RESUME MARCH

Resume March

Confessions of a Drum Corps Addict

A Semi-True Story

Mike Piskel

Resume March
Confessions of a Drum Corps Addict

Windy City Publishers
www.windycitypublishers.com

Published in the United States of America

ISBN:
978-1-953294-30-2

Library of Congress Control Number:
2022913566

Cover Photo Credit:
1979 Birmingham, Alabama. DCI Open Class World Championship Prelims
Used with permission from Sights & Sounds, Inc., Publishers of *Drum Corps World*

WINDY CITY PUBLISHERS
CHICAGO

For my family,
both on and off the field

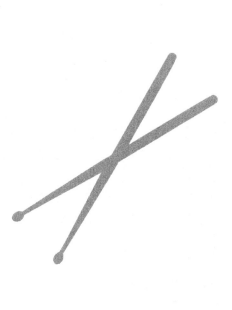

PREFACE

THE OTHER NIGHT I WATCHED comedian Jim Gaffigan rail against marching bands in parades. It was pretty funny, and it left me thinking about how often people use humor to mask their own ignorance about a subject. I know for a fact that I do, and that evening, it was pretty evident that Gaffigan does too. It's fair to say that most casual observers would probably identify drum corps as marching bands and vice versa, but what they don't understand is that historically there has always been a significant difference, and it should be noted that while drum corps had their beginnings as parade units, most of today's competitive marching units rarely tolerate the many hazards of marching down a street without handsome compensation.

Taking time to explore drum corps from a historical perspective reveals how the marching arts moved from the streets to the stadium, becoming one of the most exciting visual and musical experiences that audiences and performers can simultaneously enjoy. Throughout its existence, drum corps shows have essentially drawn their inspiration from our nation's social fabric, beginning with straightforward patriotic themes, to today's varied and original artistic designs. Over the last fifty years a reciprocal relationship developed between drum corps and the other performing arts as many elements from each have been widely shared.

Anyone who is familiar with drum corps can see the influence of its unique choreography on modern pop and hip-hop concerts, Super Bowl halftime shows, Olympic ceremonies, competitive cheerleading, televised music awards, and Broadway productions. If you've never had the opportunity to experience world class drum corps in living color and brilliant sound, I hope this book provides you with a better understanding of how it became a truly original form of entertainment, while also inspiring you to take in one of today's DCI events.

Competitive drum and bugle corps has undergone a myriad of transformations throughout its one hundred plus years of existence, but historians have portrayed the 1970s as "a pivot of change," and that is clearly evident in the dramatic events that took place in drum corps throughout the decade. During the early seventies, drum and bugle corps finally emerged from the shroud of restrictions that were rooted in its association with military service organizations, and once freed, they quickly began to reap the artistic and financial benefits associated with self-governance. Marching from 1972 through 1979, I was fortunate to have experienced this renaissance firsthand and the people and events encountered during that time have been rattling around in my brain ever since. Now retired from a thirty-seven year career in high school education, I decided to write it all down.

The best stories are the ones that actually happened, and there is no doubt that those who donned a uniform and marched in a competition probably have some outstanding tales of their own. Mine took place within two corps in the Midwest, the Emerald Knights from Cedar Rapids, Iowa, and the Blue Stars, from La Crosse, Wisconsin. Respectively, these corps are excellent examples of classic and modern drum corps and their juxtaposition illuminates the evolution of the marching arts in a hopefully entertaining way. I've done my best to keep the events in this book as authentic as possible; however, there are segments where timelines were slightly altered to enhance their readability. Likewise, while all the major characters are real people, and the dialogue's emotion and intent are reasonable facsimiles of what occurred, they are only the approximate recollections of what was actually said over fifty years ago.

Those of you close to the marching arts know there are way too many corps, characters, show designs, and anecdotes to be chronicled in just one book, so I apologize if you don't find your story in these pages, but for the thousands of past and present marchers out there, it is my hope that reading *Resume March*, will help reconnect you with the people and events from your drum corps experiences.

~Mike Piskel

PART 1

ESCAPE

1

JULY 6, 1978

SUMMERTIME IS DRUM CORPS TIME. Walking on the hot tarmac to board a plane in thick July heat, I felt clueless about where the future might take me, but I sure knew what I was leaving behind. Leaving—well, running away was more like it. I needed to get as far away from Cedar Rapids as possible.

As long as I could remember, summer was always my favorite time of year—that was, until this one. Right before heading home from college my girlfriend dumped me, and I found myself living at home with Mom and Dad, taking a job wearing a silly hat at McDonalds and enrolling in a summer school chemistry class to catch up on credits from a rough sophomore year. All of it would've been tolerable if the corps had been what it should have, but we weren't even close. If I stayed in town any longer, I wouldn't be able to salvage the rest of summer, or my sanity for that matter.

Trying to get comfortable in the plane's passenger seat wasn't working. The guilt of abandoning my friends, compounded by my fear of flying, started my stomach rolling and put an egg-sized lump in my throat. Recent events had brewed a complex cocktail of emotions that were now mixing with the thought of taking off to join up with something much better, something that would hopefully heal fresh wounds and put summer back on track.

Every time I sensed my emerging butterflies, I choked them back down by locking firmly onto the anger that had been stewing for several weeks. It provided all the justification I needed for my escape. Closing my eyes, I pushed back my seat and fixated on the biting words that played through my head like a bad mantra: "Piskel, you're not the drum major anymore, so shut up, and do what you're told."

Unbelievable. He had to be fucking kidding. For seven years, drum corps was a dominant player in my life. It was a passion that had gradually grown into an addiction, and during that time, I'd twice been named Knight of the

2

Year, and spent the prior three seasons as the corps' drum major and de facto horn instructor. I'd given everything to the Emerald Knights, and the corps had played a significant role in how I'd come to define myself. Now that relationship was coming to a disheartening end.

After the '77 season, I thought going back into the horn line would be a preferred slow-drip solution over quitting cold turkey. I could ease out, make this my last year. As a sophomore at the University of Iowa, I was entering that age of accountability, and my mom's perpetual nagging about growing up and getting on with life had become an inescapable track on a looped tape, so after the previous season, I'd met with the corps' staff explaining that I didn't feel I could make the necessary commitment to be the drum major.

By returning to the horn line, I wasn't just walking away. My presence and leadership would still be a noted contribution. I presumed I could balance life a lot better from behind the bell of the horn than from the top of a podium. The move would initiate the weaning process and allow for some additional freedom; I could take a class, get a job, and still have time for periodic trysts with my girlfriend back in Iowa City. In the words of my mom, I could get on with my "real life." At the time, I thought it seemed like a compromise that might just make everyone happy.

Feeling the jet accelerate down the runway and its release into smooth air buoyed my spirits. The plane banked east, and I glimpsed my hometown's modest skyline. With sitcom timing, the pilot announced, "Take one last look at Cedar Rapids, cuz we're outta here!"

Hell yeah, I thought, then laughing to myself, I considered the possibility he might be executing his escape as well.

Each summer, several hundred competitive marching music organizations emerge from nine months of hibernation by performing in the first of many competitions of the season for thousands of drum corps fans across the country. Like the shock of birth to a newborn, early June is the most challenging time of year. As schools empty and older members and staff return home from college, drum corps finally have the personnel needed to complete the work that remains to be done, and therein lies the problem—the work remaining to be done.

With first shows only a week or less away, many corps find themselves scurrying to finish their productions. Their handicaps include: incomplete music, drills, and color guard choreography, insufficient numbers to fill the open spots in the drill, and uniforms begging for final fittings and alterations. This often results in sketchy performances, with some corps playing the last portion of their show parked on the fifty-yard line, and others still at a loss on how to smoothly depart the field once they've finished.

The '78 Cedar Rapids Emerald Knights were no different, and the start of the season had them scrambling more than usual. The corps was composed of a fairly young and talented lot that had grown in membership, maturity, experience, and competitive success, every year from '73 through '77. Their steady progress had taken place in spite of a confused sense of identity, inconsistent instruction, strange budget priorities, ill-conceived show designs, and at the root of it, a poor management scheme.

What they desperately needed was a steady and dedicated director with passion, vision, and most importantly, the autonomous power to put the corps on a well-defined path. Instead, the Knights' operations were ruled by a board composed of well-meaning parents, whose decisions were unfortunately predicated on keeping the corps going and their kids safely occupied. Without a mission of growth, achievement, and education in the performing arts, they were anything but a proactive organization.

The corps' origin was a prelude to the struggles they would encounter throughout their existence. The Emerald Knights were born out of a strained relationship with the Cedar Rapids Cadets, a competitive Midwest drum corps with notable regional success. In 1960, the Cadets formed the Cadet Bees, a training corps made up of over seventy young boys who would eventually be promoted into the older unit: little guppies waiting to be swallowed by a big fish when the time was right.

4

In 1965, the big fish was looking to improve its status and separate itself from the anonymity of its name, and the Cadets became the Grenadiers. With the name change came the desire for a new look, and in order to purchase new uniforms, they appropriated funds from the coffers of their feeder corps. This move so infuriated the hard-working parents of the Cadet Bees that, in the middle of summer, they packed up their little boys and formed the Emerald Knights. Despite the competitive success of the Grenadiers, without the supply chain of trained members and their fundraising parents, their days were limited. The big fish soon went belly up, and the Emerald Knights were the unescorted small fry left behind.

By 1970, the only remaining drum corps in Cedar Rapids was the Emerald Knights. Girls soon joined the ranks, but the organization was still run like a training corps, which was directly reflected in their stated mission: "Instilling the spirit of good citizenship while working with others, and at the same time, to learn coordination and a thrilling form of music."

After the founding director moved on, the parent board looked within their limited circle for a corps manager, someone who was willing to take on the responsibility, yet remain accountable. It was a model that didn't bode well for the development of a top competitive drum corps, and sadly, as the corps matured, the management scheme didn't, with the director's position becoming a revolving door.

Filling that void for '78 was a guy named Fred Beyer. He was well-spoken, muscle-bound, early thirties, with a neatly trimmed beard and nicely pressed clothes. The parents thought they had a winner. Unfortunately, he lacked the vision, passion, and drum corps savvy to direct a corps that had finally arrived on the cusp of national prominence. Members weren't quite sure of his motivation, as he was frequently absent from winter rehearsals, and when he was there, he seemed dismissive and impersonal. Unlike the prior four years, there was a complete disregard for the transparency of earnest communication that the older members had grown to expect.

Caught up in our success from the '77 summer season, several of the veteran members, including myself, initially had high hopes for the new guy running our corps. That September, with momentum on our side, we enthusiastically approached him with the idea of playing an Emerson Lake and Palmer themed show. They had recently released their *Works* album, and several of us had already worn out the vinyl.

That Saturday, four of us met at Fred's apartment and pitched the idea for a repertoire that, in Keith Emerson's words, was "...rock fused with European-influenced music." We played their rendition of a movement from Prokofiev's Scythian Suite, "The Enemy God Dances with the Black Spirits." Classical, dark, and powerful, it would make an impressive opening statement and other ELP tunes could do wonders shaping the identity for a corps called the Emerald Knights. Fred told us he liked the idea but had reservations about whether we could perform it.

How the hell did he know what we could play? Coming off the best season in corps history, last year's brass arranger, Dr. Cliff Colnot, stated his one regret for us was that he didn't pen a more challenging program. After sharing tapes from our previous years and telling Fred about the quality of musicians in the line, we left his place feeling we had convinced him it was the way to go.

Less than two months later, any ideas and influence we thought we secured had been discarded like trash thrown from a car. The first practice of the '78 season saw the corps' largest turnout of veteran and prospective members. This should have been the time to tell us how this would be our year of dominance and distinction. Instead, Big Fred sheepishly stood in front of one hundred and fifty eager young people and shared uninspired and nebulous plans for the upcoming season, after which nearly seventy brass players found they were still without a horn instructor. Several of the section leaders from the year before took it upon themselves to scrounge equipment, lead warm-ups, and begin work on a jazz version of "Strike Up the Band," which we'd surprisingly found out was being touted as next year's opener. As for Emerson, Lake, and Palmer, well, as their song says, "C'est La Vie."

The lack of staff, preparation, and enthusiasm from management was definitely a red flag, and any momentum we might have carried into our winter rehearsal season nosedived like a sad paper airplane. By the next practice, some of our prospective members had already bailed, and I probably should have as well, but the years of investment and the steadfast resolve of many of my corps friends spurred me on, and blind faith had me commuting back to Cedar Rapids for rehearsals and camps.

Throughout the winter Fred became increasingly more aloof and he appeared disillusioned with his newfound role. In his defense, he may have been overwhelmed by the lack of definition of the job and its overall scope. Between the executive board's restrictive protocols and a suddenly shrinking revenue stream from declining bingo receipts, most novice directors would be at a loss. Because he was rarely seen at rehearsals, a skeleton crew of staff ran the practices, and I realized that the course of our season would most likely set sail on a ship without a rudder, or a throttle for that matter.

～≈～

FRIDAY, JUNE 9, 1978

Our summer's competitive season kicked off with a ragged performance in Platteville, Wisconsin. Like many corps, we lurched through our thirteen minute program, and it became very apparent that I'd been a much more talented drum major than horn player. Like a bad dream, I watched the long-haired brass judge disgustedly shake his head as he recorded tick after tick on his clipboard. It had been four seasons since I played lead soprano, and it was clear to both of us that it sounded that way.

Sitting second chair in a section of fifteen trumpets during my senior year in high school, I was a decent player, but no virtuoso. Instead of telling people I played the trumpet, I always told them that I played "at" the trumpet. Now majoring in secondary science education at the University of Iowa, I no longer practiced with the discipline required to get my chops ready to sustain the challenging upper register phrases, and that night on the field, I struggled with playing the music, marching the drill, and maintaining the stamina to do both.

I was out of drum corps shape, but so was the entire corps. We barely scored forty of the one hundred possible points. The end result of the evening's five corps lineup left us mired in fourth, way behind the Madison Scouts, La

Crosse Blue Stars, and Dubuque Colts, and barely edging out the Cedarburg Pioneers. The opening weekend included two more shows, and the following evening in Fort Dodge, Iowa, we weren't much better, almost thirty points down from the victorious Phantom Regiment. Closing out the weekend at our own hometown competition, the end of our performance brought only demoralizing polite applause, mixed with the embarrassing cheers of over-zealous parents. Since we were performing that night in a judged exhibition, mercifully our score wasn't announced.

The advent of drum corps competitions dates back to the early 1920s, and from its inception, the scoring system was always predicated on a scale of one hundred points. In order to achieve some sense of objectivity, multiple judges were involved, each evaluating a specific category of the performance. These scoring elements were what one might expect after watching a performance, and those early American Legion and VFW sponsored competitions included the obvious captions for marching, bugles, and percussion expertise and execution, but they also included a penalty category for specific cadence and national flag requirements along with the inspection of uniforms and individual appearance. All scoring was punitive, with each notable error resulting in a small deduction from the maximum score.

As with any subjective evaluation, a host of variables could influence the results. Biases aside, a lot depended on the training and skill of the judges, the uniformity of their tolerance for errors, and the role fatigue and context might play, as some national competitions featured a mix of marching units from different performance classes spread throughout several days of competition.

In time, there was a concerted effort to mitigate those issues. Detailed adjudication procedures were laid out, and subcategories on judging sheets were also developed to aid in uniformity and ease in tabulation. Each mistake was recorded with a small coded identifying mark on the sheet, and the resulting term, "tick," was coined. Each tick resulted in a deduction of one tenth of a point.

It wasn't until the 1950s that the category for general effect, i.e. audience appeal, showmanship, performance quality, and show demand became part of the total score. Now ten of the one hundred points possible were awarded rather than deducted. The remaining ninety points included thirty for marching execution, twenty points each for execution of drums and bugles, ten points for cadence/ tempo requirements, and ten points for the inspection.

By the mid-seventies, scored inspections had thankfully gone the way of the dodo, and judging had transitioned to focus more on performance and show design. Now judges were given a ten point range of credit to be awarded for general effect in each category of marching, bugles, and percussion. Execution in those same categories were further subdivided to record errors, as well as a build-up of points for difficulty and musicianship.

Historically, many drum corps judges came from military service organizations, and they often possessed little to no fine arts experience. Thankfully, as the activity evolved, so did the requirements for becoming a judge. Again the seventies brought notable changes, with more judges showing up with college and high school music education and fine arts performance backgrounds. In an attempt to standardize scoring, judges went through training requirements that included clinics, conferences, and stints as trial judges before being allowed to adjudicate an actual competition.

By 1978, the scores at major shows were derived from a slate of eleven judges along with an official in charge of timing and penalties. The major competitions had eight judges on the field: two each for marching, percussion, and brass execution, and additionally two analysis judges, evaluating the difficulty and musicianship within brass and percussion. Up in the press box, a panel of three general effect judges graded marching, brass, and percussion, with the marching judge having a subcategory for color guard performance.

The scores in the captions where points were awarded had the added dimension of real-time analysis of the performance with cassette recordings. Now the staff could listen to the judges' rationale for a given score and then determine its value for instruction.

In order to reduce show expenses, smaller competitions eliminated the duplicate judges for the execution categories. During each competition, a host of tabulators would sift through the score sheets to count and double check the number of ticks, add in the sub caption scores, include any penalties, and then determine the overall winner.

Full corps finales assembled the competing corps back on the field in their parade formations to anxiously await the results. Hosting officials would present trophies to the drum majors, who were brought front and center. The corps would then play themselves off the field in reverse order of finish, and often the winner of the show would treat the remaining audience to an encore standstill performance.

Despite the time lag between the last competing corps and the finale, tabulators and judging crews often struggled to expedite their calculations, and often delays took place requiring anecdotes and improvisations from show announcers. Some regional and national championship shows would have a preliminary competition over several days and the evening finals could last close to four hours.

At local and regional shows, judges and corps' staff gathered after the show for a critique, which provided instructors the opportunity to seek feedback about the scores and determine what they should prioritize for their instruction. With corps often only separated by tenths of a point, animated conversations between judges and staff often took place.

The only thing keeping my head up during our show's finale that night was the nucleus of stalwart veteran members, many that I had grown up with over the past seven years. The nature of the activity made it one very big team that in time had grown into one very large family. We practiced, traveled, ate, slept, showered, joked, argued, performed, celebrated, and cried together. The shared secrets, and scars formed from our collective time on task formed bonds that were authentic and tight. That night, it became apparent to me that those relationships would be the key to squeezing some satisfaction from a summer of mediocre drum corps.

The following weekend we crossed over the northeast corner of Iowa to the Mississippi River town of Prairie du Chien, Wisconsin, where impressive dolomite bluffs formed the boundary of the town. It was a backdrop that provided the perfect acoustics for an evening show at the local high school stadium.

That Sunday, a buckling jet stream brought volatile weather patterns with it. Warm, sunny skies were instantly transformed by fast moving fronts resulting in crashing temperatures and storms. The afternoon rehearsal had us experiencing both extremes, one moment happily making vitamin D, then abruptly chased off the field by a stark charcoal bank of clouds ushering in meteorological mayhem. Pealing thunder and strobing bolts of lightning scared the shit out of us, as huge pelting raindrops stung skin and soaked T-shirts and cut-off jeans tight to bodies. We ran for cover into the school's gym. We weren't alone; joining us were several other corps that had also taken refuge there.

We'd been assigned the use of the gym for housing, and our personal belongings were a collage of duffels, sleeping bags, and open suitcases scattered across the floor. Awkwardly, several hundred people sought open floor space and thick humid air quickly filled in any remaining gaps. It was dank, dark, and noisy, but as quickly as it began, the storm moved on, and so did the other corps. When the gym emptied, our staff gave us a break to dry off and reorganize.

Steam rising off the asphalt parking lot, I dodged puddles back out to the practice field to get my horn case, and passing by the Blue Stars' equipment truck, I heard my name being called. "Piskel?... Hey, aren't you Piskel?" A short, stocky, hirsute guy in jeans and T-shirt, sporting large aviator glasses above a significant mustache, strode towards me.

"Yeah, I am," I replied, surprised that someone from the corps knew me. "Do I know you?"

"I thought that was you in the gym," he said, smiling. "I remember you from some shows last year...I'm Pierre. I marched with Charlie Lilly in high school before joining the Blue Stars. I aged out last year, and now I'm on their brass staff...Is Charlie here?"

Realizing our connection, I replied, "No, he instructed us throughout the winter, but it was a pretty rough off season...lots of transitions going on." Sighing, I continued, "I think he could see where we were heading, and he wisely decided it wasn't worth it. He's working in Iowa City this summer and taking classes." Then I tentatively added, "Maybe I should have done that too."

"Really? But aren't you their drum major?"

I quickly filled him in on the move I'd made, and recognizing that I probably wasn't in the best place, he quietly offered, "Interesting that you're playing soprano now, so...would you ever wanna march in the DCI Finals?"

Confused, I asked, "What are you talking about?"

Furtively looking around the parking lot, he explained, "You could march in finals with us this year...it's a rush, I've done it for the past three seasons. It'll be an experience you'll never forget. We're good, but we still need three more brass players to fill out our line...two sops, and a bari." His eyes flashed with fervor as he energetically continued, "You don't seem all that fired up about your situation...you could come take one of the remaining soprano spots." Pausing, he then definitively stated, "We're going to make finals. We always make finals...why not end your year marching with us?"

Wow. The dark clouds that had cleared moments ago now seemed to have moved directly into my head, and the abrupt proposition jump-started a montage of possibilities before letting my sense of propriety take over.

Pragmatically, I snapped back to reality, "No...I mean, thanks, but I can't. I've pretty much decided this is my last year. I'm going to go out the way I came in, playing horn for the Knights. I have too much invested to just up and bail."

Perhaps realizing his offer had been a little too presumptuous, Pierre tempered his enthusiasm. "I get it, you're loyal. Charlie told me you were a diehard when we talked last Christmas. Oh well, it was worth a shot. Good luck man. See you in Denver."

Still reeling from the offer, I trudged off mumbling, "Yeah, see you around." Heading back into the gym, I thought, *could I really do that?* Leave my corps, just take off in the middle of the season to join another one, a better one—a corps like I'd always wanted us to be, a perennial world championship finalist, where I imagined every member marching with purpose, pride, and commitment. A corps staffed with talented instructors that taught you the skills and techniques necessary to reach a potential you didn't realize you possessed. Where the summer was spent competing against the best from all over the country, in competitions packed with drum corps nuts who had you on their list of favorites. Where you performed late enough that the stadium lights caused your corps to shine like silver coins on a cloth of green. A corps that could march their asses off and push the stands back twenty feet with their sound. A corps with history, tradition, and talent, one that was able to generate enough energy to send a charge through themselves and the crowd for a full thirteen minutes. *Could I really leave my corps to do that?*

Even considering it felt like a mortal sin. *Nope, do what's right Mikey, stay true to yourself and your friends. Remember loyalty and dedication? Isn't that what part of marching in corps is all about? Let it go. Refocus. The Knights are good enough—hell, we're family. We'll get better. We'll have some successes this season—just keep it together.*

Entering the gym, I sat down center court for a corps meeting. Beyer stood in the middle of our large huddle, pontificating, "The weather looks like there could be storms this evening. If it's raining, there's going to be a standstill performance in this gym. Since we don't have a lot of time left before dinner, we're going to practice right in here. It'll give us a leg up on the competition…I think we could win this thing."

Was he delusional? This was the moment he chose to spread managerial wings and suddenly express some enthusiasm? Thinking about winning a standstill competition was priceless. Someone needed to clue him in that indoor performances were usually done only for the benefit of prepaid ticket holders.

Suddenly Big Fred was back in charge, and he ordered the drums and horns up onto a small stage at one end of the gym. Packed tight in the dimly lit space, I could smell damp clothes mixing with ripening body odors. Horn players were staged two rows deep on either side of the drumline. On the gym floor below, Byer had the guard spread out into a large arc, and with nowhere to run, we played through the full show. As the stage closed in around us, thirteen brutal minutes seemed like an eternity.

Thirty-four brass players and a full drumline all crammed on the small stage did no favors to Tchaikovsky's never-ending year of 1812, nor to the rest of our music. The drums echoed off the hardwood floor like BBs rattling in a tin can, and the baritones blaring behind me triggered ringing ears and a pounding headache.

After the noise thankfully ended, I stepped out of the formation and relayed to the staff that from up here we couldn't discern one note from another, asking if there was any chance we could spread the horns and drums out on the gym floor.

That's when Beyer snapped, "Piskel, you're not the drum major anymore, so shut up and do what you're told. Let us take care of it."

There I was, pushed off a steep mountain trail by an anonymous passing hiker. No way did my earnest plea warrant that response. Now in funeral service silence, I felt way too many eyes on me. Deflated, I stepped back into line, lowered my head, and quietly stewed. I wasn't mad at Fred; he truly was clueless. I was mad that it had ultimately come to this. We were victims of our own small time drum corps dysfunction, facing the consequences of the blind leading the sighted through the very long maze that is a summer of drum corps.

Left with a hollow heart, headache, and an ever-expanding sense of frustration, my thoughts began to race. *Maybe the Emerald Knights weren't my corps anymore, maybe he was right, and my voice no longer needed to be heard. Maybe I didn't matter anymore. If not, then what the fuck was I doing here?*

Suddenly I realized I had another option; an absurd gift, presented with Swiss quartz timing—it was a way out that only moments earlier I'd convinced myself not to consider. Our practice ended, dinner and pre-show warm-ups were scheduled. I wasn't hungry; what I wanted was some space. I took a walk—right back to the Blue Stars equipment truck.

There wasn't a cloud in the sky. Thankfully, there'd be no standstill, and the cool air also cleared my head and calmed my indignation. The Blue Stars had finished their practice and members were scattered around eating dinner and starting their pre-show routine. After finding Pierre, I led him away from sensitive sightlines and told him I'd reconsidered.

"You serious about this?" He seemed rejuvenated. "This is fantastic, we can really use you. We're going to be great, we have good chemistry, you'll see."

Sensing his contagious enthusiasm, I responded, "I believe you, but I have several things I need to take care of before I can join you guys. I'm taking a summer school class that doesn't end until my final on the fifth of July."

"That shouldn't be a problem. You can catch up with us on tour." Pulling a schedule from his pocket, he scanned through it. "When you finish school, we'll be heading into Allentown for the DCI East Regionals. We can have someone meet you there. I'll take care of the details and mail you some information and the lead sop parts…give me your phone and address."

Was this really happening? Was I being rash, or were instincts leading me in the right direction? Now, a much better adrenaline rush flooded through me, and my frame of mind was vastly improved. Heading back to the gym, I felt more like a freed indentured servant than a Benedict Arnold.

2

OUR PRE-SHOW ROUTINE REVOLVED around eating dinner, showering, getting into uniform, and warming up. My issue came with suiting up. I loathed our uniform. Our comic attire consisted of a sleeveless tunic with a field green front and black back. It was adorned with a decorative metal link belt. This was worn over a black shiny blouse with loose billowy sleeves and a broad collar that appeared to have been salvaged from a discarded leisure suit. Loose-fitting, off white knit pants were trimmed with a black side stripe and were matched with black shoes. The color guard wore the same top, accompanied by white knee-length skirts with green pleats and high black boots. The uniform was capped off with a shiny black plastic Trojan helmet, complete with a stiff white brush running down the middle. It was reminiscent of the oversized headgear worn by Marvin the Martian in the Bugs Bunny cartoons. His nasally trademark line being, "This makes me very angry, very angry indeed." Yeah, Marvin, the helmet pissed me off too.

When they were first revealed before the '77 season, I begged management to send them back, telling them they didn't even have anything to do with knights, and when they declined, I privately shed real tears. I couldn't believe the vast amounts of our hard-earned bingo money spent on them, and by June's end, our competition had already saddled us with several nicknames: The Fuller Brushmen, The O-Cedar Rapids Cadets, and my personal favorite, The Scrubbing Bubble Knights.

Photo courtesy of Dee Ann Rexroat

Portrait of a Roman Centurion? My reluctant unveiling of the 1977 Emerald Knights' drum major uniform.

I'd always been envious of the clean, professional look of the Blue Stars, and comparing our costumes against their deep navy uniform revealed stark differences. Their uniform top had a short, stand-up collar with shoulder epaulets and the pants featured a thin white and red side stripe. Accoutrements included two white cross straps across the front of the chest joined at the sternum by a small chrome buckle, a fitted white cummerbund, along with white gloves, gauntlets, and shoes. Their uniform was topped with a white pith helmet of the corps' own patented design. On the helmet's upper right side, was a twelve inch crimson feathered plume, adding presence and height. The guard's uniform was similar, only with short sleeve tops and their iconic navy hot pants, and short white majorette boots. While their uniform had evolved slightly over the years, there was no mistaking them when they took the field. Now I couldn't wait to wear it.

Photo by Jane Boulen ~ Used with permission from Sights & Sounds Inc., Publishers of Drum Corps World

1978 Blue Stars sopranos demonstrate their excellent marching technique.

Showered and dressed, I headed towards the semicircle of horn players gathering in an athletic field. Passing our percussion section beginning their warm-up, I was met with a host of red, glassy-eyed stares. I found it interesting that many of the members in our battery section appeared high. I knew a lot of our members partied, but up until now I wasn't aware some of them had decided to make it a part of their pre-show preparation.

Weed, reefer, grass, ganja, herb, or just good old pot: lots of high school and college students partook. Upon entering my freshman year at Iowa, I'd read a letter sent from university housing in complete disbelief. It outlined the school's liberal policy on the standards of student behavior for residence halls, stating: "The use of marijuana, LSD, hallucinogens, or other dangerous drugs or controlled substances will not in itself be regarded as an act calling for Residence Services disciplinary action." Heck, it seemed like they could've cared less if we turned our dorm into an opium den. Once school started, I was repeatedly proven right, as its earthy skunk smell often wafted from open doors, revealing bongs set along dorm room walls like tools in a workshop. So prevalent was the odor in my dorm hall, The Beth Wellman House, that it was rechristened, "Wasted Wellman."

At college, I really wasn't much of a drinker, but I was no saint. I partied regularly and was partial to the primo stuff like Colombian Gold, Panama Red, Maui Wowie, and various other exotic strains of sinsemilla. I preferred it to alcohol, as there was no accompanying lampshade stupidity, vomit, or lingering hangovers.

For me, weed was a fun way to chill after a day of classes and an evening of studying. Pot heightened my senses; it lent music an acute mesmerizing fuzziness, conversations were seemingly more engaging, dorm food tasted way better than it should have, and when enjoyed with my friends, outrageous hilarity would often ensue—even when things weren't quite all that hilarious. Getting high provided a fascinating change of pace, and as far as I was concerned, it wasn't all that different from my parents' habit of obtaining a buzz from an after-work martini, or the Wisconsin supper club-sized old fashioned cocktails that they and their friends regularly enjoyed on bridge night.

But for me, the beauty of drum corps was that it didn't need any adulterations. It provided its own pure rush: a unique natural high of adrenaline mixed with ample amounts of dopamine and endorphins, purely extracted from the unique combination of competition, music, travel, friendships, arduous protracted practices, and performing to appreciative crowds on a warm summer's eve. Drum corps season immersed you so deep into the moments of your own life, you could easily forget everything else going on outside of it. It was all the escape I needed.

Fundamental to the drum corps experience was the competitive performance of a thirteen-minute show. Big or small, I treated them all with a certain reverence. Competitions weren't just about the other corps at the show, they provided a tangible measure of improvement from one performance to the next. It was a game that took place within yourself and the entire corps, trying to see just how much better you could be. It was a test of mettle under a complex collection of hurdles, and each performance provided the opportunity to see if your attempt at perfection aligned with your perceived individual and collective potential.

The ultimate team sport, drum corps competitions also gave members the chance to enter the elusive "zone." That rare occurrence which requires a myriad of variables to precisely align in time and place, and like a spiritual event of shared energy, brain waves, hearts, and souls are magically synchronized into one fluid machine. While it's one thing for five people on a basketball team to simultaneously find the zone, it's an entirely different phenomenon for a team the size of a drum corps. I'd experienced it only a few times, but every new competition provided the exciting possibility that it could happen again.

Now, a number of my own teammates were sabotaging our machine before we even had the chance to fire it up. *Were we growing apathetic with the realization we had lost a step from last year? Was it from the lack of leadership from management? Or was this just one more symptom of a corps adrift without a well-defined mission?*

It was way too early in the season for apathy to have infected our ranks, yet here it was, forcing me to see the reality of what we had become. I'd lost—we'd lost, and walking past the stoned drummers, I had a new angle of perception, revealing something that my naïve ideologies hadn't had the foresight to consider.

I wasn't sure of those percussion members' motivation, but their apparent indifference tempered some of my guilty feelings. I was amused that a number of signs were pointing me towards leaving the corps. They couldn't be ignored, and my confidence to follow through was growing exponentially. It was overwhelming to realize how far the Emerald Knights had drifted from last year's success. A host of dashed dreams, I quietly joined the arc of horn players beginning our pre-show warm-up.

~ ~ ~

Waiting in line to enter the stadium usually made me feel like a gladiator readying for the arena. Okay, maybe the goofy helmets helped, but the sights and sound of the other corps performing, along with the crowd's response, all combined to set my senses tingling. No matter how tired I was, the anticipation of performing in competition could always squeeze out some residual energy to rebound for the show. Tonight, however, I was running completely on empty, and surprisingly, it was my best performance of the year. Indifference seemed to have quieted my nerves enough to calmly execute each segment of music and marching. While I was intrigued, I took little satisfaction from the experience.

With no true program coordinator, our show design came together like a last-minute potluck dinner missing its main course. How it had been selected was a pure mystery, and it seemed to be pieced together like an early David Lynch horror movie.

The show opened with a jazz version of "Strike up the Band." It was the best arrangement of the lot, but quickly disintegrated from there. After being appropriately struck up, we transitioned to our drum solo, taken in part from the theme from the *Rocky and Bullwinkle Show*. It was heavy on the xylophone parts and a little light on the stupid moose and squirrel. Even more absurd to us, and no doubt the audience, was our concert number, "Look What They've Done to My Song, Ma." I thought our version should've been renamed, "Look What They Done to my Corps, Ma." The arrangement was from a semi-popular folk pop song released in 1970 by the singer, Melanie. Her one big hit had been the kitschy "Brand New Key." Neither song conjures up much drum corps excitement, and as far as I was concerned, her music should have been relegated to the soundtrack purgatory heard only in elevators and grocery stores.

The show concluded with a dreadfully drawn out production of the "1812 Overture" (after all, what goes better with folk pop than Tchaikovsky?) Our arrangement was performed by thirty-four mostly talented horns, desperately searching for another thirty-four. The parts were challenging, and our small horn line didn't have the stamina, volume, or quality of sound to sustain the grandiose musical phrases to their full emotional conclusion.

Seventy thousand troops had perished in the battle of Borodino, and each night we fell victim to that same fate. Perhaps if we'd have had the actual cannons, we could have blown the piece out of its misery. Tonight, we were lucky enough to begin and end together. Maybe a partially stoned corps was the key to performing a show that was conceived in its own cloud of dubious smoke.

The cool evening had all five corps gathered on the field for the finale, as a fourth place score of 44.1 was revealed. Despite my improved performance, it was no better than the week before. The Blue Stars won the show with a score of 67.6, distancing the second place Colts by over sixteen points. Last season the Emerald Knights had debuted with a score of 54.3, taking second place to a strong Phantom Regiment. Now, with two weeks of semi-hard data, we faced the reality we weren't close to the same corps.

Heading back to Cedar Rapids on a bus full of sleeping Emerald Knights, I was alone with a flood of new thoughts. I was never good at carrying the burden of others' secrets, and now I had my own to tote. I considered the best tack was to keep on marching and hopefully keep my mouth shut until I left town. Quitting right now would only expose me to the inevitable fallout; friends would ply me with guilt, while others could make it even more painful, as, hypocrite, traitor, and asshole, were the words playing out in my imagination. *Nope, don't do it Mike, stay the course, continue to work, go to practice, finish summer school, then just slip away.* That was the plan, but there was just one sizable problem, and pulling into town two hours later, I was still wondering how my parents would respond to this scheme.

3

MOM AND DAD WERE A formidable team, well-practiced from twenty-five years of marriage. On all things domestic, Mom took the point. She craved order and control. Hell, she even ironed underwear. Who does that?

Dad had learned early on to accept his "yes dear" role and was a diligent and faithful partner. The Sergeant in Arms, he oversaw enforcement of the family tenets whenever my brother or I got out of hand, often doling out stern statements of finality like, "Because I said so," or, "You got a lot to learn, boy," and his favorite rhetorical question, "Do you understand?" These were accompanied by his unique talent of flashing the combined look of anger, fear, and disgust, as quickly as the raised hackles on a dog. It scared the crap out of us.

As kids, whenever we misbehaved, he'd pull his belt from his pant loops, while simultaneously asking, "You want a strappin'?"

Hell no, we didn't want a strappin', and doing our best to dodge a bullet, we soon became conditioned to instantly modify our behavior, praying he'd restring it back around his waist, like a gunslinger spinning his six-shooter back into its holster. However, if the belt cleared that last loop, we'd feel its sting at least once.

Thankfully, "The Belt," as an instrument of compliance, came to an end on a particular night that has since gone down in Piskel family folklore. One winter's eve, a painfully long dinner was made painfully longer by the dreaded presence of peas on my plate. I couldn't fathom putting the wrinkled, tepid, mushy green globules in my mouth, and there they now sat, lonely on my plate—mocking me.

Throughout dinner I performed subtle passive-aggressive protests, and my parents took turns dishing out statements like, "Eat your peas, or…you will not get dessert, you will not be dismissed from the table, you will sit right there until you do, mister."

After a presumably long day for an eight-year-old, I decided to take a stand. Having no sense of control over my culinary choices, along with basically no control over anything else, frustration forced me from my seat, and I stood up shouting, "These peas make me sick! I'm not eating them, and you can't make me."

Rising from his chair, my dad stood menacingly across from me, and without hesitation, he unfastened the belt in one swift, well-practiced move. Meeting his threat, I boldly grabbed my fork in defiance. It was a Mexican standoff at 1400 Parkwood Drive.

Food fell from my brother's mouth, Mom shrieked, and the belt was fully drawn from its scabbard. A river of tears flooded down my face and merged with dual tributaries of snot. I defiantly jabbed the fork towards my father and took off. Dad, in mandrill-like, red-faced bloom, struggled around the confines of the dining nook and was after me. From the kitchen to the living room, through the foyer, and back into the kitchen, we made the left turn loop like NASCAR racers desperate for more corporate sponsorship. Each lap had my brother, howling with laughter, yelling, "He's gaining on you. Hurry up, he's gaining on you!"

Stocking feet gained traction on the living room carpet only to slip wildly onto the kitchen's linoleum floor. Turning around sporadically, I'd make desperate, air-piercing jabs with my fork in my weak attempt to fend him off. I was fading, and Dad (as my brother continued to inform me) was catching up. Running out of breath and options, on the next lap I made a calculated pit stop, sliding back into my chair and using my makeshift weapon to shovel as many peas into my mouth as I could.

Mom burst into laughter, and with Tommy guffawing to the point of asphyxiation, my well winded father couldn't help but join them, as they watched me wash down the little green orbs with the last of my milk. That night the belt remained silent and was never pulled from his pant loops in anger again.

At twenty years of age, I no longer feared my parents' wrath. Now my apprehension centered around disappointing them, and it seemed my participation in drum corps had always disappointed my mom. For her, drum corps was anathema, and I was pretty sure it came from her desperate desire for complete control. My first year in corps corresponded with a long-awaited start to puberty and unfortunately it had collided head-on with my mom's early stirrings of menopause. From then on, we'd been at it for most of the time I marched.

As far as she was concerned, any time spent with drum corps was a monumental and ridiculous waste of time. Ridiculous, as in, "That's ridiculous!" It was her pet phrase to dismiss anything that didn't jibe with her myopic view of world-wide propriety. Over my years in corps there had been some "volume knob turned to eleven" arguments, most resulting in tears, slammed doors, and days of stoic silence on both our parts.

Despite her best efforts, I wouldn't fold, so resolutions often came in the form of a tense dysfunctional compromise, often manipulating me to do her bidding by using drum corps as collateral. Like forcing me to eat my peas all over again, it was, "Do this or you will not be going to the…(fill in the blank) practice, camp, or show." Thankfully, once I'd gone off to college, things between us had begun to cool down, perhaps aided by her diminishing hot flashes and the realization that I'd soon be permanently out of the house.

Mom was all about how she perceived things appeared to others, so minor relief had recently come from my visible achievements like making the honor roll, winning a scholarship from the Drum Corps Midwest Association, and articles and photos in the *Cedar Rapids Gazette* that noted my awards and contributions to the consistently improving Emerald Knights.

My dad, on the other hand, could be the key to garnering support for spending the remainder of the summer with the Blue Stars. While he never came out and said it, I truly believed he had a covert fondness for the activity. I think he liked it because he could see the passion, pride, work ethic, independence, and sense of identity fostered in me, and I know he recognized the confidence and leadership skills I'd acquired during my time as drum major. I also think he secretly thought the entire drum corps thing was pretty cool. Unlike my mom, he got it; he understood the potential for what corps could offer as a youth activity, and he even helped out with fundraising, working our bingo game once a week.

Without having to sell my soul in the process, I hoped he could bridge the divide between Mom and me, at least enough to earn both consent and the additional funding I'd require for touring the country's football stadiums. Home at last, I sank deep into bed knowing the next day I'd begin negotiations.

Monday mornings always came way too soon after a weekend of nonstop drum corps. Normally I'd sleep through them, but there was a chemistry class to take and work that followed. As the afternoon slogged on, I fixated on how to broach the evening's conversation. Five-thirty brought my dad home and out of the coat and tie he wore every day to work.

Anxiously, I knocked on the bedroom door. Hey Dad, how was your day?"

"Oh, it was work. How about yours?"

Sitting on the bed, I said, "Alright…I want to tell you about something that happened this weekend, and I figured this is the best time to do it."

The master bedroom's heavy drawn drapes seemed to amplify my retelling of the events from the weekend and how my self-esteem had taken a significant hit. Sitting next to me, Dad said I should tell Byer and the Knights to take a hike. It was the perfect segue to detail the unique opportunity I'd been given to start summer over.

Listening patiently, after a beat of silence, he flashed a rare smile and said, "Okay…but what are we going to tell your mom?"

His question carried a lot of weight. I figured the "we," in his response, meant we were now a team. I'd expected some blowback from my plan, but it didn't happen. Maybe he felt good about the fact that I was approaching him first.

I could tell my dad was mellowing. He'd stopped yelling at the TV during the nightly news. He seemed resolved to take the things he couldn't control as they came. My brother had recently married and was now an army captain stationed in Germany. One son down, one to go. Maybe he realized his time as a dad with significant proximal influence was limited, or maybe he just read the frustration in my eyes. Either way, it was one of those moments where I sensed his empathy and was reawakened to the fact that he was there for me, and that he'd always been there for me, wanting the best.

Sitting next to me, he said, "Let me lead the discussion at the dinner table tonight. Stay calm, don't get too emotional, at least to begin with…we'll make this happen."

Before leaving the bedroom, I said, "Thanks, I really appreciate you doing this. I don't say it enough, but I appreciate all you and Mom have done for me."

Dinner that night was open-faced Rueben sandwiches toasted under the broiler, served with fried potatoes, peppers and onions, and a salad. Now with the suspense of waiting for Dad to break the news, the sauerkraut wasn't doing my stomach any favors. Suddenly I wasn't so sure this was the way to go. Dad wasn't always the best at articulating his or others' feelings. He was an electrical engineer, a numbers guy, and he frequently struggled when it came to issues regarding my brother or me. I was curious how this conversation would begin, and slightly more fearful of how it would end.

As dinner wound down, he finally spoke up, telling Mom, "Mike has something very important he would like to share with us, and I think we should both hear him out."

Wait...what? That's it? That's him taking the lead? Oh well, I figured at least she'd realize that he knew what was going on before she did. I took a deep breath and proceeded to share the weekend.

When I finished, Mom got this pursed look on her lips, then looked at both of us and said, "What about school?" Not, what about anything else—just, what about school?

I eagerly explained, "Mom, I told the Blue Stars I'd be finishing summer school before going out to meet them. I called Greyhound this afternoon...I can get a bus out to Allentown that day. I'll be out there in twenty-six hours, and the bus is only sixty-four bucks."

Immediately she exclaimed, "Oh no you're not! You're not taking the bus... twenty-six hours, why that's ridiculous. I'll call the airport tomorrow and see what flights they have available. If it's not too costly, you can fly there."

Huh? I couldn't believe it. As far as I was concerned, it was my mom's finest hour as a mom in quite some time. Now I was two for two with parents on the same day; both willing to support me financially and emotionally, at a time when I felt like I needed them. We continued talking throughout the evening, now a tiny family on a mission, hammering out the logistical plans for my escape. My summer was beginning to look up.

4

MY FLIGHT TO ALLENTOWN INCLUDED a brief layover in Chicago, and the transfer through O'Hare went smoother than I had imagined. With about a half hour to kill before boarding, I found a seat by the gate, and pulled out the Blue Stars' music from my backpack.

A week after plotting my escape with Pierre, I'd received the brown envelope in the mail, where I discovered the daunting lead soprano parts. With most of it perched well above the staff, I realized that if I was going to be a contributing brass player, I'd need to make a change.

Trumpet players are frequently instructed to play on a larger cupped mouth-piece for a richer and fuller tone, and I had always diligently obeyed. Yet, most of the impressive lead sops in the Knights used shallow cupped mouthpieces, and their innate ability, buoyed by the aid of their mouthpieces, allowed them to expand their range into the stratosphere of our trumpet heroes, like Maynard Ferguson, Doc Severinsen, Al Hirt, Bud Brisbois, and Bill Chase.

The Emerald Knights' lead line was the envy of many other Midwestern corps and our ranks held four lead sops who could reach double Cs, a feat equivalent to bench pressing three hundred and fifty pounds. Even after playing all day, they'd challenge each other to see whose latex embouchures could still reach the highest, wide-open, Maynard Ferguson lip trills. They were ballsy, loud, and truly spectacular. I wasn't one of them.

I felt my best chance to reduce fatigue, brighten my sound, and handle the lead sop music was to purchase a shallower Bach $10^{1/2}$ C. The mouthpiece still required plenty of air, but at least now, I wouldn't be pushing a two ton rock up a steep hill. The trip to the music store paid off. In one afternoon, I went from a D above the staff to squeaking out a high F. At the next practice, it didn't go unnoticed.

Following my survival plan for the remaining time in the Knights, I went to school, sold Happy Meals, attended practice, and diligently spent time with the Blue Stars' musical book. In the narrow gaps between, I did my best to appreciate my parents. Life at home was getting better by the moment; turning off the ever-present television news during dinner, we had real conversations that finally broke free from the constraints of the obligatory family roles of mother, father, and son.

The atmosphere at the Emerald Knights rehearsals wasn't so comfortable. While the corps' members had aged, we hadn't matured. Sadly, we'd lost that loving family feeling we'd enjoyed during the '77 season. Younger members seemed less dependent on veterans, and the corps had scattered into little cliques. The collective effort needed for success just wasn't there, yet most of the vets marshaled on with feigned enthusiasm.

My final road trip with the Emerald Knights was a nonstop four-day swing through Iowa and Illinois, marching in the parades and competitions sur-rounding Independence Day. It was something we'd done every year since I first joined the corps, as the Fourth of July was to drum corps members what prom was to most high school seniors—you had to do it, whether you liked it or not. Fortunately, most of us liked it; after all, we played a critical role in the annual celebration. It'd be hard to imagine Main Street, USA during the pinnacle of summer without Old Glory in front of a line of flowing flags and twirling rifles, all accompanied by the patriotic soundtrack of rudimental drum beats and blaring bugles. Why, the only thing that could make you feel any more American would be watching the fireworks paint the evening sky.

Committed to keeping my secret, the trip had me battling a persistent hollow feeling, and I searched for a tolerable mindset, ultimately settling on squeezing as much satisfaction as I could from spending these last few days marching with my friends. I suppressed any anger, apprehension, guilt, or sen-timentality, by becoming a photographer of sorts, staying focused on only the best parts of each moment.

Almost a month into the season, we were finally getting into drum corps shape. With numerous full show run-throughs, and completed guard work, the corps had definitely improved, but after a week off from competition, our show in Fort Madison was pedestrian at best. We struggled with all elements of our performance: phasing, impacts, and execution. Nothing quite jelled. The end result was a whopping score of 44.3, just two tenths of a point higher than the score we received in Prairie Du Chien. What made it even worse were the corps beating us. The Wausau Story, Colts, and Geneseo Knights were all good, but not great. They were the second-tier corps that we'd been extremely competitive with last year, but now they were embarrassing us by twenty points.

The evening's show result made for a quiet bus ride, and we reached our housing in Waterloo, Iowa well after midnight. After departing the buses to the hum of a single street light, we followed a tired old custodian as he silently led us into a musty gym. Robotically, we unrolled sleeping bags and crashed before a full day that included a morning parade, practice, and performance.

Starting in 1974, the Emerald Knights had bought and brought their creative staff, mostly from Chicagoland, to arrange and teach the show. Unfortunately, good local instructors were transient, and many weren't all that proficient, the percussion staff being the one exception. With no true program director, or experienced music and visual caption heads, the Emerald Knights struggled to match the progress made by other corps throughout the summer. Rarely was there a brass instructor on trips, so rehearsals became the responsibility of the drum major and section leaders in the horn line. Luckily, many of the brass members were decent high school musicians, bred from Iowa's strong public school system, but this created its own issues, as listening to the corps from a semicircle or while on the field wasn't the same as having a critical ear in the stands. The horn line often found itself with a collection of differing opinions on how to make things better, and once music was learned and polished in sectionals, performances would typically plateau.

Most of the corps' year-to-year improvement had been due to its increase in members and experience. The '77 season saw an influx of veteran members from neighboring corps that had fallen on tough times. That year more than twenty percent of the Emerald Knights were former Clinton Nee-Hi's and Royal Chevaliers from the Waterloo/Cedar Falls area. The infusion of older, experienced talent paid off with several impressive placements at a number of regional and national competitions.

Fueled by the humiliation of our prior night's performance, there was a sense of urgency to our afternoon rehearsal. Now motivated, members and staff increased their concentration on performance levels and musical impacts, and our efforts over the next two days resulted in the corps accomplishing something we'd never done.

The Waterloo show only hosted four corps in the evening's competition, basically all of similar caliber, and a small crowd at the old high school stadium witnessed our first cohesive show. Scoring a more tolerable 51.45, the corps eked out a win over the surprised Knights of Geneseo.

Confidence growing, the following night in Streator, Illinois, produced our best run of the year. Throughout the performance, we could sense the tempos were locked in, and the authentic emotion in our music. The end result included genuine positive feedback from the small local crowd and our staff.

Re-entering the field with the other corps for the finale, we anxiously waited to hear if the scores reflected our presumed improvement. Contrived drama was delivered with the announcement of scores, in reverse order of placement. Other than the Knights of Geneseo, the competition we faced that night wasn't all that competitive. Unbelievably, there was a corps that scored a paltry 13.5, and two others in the thirties, but when we heard a score of 43.2 going to the Black Knights, there was audible relief that the color wasn't green.

The P.A. announcer followed, "In second place, with a score of 50.85..." he said, teasing the crowd with his clichéd pause, "...the Knights of Geneseo!"

I watched as the backs of members tightened and relaxed, with quiet jubilation, hushed whispers of "Yes," "Cool," and "Thank God," surrounded me, as our score of 52.5 was announced. It was one of those little victories I'd predicted the season would bring.

Ambivalent about the back-to-back wins, I was happy for us, but it still didn't fill the hollowness inside. Unlike some of my friends, I took no personal satisfaction from winning a show of this caliber and was anxious to move on.

The Fourth of July came with its inevitable midsummer heat wave, and the day was a marathon, with three consecutive parades and an evening competition. Parade appearances provided significant revenue for our corps, and every year since I'd joined, we had traveled to the small downtowns of Chicago suburbs like Park Ridge, Palatine, Arlington Heights, Schaumburg, and Des Plaines. The neighboring parade committees would coordinate staggered starting times so that marching units could hurriedly hop from one suburb to the next. Some parade routes took us through shaded residential streets, while others moved through small downtowns with red, white, and blue ruffled decorations hanging from street lights.

Today was not unlike any of those prior Independence Days. Bused from parade to parade, it was hurry up and wait before grabbing a sack lunch, dodging road apples, dealing with creeping, sweat-soaked underwear, and listening to sunburned adults with late morning beer buzzes yell at us to play something—anything. For our efforts we were presented with tiny flag waving cheers. People of all ages love an old-fashioned parade, and often, marching down a main street lined with thousands of happy faces, I felt my own patriotic stirrings.

Finishing each parade, I chugged as much water as possible and crunched ice until my teeth hurt. While the day was full of down time, it still moved fast. Parades behind us, we slammed fast food, took reinvigorating cold showers in a nameless well-worn Chicago high school locker room, then climbed back into our moist uniforms for the evening's competition.

With no rehearsal time, we relied on the residual energy from our back to back victories to manage a fourth place finish. Realizing my historic run with the Knights was finally over, I was now able to replace that hollow feeling with the sensations of sorrow, resolve, apprehension, and anticipation.

From parade rest, I listened to the announcer say, "In first place, with a score of 72.5, The Cavaliers from Park Ridge, Illinois." Smirking, I realized in just two days, I'd be a member of a corps that was beating them. I couldn't wait.

5

FEELING CONSIDERABLY MORE RELAXED ON the second leg of the flight, I predicted that in only three more hours I'd be a Blue Star. Not quite sure how the rendezvous would play out, I fashioned a makeshift calling card with "Blue Stars" on a sheet of notebook paper to improve my odds. Then, reviewing the music to the opener, I mimed the fingerings on an imaginary bugle. Focusing on my task kept automatic negative thoughts at bay.

With only forty days left in the season, holding onto any Catholic guilt would only diminish the experience. I needed to concentrate on what I was running to, and not running from. It worked. When the plane started its descent, time had evaporated like water on hot cement, and suddenly I was miles away from Cedar Rapids and the uncomfortable feelings from the morning.

The terminal at the Lehigh Valley International Airport in Allentown had all the charm of a glorified bus station. The flight had been full, and as I weaved my way to the baggage area I considered that my little homemade sign probably wouldn't stand much of a chance. Retrieving my suitcase and sleeping bag, I also realized I'd been pretty foolish to think that this part of my journey would go as smoothly as the flight. When the crowd thinned, minutes slowly started to pile up, and it was obvious there was no Blue Star welcoming committee.

After a long, lonely hour, I debated my next move. Several more planes arrived, with new crowds milling around the baggage area. Spotting the back of a Phantom Regiment jacket floating through the crowd, I saw it belonged to a huge bearded man picking up his luggage. Approaching him I asked, "Excuse me, do you have any information about where any of the corps are staying this weekend?"

He flatly responded, "No, but I do have the phone number to the DCI East Headquarters…you could give them a try."

Relieved to have something, I took it and headed for the nearest payphone. A friendly female voice on the other end of the line answered, "DCI, how may I help you?"

Not quite sure where to begin, I winged it. "Hi, my name is Mike Piskel, and..."

Before I could continue, she interrupted, "Mike Piskel, Mike Piskel! I've been trying to get someone out to the airport for the past hour...but as you can probably tell, I'm not having any luck."

I was found. A cool wave of relief splashed over me, saving me from thoughts of being stranded on the taupe desert island that was Lehigh Valley International Airport.

"Have you had anything to eat?" she asked.

"No, not since breakfast."

"Well, go get something, and call me back in a half an hour. Maybe by then I'll have a ride for you. You're going to be staying here with us...the Blue Stars have a show tonight and won't get here until tomorrow."

I went to the airport cafeteria and discovered that the phony flavor of a gray burger and soggy fries aligned perfectly with the institutional décor of the airport. It didn't matter. There were real people in Allentown, who actually knew about me! After downing my lunch, a calmer voice on the end of the line told me the Blue Stars were sending someone out to pick me up.

I stepped out into the afternoon heat and this time my little sign made good, as a compact sedan with a young couple pulled up. Introducing themselves as Drew and Patti, they were newlyweds, and at that point in their relationship where everything was said in an upbeat manner, explaining they were both '76 Blue Stars alumni, having met during their age-out season.

In the close confines of a drum corps summer, love affairs bloomed often, and like spring flowers, most of the infatuations were short lived. The mutual crushes that persisted past the initial stage of lust usually fizzled out when young lovers realized they were headed back to their prospective high schools, colleges, jobs, or life in the armed services. Still, there are always exceptions, where the mutual attraction, infatuation, and the art of tolerance, well-practiced in drum corps send couples paddling down a romantic river, well on their way to permanent attachment.

Leaving the industrial surroundings of the airport, we crossed over to an older residential neighborhood of Allentown. It was marked by well-maintained large homes, parks, and broad green boulevards. Watching the scenery change, I shared my personal circumstances that led me to the corps.

The condensed version of my story complete, Drew and Patti simultaneously replied, "You made the right choice. You're going to love it. The Blue Stars are an amazing organization with outstanding people."

Drum corps' common ground provided that sense of instant familiarity, acceptance, and trust, and we easily chatted about our backgrounds, their love story, and the Blue Stars. Even though they were no longer with the corps, listening to them made me feel as if I'd already been unconditionally adopted into a brand new family.

It was late afternoon when we pulled up to a stately building on a quaint old college campus. School out, there was little pedestrian traffic, and the setting provided a welcome mat I hadn't anticipated. The campus was composed of colonial style red brick buildings, bearing clean white pillars and domed towers surrounded by a picturesque landscape of mature hardwoods and evergreens. Drew and Patti cheerfully wished me luck and sped off. Picking up my gear, I headed towards the two-story building with a small temporary sign taped to the door. Typed block letters spelled out "DCI East Headquarters."

The building's foyer led to a large room that seemed part office, and part living room. It was complete with a formal fireplace mantel, ten foot ceilings, an ornate oversized wooden desk, and large framed still life paintings. One part of the room featured a long meeting table, and nearby were comfortable overstuffed leather sofas and chairs. One wall had rows of paned windows and French doors that looked out onto a small patio and lush courtyard. The late afternoon sun illuminated little dust particles that danced in the air.

A short young woman looked up from the phone at the desk and greeted me with tired, warm eyes, "Hi Mike, I'm Kris. I'm glad you made it...you can set your belongings down in the corner and we'll get you a room after dinner." Her appearance fit her professional demeanor. Dark hair in a ponytail, she had light makeup under stylish plastic framed glasses, and wore a navy polo with an embroidered DCI logo, and khaki shorts.

Her welcoming tone put me at ease, and after phoning my parents for a reassuring chat, I sat down on one of the plush leather couches. It was in stark contrast to the cramped plane and the hard plastic chairs in the airport. Finally I could relax and organize the thoughts running through my head. Closing my eyes, I considered that this detour might actually be a better route than being thrown into the mix of a corps on the eve of the season's first big show.

I'd been given the rare gift of a total reset, and I wondered how tomorrow would play out. *Did I have the talent to play lead sop for a top-level DCI corps? Dropped into the middle of their season, how would I assimilate into their culture? What were their routines, protocols, expectations? With the season so far underway, how long would it take before I fit into the complex moving parts that were the Blue Stars?*

Reminding myself to stay in the present, I was helped along by the distraction of people streaming into the grand room. People I knew, but who didn't know me. They were directors, program coordinators, and staff from some of the top corps in the country. I recognized them from past competitions, and from photos in *Drum Corps World* and DCI publications. They were there to pick up their contest information packets and banter with each other and Don Whiteley, the charismatic public relations director for DCI.

In 1969, Whiteley was the public relations director at a local Denver ABC television network. While attending a Broncos game, he feasted eyes and ears on the Troopers from Casper, Wyoming performing during halftime and quickly caught drum corps fever. After befriending the Troopers' iconic director, Jim Jones, they joined forces to organize and promote a wildly successful show called Drums Along the Rockies. The competition was held at Jefferson County Field in Lakeland, Colorado. Fans packed into both sides of the stadium, and in order to appease the huge crowd, they had every other corps perform to opposite sides of the stadium.

Whiteley was instrumental in moving the marching arts activity forward by initiating the formation of the tabloid, Drum Corps World. Shortly thereafter, he was taken on as a volunteer for the newly formed governing body of elite competitive drum corps, Drum Corps International. After Whiteley quickly proved his expertise, the 1975 DCI board of directors hired him to be their full time public relations director.

Don wasn't just an idea man, he was a hands-on "get the stuff done" kind of guy. Equally comfortable in the field as well as an office, he made sure that new regional drum corps shows came off as organized, well publicized, smooth-running events. During his DCI tenure, he developed drum corps shows throughout the untapped southern and western regions of the country, he procured televised championships on PBS, complete with celebrity hosts, and initiated numerous marketing schemes, even convincing local Baskin-Robbins ice cream parlors to name flavors after nearby drum corps. He also organized seminars at the annual DCI congress, where new and established sponsors could learn how to promote and run efficient shows for maximum profit, fan enjoyment, and the performing corps' benefit. Amazingly, in only a few years, he'd taken drum corps from its cloistered cult-like status, into the mainstream of American culture.

Whiteley's outgoing personality matched his commanding appearance. He was a tall, barrel chested, middle-aged guy, with honest eyes set below a high forehead that was topped with thin, combed back black hair. Freshly shaven and dressed in pressed navy slacks and a long-sleeved blue dress shirt, sans tie, he moved easily from conversation to conversation. He knew everyone—surprisingly, even me.

Approaching with a ruby-cheeked smile, he said, "So Mike…you sure you want to march with that rag-tag Blue Stars outfit for the rest of the summer?" Winking, he continued, "I think you should give up that idea and come work for us. You'll see a lot more shows and have a lot more fun."

Laughing, I told him how with Kris's help, I'd gone from lost to found, and appreciated them letting me spend the night. He replied, "Oh you're not getting this for free, we'll put you to work before too long…we have to get something for our hospitality."

With that, several more polo shirt wearing staff members arrived carrying the familiar large red and white buckets and bags of Kentucky Fried Chicken, along with iced coolers of soft drinks. I pitched in, assisting in setting up a buffet line on the room's long table as an impromptu dinner party took shape.

There I was enjoying Thursday night fried chicken with DCI officials, top drum corps directors and staff, all talking about the first big showdown of the best corps in the country, in a beautiful room that spilled out into the shaded courtyard. I was in heaven.

Helping to clean up after dinner, I could tell Kris was spent from the day's hustle, and I asked if there was anything else that I could do. It wasn't going to get any easier for her. Tomorrow morning kicked off a thirty-four corps preliminary competition, with the top ten moving into finals on the following day. Informing me that we were done for the night, she set me up in a room on the second story of a small nearby residence hall.

I too was feeling the effects from a day's travel and felt lucky to have the chance for one last night in a bed, before trading it in for a bus seat and gym floor. The sterile, narrow dorm room held two twin bed frames, and I unrolled my sleeping bag on top of the thin mattress on the one with the best view of the courtyard below. Dragging myself down the empty hallway, I located a large communal bathroom, let a hot shower wash away the day's dust and welcomed the lingering fatigue that remained.

The still silence of the empty dorm was another unexpected gift. I cranked open the room's tall single window to let the fresh night air replace the room's Pine-Sol odor. Staring out over the commons, dusk was surrendering to darkness and replicas of old-fashioned street lamps suddenly blinked on. They lit a curved pattern of walkways and cast long shadows under trees and benches.

The heat in the room slowly dissipated, and with it, so did the last of my stress. Sitting on the bed, I propped my pillow against the wall, leaned back and took in the cool evening air. Through the window, the night sky was beginning to show itself, and to block out the ambient light I curled my hands into a simple spy scope and raised it to one eye. Now I could see the brightest stars just starting to flicker. Smiling, I realized that tomorrow there'll be other stars coming out to play, and I'd be joining them.

PART 2

FIRST DAYS

6

FRIDAY, JULY 7, 1978

WHEN THE FIRST SLIVER OF light slipped through the window, I stirred and gathered loose thoughts for the upcoming day. A night of deep dreamless sleep had me refreshed and antsy, and a quick shower cleared the remaining morning fog from my mind. I pulled on a favorite white short-sleeved sweatshirt, faded jeans, and white Puma tennis shoes, repacked my gear, and headed back to DCI's beautiful temporary office. Sunbeams were streaming through the French doors, heralding clear skies and temps that were already in the seventies and I was greeted by Kris's now-familiar smile and the smell of a fast food breakfast. She must have been up early, as the meeting table now displayed a large pump thermos of coffee, small cartons of orange juice, wrapped Egg McMuffins, and an assortment of fresh donuts. I dug in.

Joined by other DCI staff, we were still feasting when an effervescent Whiteley arrived. Tossing me a set of keys he chuckled, "Come on, you've got some work to do before I turn you over to the Blue Stars. You're my chauffeur this morning...you do drive, don't you?"

"Yeah," I replied, "but I'm not so sure I'd have any idea where I'm going."

"Don't you worry about that, I'll navigate," he said, pouring cream into his cup and grabbing an egg muffin. "We just have to pick up some film from the drug store, and then we're off to the stadium." Between slurps of coffee, he bellowed, "Let's load up."

Decked out in their DCI polos and white shorts, Kris and two other young staffers piled into the back seat of the huge Lincoln Town Car. Unbelievably, there I sat in the driver's seat with Whiteley as my co-pilot. The car was cavernous, a floating sofa that dwarfed our family's Delta 88. I'd never driven anything like it. As promised, Whiteley navigated, and I maneuvered the rolling boat through quiet neighborhood streets. Driving Don and his posse added another layer of excitement to the building anticipation of meeting up with the corps. The trust Whiteley had in me bolstered my confidence and contributed to a growing feeling that I'd made the right decision. I'd left Cedar Rapids only twenty-four hours ago, but it seemed I had been gone for much longer.

Allentown School District Stadium was in its second year of hosting the DCI East Championship. Prior to that, the show was held in Lowell, Massachusetts, and hosted only East Coast corps. After the move to Allentown, Whiteley opened it up to touring corps from across the nation, and the 1977 show featured a lineup of twenty-eight corps in prelims, with the top ten moving on in finals. That show was won by the Bridgemen from Bayonne, New Jersey. Beating the rest of the strong East Coast contingency along with the corps from Canada, Illinois, Wisconsin, and California.

The stadium was built into a large hill and held 15,000 spectators, with the lion's share of those seats on the press box (concert) side of the field. Its modest size was perfect for ensuring a sold out regional competition, which was always a publicity strategy for DCI. The steep, curved seating arrangement and its sound-dampening hill provided great acoustics, and most of the seats were better than good for viewing a show. The first row of bleachers started ten feet up from the edge of a track that ringed the field, and the close proximity of the audience made it easy for corps to transmit the collective and individual intensities of their performances, and even easier for rabid East Coast fans to reciprocate with rowdy, energetic ovations.

Parking in a small reserved lot close to the stadium, we made our way through a back entrance onto the field. With gear awkwardly in hand, I thanked Don and Kris, and climbed into the stands. I had my pick of seats between the scattered clumps of early morning fans, and as soon as I'd sat down, I saw Don scanning the stands and then signaling me to join him. Leaving my gear, I hustled down just as the Bridgemen were entering the field.

The day was already beginning to warm, and Don was already beginning to sweat through his shirt. He said, "Hey, you looked lost up there by yourself. You should hang out here and watch some of the corps from the front sidelines." Surprised that he was even considering me, I took him up on his offer.

"Get ready, the Bridgemen are going to blow you away, these guys have a great show, they've been on a mission since last year's disqualification in Denver." Pointing at my suitcase and sleeping bag in the stands, he continued. "Feel free to stay down on the track as long as you like. However, you may want to stash your stuff up at the Blue Stars souvenir stand. Anyway, from here on out, you're on your own, good luck. Enjoy the rest of your summer…oh, and one more thing, the moment you see Doc Kampschroer and Moe Latour tell those jokers hello for me."

Following Don's advice, I moved over to the fifty-yard line, where I leaned against the backstop of the stands as the Bridgemen finished setting up. Their opening formation had them set in concentric arcs splitting the fifty. Surprisingly, the horn line was toting brass-lacquered horns. Initially I thought the finish gave them the look of a marching band, but the more I considered the entire package, the more I decided it fit with their overall vibe.

They made a pretty funky visual statement decked out in their knee length, banana-yellow colored coats. The uniforms were topped with outlandishly oversized black fedoras, each accented by a red tie-dyed scarf for a headband. The guard wore the same fedoras with similarly styled coats yet in black, and the rifle line was front and center, shrouded in black capes. The drum major and guard captain were identified by their white coats and hats that matched the goose-white acrylic shells of the snares, tenors and basses.

In a blasting opening fanfare the rifle line shed their capes in a sequential ripple, revealing funky Smurf-blue hooded bodysuits trimmed in silver sequins, and the color contrast worked well to draw my eyes to some pretty unique rifle moves. Meanwhile, the horn line buzzed through a backfield move while their phenomenal soprano soloist, "Diamond" Jim Brady, set the stage with the melody until two parts of the drill formation perfectly fused for a high octane impact. The entire opener was a mashup of the De Falla's "Ritual Fire Dance" and Aram Khachaturian's "Sabre Dance." The tight and talented soprano section was backed by beefy, honking low brass, and some quintessential East

Coast mellophones, who'd never met a triple forte they didn't love. The lacquered horns had a warm sound that the brass line pushed to the edge of their carrying capacity. *Yeah—I guess I was being blown away.*

Just as quickly as the rifles had shed their capes, the remainder of the guard transformed their appearance. Rising up from behind small black screens on the near side of the field, they now carried reflective foil-covered shields and cutlasses, and their black coats were opened revealing a red satin blouse and yellow belt. Completing their look, they had traded their black fedoras for yellow Cossack hats. Suddenly they were doing synchronized dance moves while sitting on the backs of the kneeling blue clad rifles. I'd seen Santa Clara's rifle line do their standing ovation-inspiring bottle dance to *Fiddler on the Roof*, but this guard work took things in an entirely bizarre, and I thought, wonderful new direction. The dance choreography mixed seamlessly with the more traditional guard work, making every move watchable.

Their show wasn't hip, it was hypnotic. Wearing the long coats and using a low leg lift gave the corps the appearance of floating across the field. Drill sets were framed and accented by a flag line using long, thin, rainbow-colored banners. Up close to the action I scanned for younger members, but there weren't any. Gone was the traditional drum corps' clean-cut military appearance, and many of the guys sported beards or mustaches, with long hair and ponytails trailing from the back of their hats. The corps seemed cool, mature, confident, and definitely locked in.

At 8:30 a.m., their concert number, "Harlem Nocturne," somehow turned a football field into an after-hours nightclub stage. Brady soloed again, this time backed up by a baritone ensemble, surrounded by guard members dancing in ways that would make parents cover their little one's eyes. This led into a full ensemble impact that filled the stadium with a curtain of sound. Holy shit, without ever seeing any of their competition, I was ready to give them the crown.

The musicianship demonstrated during the percussion feature was just as mesmerizing as their brass line in concert. Not just a tight line of snares and tenors, the entire percussion section created a festive Caribbean/West African sound. It was complete with agogô, and roto toms, all visually supported with a funky horn and guard synchronized dance that made me want to join in.

Two calling soprano solos dueled across the field, taking the corps into their production number of "Spanish Dreams". Again the music featured Jim Brady. This guy had it all going on, and I thought his sound on a G bugle rivaled that of any studio trumpet player. With unbelievable chops, he was in complete control of an upper register that delivered genuine goose bumps, and his melodic solo then segued into a tasty swinging lead soprano feature, before the whole arrangement turned into a smokin' hot ensemble with Brady's bugle once again soaring through the morning air.

Even though the stands held only a fraction of their capacity, every element of the corps was bringing it, as they seemed determined not to lose an opportunity to maximize their personal adrenaline rush. Finishing their show with their patented "William Tell Overture," they brought the eager early-morning audience to their feet, and a sobering reality to me, as I realized just how much I'd have to up my game to play in this league.

From New England to Washington D.C., the East Coast was always a beehive of America's drum corps scene, and the Saint Andrew's Bridgemen could be considered an archetype of the many junior drum corps located there. Competitive drum and bugle corps originated as an adult endeavor, born from the patriotism of veterans returning from the two big wars. By the time the late fifties and early sixties rolled around, thousands of kids of drum corps parents were coming of marching age, and neighborhood junior drum corps were popping up everywhere. While many were sponsored by the local chapters of the American Legion and Veterans of Foreign Wars, corps also grew from the likes of the Catholic Youth Organization, Police Athletic Leagues, Boys and Girls Clubs, and scout troops.

During this time, band and other music education opportunities in public schools weren't quite up and running, and many adults saw drum corps as a great way to get their kids off the summer streets and involved in a wholesome youth program that centered around a patriotic, disciplined, team-oriented, musical activity. Most of these young people didn't have to be persuaded. Much of the U.S. was still basking in the afterglow of our victory overseas, and the children of veterans had inherited that same strong love of country. Having watched their parents and older relatives and friends become involved in senior corps, when provided with their own opportunity to march, many were eager to join in this fast-emerging, uniquely American activity.

Bayonne, New Jersey, industrial and military port of call, was home to a large Polish-Catholic, working-class population, and St. Andrew's Parish was a hub of teen activity during the baby boom. Newly appointed assistant pastor, Father Donovan, was a big proponent for the neighborhood's young people, and his parish held some of the best CYO dances in town. Early in 1965, he proposed that the church start a drum corps and the St. Andrew's Bridgemen Drum and Bugle Corps (named after the majestic steel arch bridge that connected Bayonne to Staten Island) was born.

Father Donovan recruited parishioner Ed Holmes to become the director of the corps. Holmes embraced the activity and became a key player in their success. When funds were sparse, he poured his own financial resources into the organization. Ed and his wife were childless, but they often joked that they were the parents of one hundred and twenty-eight kids. Ed's organizational skills and dedication spurred a fast-growing membership, and at the end of their first summer, the Bridgemen debuted alongside Broadway Joe Namath, performing at a New York Jets intersquad game.

In 1966 they started a cadet corps to ensure well-trained members would continue to fill their ranks. New Jersey's Garden State Drum Corps Circuit was rife with working class neighborhood corps and the Bridgemen's early seasons were spent marching in numerous parades and competing in two to four shows each weekend. Clad in white and black West Point cadet uniforms, trimmed with gold and topped with classic military shakos, they looked like many of the corps of the sixties era.

What separated them from other East Cost drum corps were the people involved in the organization. Holmes not only gathered a critical mass of members needed for success, he also procured a great instructional staff to teach dedicated, disciplined kids, who, by the nature of their blue collar work ethic, had the one other required component for success—desire.

The Bridgemen were initially a collection of neighborhood kids who had played together all their lives. They stuck around and continued to grow up within the corps, all the while developing strong music and marching skills. By 1968 and '69 they were Garden State Champs, and in 1970 they were regularly winning regional shows.

The corps was best known for its talented horn line, and their twice-weekly practices were ramped up to four days a week and weekends. The extensive rehearsal schedule developed amazing talents that were showcased throughout their music. Common to every corps' performance were the drum solos that separated musical productions throughout a field show, but St. Andrew's also incorporated a trademark triple tonguing bugle feature. Sounding more like a percussion exercise than music, twenty-two sopranos spit out notes with such machine gun-like precision, it often required a moment of processing before a stunned crowd would break into appreciative cheers.

Almost overnight, the Bridgemen became formidable competition for the other established East Coast corps that included: The 27th Lancers, Muchachos, Garfield Cadets, St. Rita's Brassmen, Blessed Sacrament Golden Knights, Polish Falcon Cadets, and Boston Crusaders. In 1972, they were one of a few eastern corps to complete an extended two-week tour. At the inaugural DCI World Championship in Whitewater, Wisconsin they finished twelfth in prelims, obtaining the last spot in the coveted finals, and with that distinction they were the first corps to perform during the evening of the DCI championship show, ultimately finishing eleventh overall.

The following year saw them placing ninth at the World Championship, but then things started to unravel. Many of the original members of the corps had reached their age-out year of twenty-one, and the younger members weren't ready to replace the veterans' maturity and experience. The Vietnam War's controversial nature, and the liberal youth movements that came with it, were shifting gears in the cultural pursuits of young people. Local membership was declining, and in 1974, the corps dropped to twenty-sixth place at DCI's World Championship, falling one place out of DCI's associate member status. By 1975, they were struggling to score seventy points and decided not to compete in the DCI Championship, even though it would be taking place in neighboring Philadelphia.

Unwilling to fold, Father Donavan and Holmes conspired to make one last big push for the '76 season. Advertising for members in local papers and drum corps publications, they upped the ante by hiring a well-known, and well-traveled program designer by the name of Bobby Hoffman.

Hoffman was truly one of a kind, and arguably did more to advance the marching arts than any other individual in the activity. Baptized into drum corps in the early fifties, Bobby immersed himself into the activity playing tenor drum in a small New Jersey neighborhood corps. As a young adult, he matured into a wicked good timbale player for the Hawthorne Caballeros, one of the top senior drum corps of the times. In the mid-sixties he transitioned to become a drill writer and instructor for several top corps and winter guards. At the end of the decade he was teaching and writing drill for the long-established and successful Garfield Cadets.

Always pushing the boundaries in drill design, Bobby moved away from the common squad parade formations, to more stylized drill forms that pleased the eye and provided optimal staging for the corps' musical selections. He also took other risks with the military-inspired activity, including a peace sign in the Cadets' drill during the turbulent times of the Vietnam War.

In 1973, his talent as a drill writer carried him to southern California, where he worked with Drum Corps International's inaugural champion, the Anaheim Kingsmen, but by 1975, with the corps struggling financially and temporarily shutting down operations, he started his migration back east, stopping briefly at the bluffs of the mighty Mississippi River in La Crosse, Wisconsin, where he wrote a creative drill for the Blue Stars that included a seven minute medley of songs by the horn-infused rock band, Chicago. Hoffman's drill featured a marijuana leaf formation, along with the spelling out both CTA (for the band's original name of Chicago Transit Authority,) and Chicago. Despite fielding a relatively small corps, the Blue Stars still had one of their best seasons, finishing fifth at the World Championship in Philadelphia.

With the promise of complete creative freedom, Hoffman was lured back to New Jersey to coordinate a Bridgemen resurrection like no other. Lean and tall, sporting aviator framed glasses and a well-conditioned afro to complement his mod attire, he was both an imposing and incongruous site at a drum corps practice. Young people were captivated by him. He had style, charisma, and possessed a creative genius that was enhanced by his years of drum corps experience. Hoffman was also personable, observant, well-read, worldly, and open to suggestion. He loved rock and roll and was in touch with the times. In addition, he was intrigued by the canvas that Broadway theater provided as an art form.

Free thinking Hoffman approached the Bridgemen as a general contractor performing a complete rehab. He had the framework of a drum corps, but not much more. To start filling it in, he began with their look. Their old cadet-style uniforms were wearing out and would be costly to replace. The drum corps uniforms of the times basically fell into several categories that included: cadet-style jackets, shiny satin shirts complete with ascots, cummerbunds and gauntlets, themed uniforms of nautical, western, or Spanish influence, or inexpensive scout or army surplus uniforms. Headgear included plumed military shakos, tams, cowboy, gaucho or Aussie style hats.

Bobby's creativity led him to consider several visions for the corps' appearance. His original idea of having different sections of the corps in a variety of pastel-colored long coats and large busby hats, was swiftly vetoed by the corps membership. Reportedly, one member of the percussion section, who was also aligned with the Hell's Angels Motorcycle Club, colorfully told Hoffman there was no way he would be caught dead in such a getup. But Hoffman wanted large hats to help define his drill and momentarily he was at a loss. Then, while attending an evening with Stevie Wonder at the reopening of the Apollo Theater in Harlem, flashing cameras caught Hoffman's attention and he spotted a concert patron stepping out from a stretch limo sporting a funky felt fedora and a bright yellow coat with his initials emblazoned on large pockets. This flashbulb moment lit up Hoffman's imagination, and at that moment, the banana-colored zoot suits began to take form

Coincidentally, their new look allowed for several sweeping visual innovations to take place. The zippered coat made for quick costume changes in the color guard and because of its length, he devised a low leg lift style of marching that would enhance the musical performance of brass and percussion players. The traditional high march time always demanded a great deal of stamina from members, but now with the calisthenics removed, more of that energy could go into the performance of music and drill.

The Bridgemen's new visual identity would also spur the development of a new musical one. Hoffman had the corps move more towards music from contemporary jazz and rock genres, along with Broadway music that was easily relatable for members and the audience. He kept brass arranger Larry Kerchner, encouraging him to break traditional barriers with his writing. Kerchner did just that, beginning with a revamped "William Tell Overture" that included some jazz riffs and uniquely drum corps-esque twists on the original phrasing. Tom Pratt was told to "go crazy" with the color guard; quick costume changes and Broadway choreographed dance moves followed. Drill writers Greg Pych and Jim Messina opened up the drill with flowing lines, asymmetrical rotations, and drill sets designed to enhance the musical performance.

Hoffman also invited an old marching buddy, Dennis Delucia, to join him as the drumline's caption head. Delucia was cerebral, innovative, and professional in his instruction and arrangements for percussion, weaving color, texture, and musicality into what traditionally had been a strict rudimentary foundation. With the rumors of Hoffman's significant changes circulating, the corps attracted new members from all up and down the East Coast, and as far west as Tennessee. Gone were the days of neighborhood kids forming a drum corps, as talented imports were now becoming the norm.

In early June, the revamped Bridgemen unveiled their new look and sound at their own show, the Tournament of Champions. Keeping things under wraps, the corps marched the late morning parade in just black pants, and member jackets. Last to perform that evening, they entered the stadium with a police escort. The hometown crowd was completely ambushed, and the surprises kept coming as the drum major was delivered to the field in a limousine.

Early scores had them all over the place, as judges tried to figure out just what they were doing, but by the end of the 1976 season, the transformation was complete. At the DCI Championships in Philly, the corps finished off their innovative show with a seemingly endless final note, capped off by the entire corps falling to the ground in a mock faint. With 24,000 fans roaring their approval, the Bridgemen finished in sixth place, marking an unprecedented jump of twenty places from their last DCI World Championship appearance.

Jimi Hendrix said, "Knowledge speaks, but wisdom listens." Hoffman's open-minded approach allowed for others to take ownership of many of the innovations in show design. His philosophy allowed for creative input from the staff, and members as well, as they took their patented "knock" arm swing from the contra base section goofing around while marching in file to a competition. Watching African Dancers in a parade during the 1977 season, Hoffman, along with his visual staff, came up with the Bridgemen shuffle: a brass and guard dance feature during the drum solo that was becoming a trademark move and crowd favorite.

Bobby's vision helped create an identity for the corps that went far beyond their uniform, and in doing so, he made drum corps accessible to a wider audience. Once the shackles of the restrictive rules of the VFW and American Legion had been removed, the Bridgemen's numerous innovations became a clarion call for what drum corps had the potential to embrace. Blazing trails, Hoffman and the Bridgemen had initiated a transformation that was adopted by many other corps, and creative show designs continued to evolve throughout the activity. Bobby once stated, "You've got thirteen minutes to do whatever you like." And while controversial for some, what Bobby Hoffman liked, was also what a lot of other people did as well.

I could have watched the Bridgemen's show over and over again, a testament to just how good they were. However, my eagerness to meet up with my new corps overcame any desire to stay down on the track. Running back up into the stands, I gathered my stuff and climbed the stairs to the top of the hill. Along a walkway outside the top of the stadium, I found a collection of small trailers, canopy tents, and tables, forming a flea market of souvenir booths. Many were just opening up to catch the growing prelim crowd, and all of them hawked silk-screened T-shirts, buttons, bumper stickers, keychains, and other trinkets to help put gas in the buses and food in the mouths of the corps caravanning throughout the country. Behind the table of Blue Stars paraphernalia, I met the smiling bright eyes of a short, attractive woman with bobbed reddish-brown hair and perfect teeth.

Seeing my suitcase and sleeping bag, she greeted me warmly, "I'll bet you're Mike, I'm so glad you're going to be joining us, we've heard good things about you…Pierre told me to be on the lookout, and here you are, bright and early. I'm Barbara Kampschroer."

Realizing I was speaking to the director's wife, I told her about my trip and the interesting experiences I had with Whiteley and his staff. We spent the remainder of the morning selling souvenirs and talking over the sound of the competing corps. For less than $200 I paid my tour fee and dues, which included the cost of my monogrammed Blue Stars corps jacket. As a bonus, Mrs. K supplemented my wardrobe with a white T-shirt featuring an anonymous Blue Stars' soprano, tympani, and guard member, surrounded by a five-point star, and I quickly changed into it.

7

WEARING THE SHIRT AND WORKING the booth with Mrs. K made me feel more like a member than a fan, and by late morning the prelim crowd had grown to a respectable size, and with it, so had my excitement. After the judges' lunch break, the Blue Stars were scheduled to begin the next block of competition and as they were filing on the field, Pierre enthusiastically greeted me at the booth.

He was accompanied by a tall skinny blonde kid with broad shoulders who looked to be about eighteen. Pierre introduced him as Tim Hoover, a baritone player the corps picked up when we got into Pennsylvania. The three of us then hurried over to the fifty-yard line, standing in the aisle separating the upper and lower section of stands. Like myself, Pierre was obviously fired up to watch the corps perform. Talking over the din of the crowd, he declared, "Wait 'til you see how much we've improved since Prairie du Chien. With you guys here, we only have one more spot left to fill and we'll have a full corps."

This was my first actual chance to watch their show, and we had a prime location. The sun was high in the sky, and while hot, it wasn't oppressive. The line of members moving onto the field stretched out across the back sideline from one end zone to the next. The guard was wearing the classic blue shorts, but also had on red turbans and long navy capes draped over one side of their shoulders. It seems the Bridgemen weren't the only corps sporting costume elements this year. Their opening set was three vertical lines, one on the fifty, and two others on each thirty-yard line. Each line had horn players in front followed by guard members. The drums completed a midfield horizontal cross with the brass down the fifty.

The P.A. announced, "From La Crosse Wisconsin, The Blue Stars. Drum Major, John Brown, is your corps ready?" With his quick salute their show began with a tense percussion intro that had the corps unfold the vertical files into a giant diamond pattern across the field. What followed was the opening

impact of their powerful fanfare, inspired by a movement from the guitar concerto, *Concierto de Aranjuez*. The music then transitioned into Bill Holman's
arrangement of "Malaga," a la Stan Kenton's Big Band. The majestic opener featured multiple tempo changes and brass hits, along with a Spanish swing-style
phrasing. The visuals were accented by some captivating guard work, including
the rifle line throwing triples over the flag line's head choppers, followed immediately with the guard side stepping toward the audience with a dramatic dance
move complete with seductive facial expressions. The opener built to its climax
with two sopranos trading bold jazz licks front and center while the rest of the
corps accompanied them with an exciting up-tempo finish.

Right there in high fidelity, the cool parts I'd been practicing for several
weeks were coming alive. It was exhilarating to be in the midst of an East Coast
audience that seemed to have an insatiable desire for the higher, louder, faster
aspect of drum corps arrangements, and as the opener concluded, they let
loose with a much more raucous response than the applause that first greeted
the corps. The Blue Stars were definitely hyped.

While not on par with the Bridgemen's volume, they weren't far behind. The
baritone and middle voice sections of the horn line were impressive, while the
sopranos seemed to be a couple of notches down on the volume knob from
balancing out the brass sound. The two holes in the lead sop section probably
didn't help, and I joked to myself, *Mikey to the rescue.*

They followed up the opener with their percussion feature. It was a selection
from *The Suite for Flute and Jazz Piano,* by pianist Claude Bolling, and the selection gave their two mallet players a playful opportunity to show off their talents. The guy on the xylophone was technically flawless and superbly musical,
and while the battery section wasn't quite the caliber of the Bridgemen's they
sure held their own with the challenging arrangement.

The distinct intervals of the three holes in the brass drill were easy to follow
and watching my spot move about the field I became increasingly aware that I
was really doing this. Soon both the gap in my summer and the drill would be
simultaneously filled.

The drum solo provided a smooth segue from the Latin opener to a four
minute production number of a medley of traditional Jewish songs. The
arrangement included the hauntingly beautiful melody of "Jerusalem of Gold,"

the bold Israeli National Anthem, "Hatikvah" (Hope,) and the well-known "Hava Nagila" (Let Us Rejoice.) The selection was a modified arrangement of last year's opener, and it provided the corps with an opportunity to create a variety of musical and visual moods representing the struggles, celebrations, and steadfast determination of a strong and faithful people.

The guard work came complete with festive traditional Jewish dancing, and the drill featured a segment where three large circles on the field unfolded into a dramatic brass and percussion company front, that featured a side stepping, slide-drag marching style that hinted of the bottle dance. The entire ensemble then built to another powerful push to the front sidelines with the soaring melody of Henry Mancini's, "Exodus." Both hopeful and ominous, it engaged performers and audience on multiple levels, and I couldn't wait to be part of the corps that performed it.

The concert of "Backwoods Sideman," a Buddy Rich Big Band chart, was another holdover from the '77 season. The allegro tempo of the tune was considerably faster than what I had been practicing and while listening to it live a significant learning curve took place. The chart began with a mellophone duet consisting of up tempo sixteenth note runs that were eventually mirrored by the entire brass line. The original piece featured two saxophones trading solos, and the corps' arrangement included an amazing musical battle between a soprano soloist and mellophone. By the number's end, the entire corps was bopping along with the music and a dancing rifle line had traded their weapons for red and white or blue and white golf umbrellas that were opened, closed, and twirled to accompany the crescendos in the music. It was a novel effect that perfectly complemented the fun music. The crowd loved it.

The closing number was the subdued and beautiful '76 pop ballad, "Come in From the Rain," by Carole Mayer Sager and Melissa Manchester. The melody was carried by a baritone soloist with such a rich warm sound and smooth phrasing that it sounded like he'd traded in his chrome-plated bugle for a slide trombone. When the entire brass section joined in, the drill unfolded into a five-point star formation encircled by the entire guard. The formation then quickly dissolved at the end of the phrase, and reopened into a four-point star, as another swelling crescendo had the entire corps performing a slow push toward the stands before fading to pianissimo.

54

From there the corps transitioned to its up-tempo finale, "Tiger of San Pedro," composed by Buddy Rich trumpeter, John LaBarbera. Starting with a pianissimo groove, the drill had the horn line divided into three sections from side one, side two, and a midfield section of sopranos marching backfield at half tempo. The music continued to build in tension and volume until all three sections ultimately converged around the percussion. Forming a tight diamond pattern, the center section of sopranos rotated 180 degrees towards the front sidelines and attacked the crowd with a wickedly brisk melody. The guard outlined the entire ensemble. Like the props on fighter planes, ten rifles spinning in double time led the way. Higher, faster, louder Latin phrases were followed by an even louder wall of sound as the brass members spilled out along the front sideline. The fans were digging it as goosebumps were being delivered ala Blue Stars, and the final notes pulled the crowd from their seats in an appropriate tiger roaring ovation. Olé!

Yep, much better than I had anticipated, and I had anticipated really good. "That was outstanding," I exclaimed. Pierre and Tim nodded in agreement.

Pierre looked pleased. "Yeah, they were really kickin' it...our best show this season. It's only going to get better from here, with our fantastic improvement and a full corps for the second tour, not only will we make finals, we have a great shot at a big move up in the rankings."

We caught up to the corps out in the small parking lot where I had parked the Lincoln, and members stood silently in a circle around a well-tanned, middle-aged man with sleepy eyes, straight jet-black hair and thick mustache. As he spoke, they focused on his every word, before the drum major dismissed them to a full corps shout of "FCO."

Excited and sweaty Blue Stars broke from their huddle and immediately began to pack up their equipment. Plumes were slid into cardboard tubes neatly arranged into two large wooden boxes, and drums, flags, rifles, and helmets were carefully placed in racks on their long fifth wheel equipment trailer. Other than the large contra bass bugles, brass players carried their horns onto the buses. The upbeat mood of the members seemed to reflect the sizzling performance they'd just delivered, and it felt like a great time to be thrown into the mix.

Pierre then introduced me to the little tan man as "Mike, the soprano player from Iowa." With a slow, resonant, Southern accent, he humorously reciprocated, telling me he was "Moe Latour, the tour manager, from Louisiana." Trying not to stare, I couldn't help but make a comparison with the cartoon character, Deputy Dawg. Asking me my age, he then pointed to one of the buses where he said I'd find a seat.

The idling buses spewed diesel exhaust, and it was like the telltale scent of fresh water to salmon on their spawning run. Familiar territory, it eased the anticipation I was sensing for my first interaction with corps members. While not quite first date jitters, I was apprehensive as to just how I would be received.

I lugged my stuff onto the old coach bus. It was crammed with members standing between the seats and in the aisle. Most of the guys were still in white, sweat-soaked T-shirts and the bottom half of their uniforms. Many of the vinyl seats were covered with faded bath towels. The aisle was further divided by hanging uniform tops strung from the luggage racks, delineating every-one's miniscule personal territory. Sidestepping my way through the narrow gauntlet, I was asked more than once if I was the soprano player from Iowa, and I was almost to the back of the bus before a brass player pointed out my assigned seat. As with the Bridgemen, I was struck by the ages of the members. I was used to the Emerald Knights, where even as a fourteen-year-old rookie in '72, I had always been one of the older members.

My new seat partner had already settled in next to the window. I plopped down next to him. He smelled of sweat and cigarettes. I introduced myself, and he told me his name was Dan Quinn. The taped drumsticks in his lap told me he was a member of the snare line. Wanting to make some connection with the guy I was going to be sitting next to for the remainder of the summer, I asked, "So how was your show?"

"Pretty good," he responded curtly. "We were locked in."

"Sorry to cramp your style," I apologized, before we began trading brief intros about ourselves.

I found it astounding that he'd been in the Marines for two years, and that at twenty-one, he'd chosen a summer of drum corps to transition back into civilian life. Soft spoken but with an edge, he seemed entirely indifferent to the fact that I was there, and I knew our conversation was over with when he leaned against the window and closed his eyes.

As the bus headed back to the corps' housing, members seated nearby were getting their second wind and began peppering me with questions about my corps experience. I was glad to turn my attention away from my sleepy seat-mate but at that moment they were all just faces without names and I felt like a prospective employee being subjected to a group interview. It was a relief to finally be with the corps, but I craved some space and fresh air for a more comfortable meet and greet. Thankfully our commute was brief.

The corps' housing was an old three-story, square brick high school, occupying its own block in a residential neighborhood. Just inside the building was a hallway leading to the gym, and brass members placed their horns back into black cases, meticulously lining them up by section in front of the school's trophy case. The large gym had retractable wooden bleachers that provided a place for uniforms to hang and dry.

Finding some space on the guys' side of the floor to fit my gear into the puzzle of sleeping bags and suitcases, I watched their routine unfold. I was impressed with the deliberate, synchronized movement of corps members going about their business, and as my presence became more apparent, I was met with stares that melted into the smiling realization that I must be the new guy. Showers were quickly taken in the adjacent locker rooms where the smell of soap and shampoo mixed in with the odor of the old gym.

After arranging my stuff and unrolling my sleeping bag, Pierre asked me to join him out at the equipment truck, where I was given my soprano. After paying him for two pairs of white cotton gloves, I added them to the case bearing a stenciled white number twenty-three on the end.

"We're holding sectionals after dinner…so bring your music with you," he instructed. "You and Hoover can then just hang out in the stands when we do our run-through."

I took the case back into the hall and neatly positioned it on the end of the line of sopranos. Looking up, I was met by one of the members I'd talked with on the bus. Toting a plate and silverware, he introduced himself as Brett Johnson. He was about my age, and slightly shorter than my six feet. He had a medium athletic build and a smiling round face framed by a John Denver haircut. With a soft, deferential Southern accent, he shared that he was one of the lead soprano soloists and invited me to join him in the cafeteria where several of the corps moms and support staff had dinner waiting for us.

Standing near the end of a long line of hungry people, Brett said, "Don't worry about plates and silverware, the ma's will give you what you need. We clean them up after every meal and keep them with our stuff." Then, taking on a more somber tone, he said, "I want you to know you can have either of my solos, or both if you want."

Completely nonplussed, I stammered, "Huh? What are you talking about?"

"Well, Pierre said you were a soprano soloist in the Emerald Knights, and when I heard you were one of those guys I figured..."

Cutting him off mid-sentence, I said, "No...well, yeah, the Knights do have some great sopranos, but unfortunately Pierre wasn't aware that I'm not one of them. I just hope I can keep up with you guys...I'm still getting my chops back after being their drum major for the past three years."

Looking somewhat relieved, he said, "Wait, you were their drum major? Pierre told us you were one of their best screamers?"

"I wish...I was back in the line playing lead this year, but I'm not quite in the same league as those guys."

Other curious members joined our dinner line, and Brett continued, "I'm sure you can hold your own, we'll help you learn the music as fast as possible, and if you need a place to live when we get back to La Crosse, you can stay with us."

"Yeah, really? Thanks...I was wondering what I was going to do for housing."

It was one less thing to have on my mind as it spun in fast forward. I couldn't help but think that there was no way this guy was for real? He had to be one of the nicest, most genuinely sincere people I'd ever met. A real Southern gentleman in the making, and not anything like what I had expected for my first encounter with a Blue Star—*and who was the "we" he talked about*? Then I anxiously considered what in the hell I'd do when Hill and the horn line realized I wasn't the second coming of Maynard Ferguson.

The "we" turned out to be the several other brass players that joined us in the dinner line, and they all possessed that same relaxed and easy accent.

Extremely polite, almost reverent, they introduced themselves as Alton, Robbie, and Perry. They were all music majors from Louisiana and Mississippi. Collectively they told me that anybody from south of Illinois went by the misnomer of Southern Bastards.

Our dinner was decent: spaghetti with meat sauce, raw veggies, bread, and large athletic coolers of watered-down fruit punch. The corps meal system was efficient, and the line moved fast. Seconds were gobbled up quickly by members burning thousands of calories a day, and despite my hunger, I held back out of deference to them.

My first meal with the corps was good enough, and I was relieved to be able to share it with my new inquisitive friends, as they continued to grill me about my corps experience between bites. As we finished eating, Moe came into the cafeteria and announced that the corps had scored a 72.8 which put the corps in ninth place. It was their highest score of the season, and conversations instantly ramped up about the progress being made.

The corps' drum major, John Brown, calmly moved through the cafeteria, stating that practice would begin in ten minutes. Judging from his easy demeanor and friendly rapport with everyone, he was well liked. He had tan Ken doll good looks, with medium cropped brown hair and matching eyes, and like so many of the past Blue Star drum majors, he was a great face for the corps

Dinner finished, plates were washed, rinsed, and then rinsed again in a second tub filled with a mild bleach solution to ward off a corps-wide epidemic. I put my plate and silverware into my suitcase, changed into gym shorts, found my trumpet mouthpiece, and slipped it from its silicone case. Walking over to the horn cases I could feel my heart rate elevating as my tongue withered in a bone-dry mouth.

Why'd Pierre tell the brass line I was one of the best horn players in the Emerald Knights? Getting out the horn, I realized both valves needed oil and borrowed some from a tall, blonde, high school aged soprano player. Unscrewing the valve caps, I felt my hands starting to shake. Nerves taking over, I realized I'd left my music back in my backpack and hurried to get it. Flustered, the one thing I didn't want was to be the last one to join the rapidly increasing semicircle of brass players.

Not sure if there was any particular pecking order in the soprano section, I stood on the end of the growing arc. Almost immediately the brass instructor strolled over to greet me. Stating flatly, "Hi Mike, I'm Don Hill, it's good to have you here. We're all still pretty warmed up from a day of playing…why don't you take it around the corner of the building and loosen up on your own. You can join us when you're ready."

That was it: no pretense, and little formality. I figured Pierre had most likely already filled him in about who I was, and what I was capable of bringing to the table, albeit incorrectly.

Pierre, aargh! What have you done?

Walking toward the school, I took note of my surroundings. The neighborhood was comprised of modest, aging, two-story frame homes. The schoolyard included crumbling and cracked asphalt with large patches of dead grass, weeds, and dusty bare ground. Some of the paved areas were marked off with basketball courts, and a football field surrounded by a black cinder track completed the campus. The entire border of the school's property was enclosed by a rusty chain-link fence.

The sun was still high in the sky, and it helped warm the chill running through me. I filled my lungs and slowly blew air through the horn to calm myself down. *Where to start?* I began by playing some lower register long tones. Taking my time, I found some rhythm as I progressed through a collection of basic exercises I had played both on soprano and trumpet: lip slurs, articulation patterns, and scales. The horn played decently enough. Gradually regaining my composure, I progressed through my slow, steady warm-up. I couldn't hear anything coming from around the corner and I assumed Hill was critiquing the performance from earlier in the day. Finally ready to let loose with a little volume, I took a deep breath and smoothly ran up two octaves of an F major scale. The warm-up, the mouthpiece, along with plenty of air and courage, all worked together. Playing a solid high F, I held onto it with satisfaction. Feeling pretty good, I rounded the corner to join the line, and was met by an energetic round of applause from the brass line and staff.

Whoa, was that for me? I felt a wave of genuine and gracious acceptance by them, and a tsunami of relief from me. It was the best drum corps-derived emotion I'd had all summer. Brett took me down the soprano line and intro-duced me to the other eight lead sopranos, then I found my place in the large arc with fifty-two other brass players.

The rest of the evening flowed with the pace I'd witnessed all day. During the brief brass warm-up, I did my best to fake my way through the technique exercises they played. After spending some time tuning, Hill covered some of the phrasing considerations in a few parts of the Jewish medley, and ten-tatively I joined in. When the brass line moved to the field, I took a seat with Hoover in the bleachers, where we were joined by a large number of curious neighbors investigating the musical army that had invaded their turf. The streetlights blended with the last remnants of sunlight to illuminate the corps as they set up for the evening's final run-through. Several staff members ran throughout the brass line with last minute reminders of drill responsibilities, and Hill and Pierre eventually joined Hoover and me at the top of a small section of bleachers. Despite the pedestrian setting, it still had the feel of a performance and while most members were quiet, a few fired up themselves and others with words of encouragement.

Whether in practice or a performance, each of the hundreds of full run-throughs during the season captures that moment in time in its own unique way, and tonight's vibe was totally different from the sunny afternoon show in the stadium. Along with the diminishing light, the ambient sounds of the city were subsiding, and even the curious neighborhood crowd seemed caught up in the suspense of the moment.

Off the line, the music's opening statement reverberated loudly through the neighborhood and the accompanying sounds of pounding feet, rifles and flags spinning, and horns snapping were all delivered in pristine fidelity. Without uniforms, individual personalities began to take shape. No helmets to provide anonymity, their faces expressed the effort being put forth. Damn they were good! The intensity of the opener's soprano duet up close sent shivers through me, and having the benefit of a second viewing, I started to pick up on the multitude of responsibilities I would encounter once I was actually marching.

When the run-through ended, our new neighborhood fans cheered loudly, and little kids marched back home with their parents. The corps pulled in close around the drum major's podium and the schoolyard reclaimed the quiet of a summer's eve. Moe revealed the schedules for the remainder of the evening and tomorrow's performance. The corps was brought to attention and for the second time that day, was dismissed, prompting another full corps chorus of "FCO!"

Heading back into the school, I asked Brett what that was all about, and he explained that it stood for the corps' motto, *Finis coronat opus*, which translates to: "The end crowns the work," or, as he explained it, the true value of your effort cannot be realized until it is finished, and now realizing the tremendous amount of work ahead of me, and the short time I had to get it done, it seemed to make good sense.

Guard and percussion equipment loaded back onto the fifth wheel, horn cases again precisely lined up, I watched the off-duty dynamics between members unfold, as quiet conversations floated through the groups of members sharing snacks of PB and J. Lights out by 11:00, the sounds of sleep instantly filled the gym.

LYING THERE IN THE DARK, my brain wasn't quite ready to let me shut it down for the night. Staring up at the slowly rotating ceiling fans, I began replaying the entire day with the corps, amused by how different it was from my very first experience in drum corps. That was a cold winter Sunday in '72, the weekend after my fourteenth birthday, and the Cowboys had just soundly defeated the Miami Dolphins in the Super Bowl. The game and my birthday were both fairly uneventful. What followed was that gray time of year where spring couldn't come fast enough and as an eighth grader I resigned myself to filling it with school, my paper route, the Y swim team, and like most young teens, avoiding my parents.

Completely vulnerable to new hormones on the prowl, I was a self-absorbed mess: constantly frustrated by the uncontrollable things playing out in my daily life. The list included a growing fascination and frustration with girls, finding my place in the complex junior high social hierarchy, dealing with seemingly pointless schoolwork, attempting to play organized sports, and the love/hate relationship I was developing with my trumpet. All of these were complicated by the challenges brought with assuming my new role as an only child. Tommy, my only sibling, had recently removed himself from our family dynamics, by escaping to a military academy in Lexington, Missouri. How desperate was that?

Tommy was five years older than me, and as the firstborn son, he plowed a critical wake that deflected most of our parents' hyper-critical wrath. Now with him gone, and me slowly clunking my way through puberty, it felt like my parents' sole domestic duty was to make sure I didn't majorly screw something up, like he'd done when he convinced his entire tenth-grade French class to toss their desks out the windows of their second-story classroom.

In my brother's absence, my parents' tag team approach to parenting made hanging around the house in my tight fourteen-year-old skin all the more uncomfortable, but I was unwilling to consider the drastic measures my brother had taken, so there I was, looking for my own way out.

Roger Dickinson to the rescue. Roger was the bespectacled, loud-mouth knucklehead I had befriended back in fifth grade. I first met him when my dad, dissatisfied with the staff and resources of Catholic education in Cedar Rapids, moved me into a public school.

At Grant Wood Elementary, Roger and I had both chosen to play the trumpet, and we found ourselves in a band that primarily consisted of girls playing flutes and clarinets, and boys playing drums and trumpets. Roger's big mouth and ample air had the band director converting him to baritone within the first month, and while we never qualified as best friends, we did occasionally play marbles during recess or ride our bikes around on weekends.

By junior high Roger hit his growth spurt much sooner than me. He was tall and skinny as a long-necked heron, with pale translucent skin stretched tight over a round head that was topped with stringy, straight, light brown hair. Beneath a small flat little nose, his face was dominated by thin lips on a wide mouth that continuously spewed a mixture of gravelly laughter, swear words, or smoke from stolen cigarettes. Wild as a ricochet, he was the kind of kid who'd pass on an invitation to have a lunch of baloney sandwiches, fluffy Cheetos, and tomato soup at my house, only to get caught swiping Little Debbie donuts moments later at the nearby Hy-Vee grocery store.

Roger didn't push boundaries, he completely rearranged them with impulsive, manic behavior, dragging his teachers to their emotional limits. One junior high band class found him terrorizing the flute section by shooting paper wads from a thick rubber band he'd stretched across the tubing of his baritone, and our beleaguered and gentle band teacher, Mr. Sadilek, caught him mid wad.

Like a wheel spun off a runaway wagon, Sadilek broke from his conducting pedestal and plowed through the row of startled flutists. Scattering folders, instrument cases, and music stands in his wake, he grabbed Roger by his shoulders and shook him like a box of raffle tickets. Glasses flying, hanging on to his horn, he howled and gurgled maniacally, only infuriating Sadilek more, who shook him even harder. The entire band spasmed with laughter and several of the flute players ran from the room for fear of peeing themselves.

Nothing slowed this cat down. A few months later, he was at it again, calling in a fake bomb threat to our junior high principal. He defended his misguided heroic effort, telling me he wanted, "...to get everybody out of fuckin' school, man," punctuated by laugh, cough, laugh.

After his one-week suspension was over, he bragged to me and anyone else who'd listen that it was a great idea, and would've worked, if the principal hadn't stepped out of his office to catch him hanging up the school's only payphone.

Yeah, Roger was a genuine piece of work, and the week after my birthday, from across the band room, he boomed, "Hey Piskel, I'm picking you up on Sunday at noon to go to drum corps practice. It's a fuckin' blast, you're gonna love it." (Cough, cough)

Roger wasn't a negotiator and he had zero patience for any deep, meaningful eighth-grade conversation. I really wanted to put him off, but with class about to start, I just responded, "Yeah, okay...maybe, I'll see if I have anything going on, and check with my parents."

Later, during our evening dinner, Mom and Dad were as confused as I was at the prospect of me heading off somewhere with Roger for a Sunday afternoon, but a follow up phone call from his mom had them feeling more comfortable about the prospect.

So, with Sunday morning papers peddled, breakfast consumed, and my mandatory attendance at Mass complete, I waited for the Dickinsons' old panel station wagon to pull into the drive before piling into the back with Roger and his quiet sixth-grade brother. While driving to the community college on the outskirts of Cedar Rapids, Roger excitedly filled me in about all things drum corps with his dizzying descriptions of horns and drums, to the "chicks in the guard, man." I was completely bewildered—well, except for the part about the chicks.

The main campus of the college had several temporary mobile classrooms that they allowed the corps to use. They were double wide aluminum trailers that struggled unsuccessfully to keep out the frigid Iowa winds, and a number of kids about my age were briskly unloading instrument cases from a small U-Haul truck and running them into two of the buildings.

Stepping onto the flexing floors of the classroom, I watched puffs of warm breath condense as members slid folding chairs into a semicircle. Impressively, everyone was pitching in. By the time practice began, the room had started to warm, and twenty-two guys and girls wearing white cotton gloves held an assortment of shiny chrome bugles.

Some of the horns appeared the size of a trumpet, but others were much bigger, the largest bugle even rested on the left shoulder of the chubby high school kid playing it. All of them were bell front instruments, and like the bumpers at an auto show, the chrome finish shined brightly under fluorescent lights.

A young instructor introduced himself as John Scorpil. Early twenties, mustache, straight brown hair to his collar, he wore bell bottom jeans and a button down paisley shirt, and he seemed pretty cool. After asking me a little about my age and music background, Scorpil opened up a small, black, rectangular horn case, revealing a trumpet-sized bugle with a mirror-like finish. He told me it was a Getzen Titleist soprano.

Up close the instrument was unlike anything I'd ever seen. Nestled in a navy blue felt-lined case, it was spellbinding, and it looked a lot more like a ceremonial weapon or trophy than a musical instrument. Under the convoluted tubing that led to the bell was a horizontally mounted valve that I learned was called a piston, and the weird toggle lever opposite it was deemed a rotor. Both were nestled inside short spirals of chrome tubing, and I thought, *how the hell would I play that?*

Scorpil explained that it was easier than a trumpet, and played in the key of G. I was baffled, until he demonstrated that the piston changed the pitch a whole step like the first valve on a trumpet, and the rotor dropped the tone a half step, like a trumpet's second valve. Demonstrating a scale, I noticed Scorpil's embouchure kicked slightly off to the side, but he had a bright clear tone, and his range demonstrated seasoned chops. He handed me the horn. I found it was much lighter than my trumpet. It had a hook on top of the bell that provided a grip for my right hand, while positioning my right thumb for access to the piston directly underneath. With the index finger on my left hand I could work the rotor. Giving it a try, I squirreled my way up the scale and mustered out a thin, high C. Scorpil seemed impressed enough, telling me I could try the first soprano music.

With the exception of a few high schoolers, most members were my age or younger, and the mood of the room was loose, busy, and fun, as the experienced members helped a half dozen newbies. Eventually we began playing some scales and exercises, and I found myself completely captivated by the edgy sound that rattled the frame of the beer can classroom.

Long ago, the horns on animals evolved to provide effective offensive and defensive weapons, and for eons, humans have used them for that very same purpose. Think of shofars, the ram's horn, still used by Jews to announce religious ceremonies. Biblical references have seven priests blowing shofars, and accompanied by shouting soldiers, they inspired the walls of Jericho to come tumbling down, and by AD 200, Roman legions had forty-three different horn signals for battle.

Not unlike the incredibly loud horn lines of drum corps, the early Greek Olympics included a horn playing event that was judged strictly on volume and endurance. During the Crusades, the Saracen military used horns, accompanied by large, hollow-bodied kettle drums, as a means of psychological warfare. No doubt crusading armies were scared shitless hearing the enemies' ominous music echoing in the adjacent valley. Considering the impressive acoustic volume reached by horns, we should remain mindful of the seven angels from Revelations that will blow their trumpets to signal the world's end.

The bugle gets its name from the French term "bugler" or "bugleret" which is derived from the Latin buculus, meaning young bull. Bugle horns of the day were distinct from trumpets, with conical rather than cylindrical tubing, and played with a funnel-shaped mouthpiece.

By the time of the American Revolutionary War, the bugle had become the preferred signaling instrument, and had evolved into a half moon curved tube for sending commands to light infantry, mounted troops, and ships. Near the end of the eighteenth century, the bugle was now coiled like a trumpet, and the Continental Army traded in their fifes for bugles, as they were superior at signaling from a distance and easy to use on horseback.

Like most instruments throughout history, bugles encountered an assortment of different designs. The addition of piston valves, rotors, and even padded keys increased the variety of music that could be played. Slides in bugle tubing predated the trombone. However, in the military, bugles were valveless and limited to the five notes used for the familiar calls like reveille, retreat, and taps.

In the 1850s, The Royal Artillery Bugle Band of England enlisted instrument maker Henry Distin to create a chromatic attachment to the bugle. He also devised three separate voices for the horns, expanding the range of the sound by varying the size and tubing of the instruments. From there things changed rapidly.

During the 1870s, Italian instrument innovators Giuseppe Pelitti and Son took horn building to another level. They created a brass choir sound by developing a line of seven conical bore brass instruments with a single vertical piston. Pelitti's horns were adopted by the Italian light infantry known as the Bersaglieri, and their band was notable for their unique sound and distinctive appearance, playing their instruments while maintaining a jogging pace—truly a band on the run.

Bugles were commonly used in the Civil War, and by 1860, the United States military had a New York company manufacture more than sixty thousand field trumpets and bugles. Bugle bands started to form from the signaling corps, and drums were quickly added into the mix. Since bugles were limited by their simple design, modification of tuning crooks (shaped like a shepherd's crook) were added to increase the length of the horn, allowing access to more notes. In 1880 a Canadian bugle band included snare drums, and by the mid 1880s John Phillip Sousa had written a book of compositions and techniques for the bugle bands that were becoming popular in the Washington D.C. area. In 1886, Purdue University formed a trumpet and drum corps that was the precursor to today's large university marching bands. It wouldn't be long before horns would again play a role in battle, this time however, on the gridiron of a football field.

During the 1870s, high-wheeled bicycles became a common mode of transportation, and initially bugles were used by their riders for warning devices. This is why the universal symbol of a bugle now identifies the horn button on automobiles.

After World War I, returning veterans were looking for ways to stay connected with other soldiers to share in their profound military experiences. To fill this need, a new patriotic service organization called the American Legion took root. It was founded by officers and veterans and chartered by congress in 1919. The Legion's main mission was to provide past and present military personnel support by lobbying for their benefits. It also promoted Americanism: the ideology of loyalty to the country, and its traditions of democracy, customs, culture, and flag. Within a few years, a multitude of American Legion posts sprung up across the country providing a place for veterans to gather, commiserate, and form community.

General Pershing, impressed by the European military bands he saw during wartime, urged returning soldiers to take the surplus of bugles and doughboy uniforms to organize their own marching units, and the American Legion gave them the framework to make it happen. It wasn't long after the formation of these parade corps that members started challenging each other to see who marched and played the best. In 1921, at the second annual American Legion National Convention, twenty-four musical marching units battled for parade prize money, and competitive drum corps was born. Black Jack Pershing himself took part in the first judging panel.

Eventually these parade units moved their competitions onto the football field, with the American Legion devising a set of rules that included starting and stopping locations, time of performance, required marching tempos, and presentation of the colors. With that, competitive drum corps became a popular pastime for veterans.

Most corps used three bugle voices: sopranos, tenors, and basses, with tuning crooks to alter their key from D to G. Some bugle designs were based off of the Bersag horns, and they offered up a single piston, now horizontally mounted under the bell, but standardization ruled the day. So, in order to create a level playing field, the American Legion only permitted simple military G bugles, and horns equipped with a piston were required to attach a locking device to prevent its use during competitions.

During the 1930s, instrument manufacturers were providing "how to" manuals and promoting drum corps as a viable social activity. It was quite literally the time of The Music Man, *with sales representatives descending on small towns to hawk the idea of forming a drum corps. The number of adult corps continued to grow, and junior corps, born from sons and daughters of the American Legion and VFW members, soon followed.*

By the end of the decade, the U.S. Marine Drum and Bugle Corps had adopted the single piston bugle, and all three sizes of horns. The bass bugle, pitched an octave below the soprano, was renamed the Baro-Tone bugle. Following the Marine Drum Corps' lead, the American Legion permitted the use of the piston in competitive performances.

In 1941, Whaley Royce Corporation introduced the French horn bugle, which was readily adopted by corps for its ability to access more notes than other horns. Corps looking for an additional musical edge resorted to polishing the horn's tuning slide and then employing it like the slide on a trombone to change pitch. It wasn't easy to use, so in 1957, slip slides were factory installed, along with a D rotor valve. About this same time, brass manufacturers were developing the contrabass, mellophone, and euphonium bugles. Horn lines were finally catching up to the brass choir instrumentation initiated by Pelitti some eighty years prior.

These moves were not without controversy, as drum corps "purists" vehemently fought the changes, and heated debates took place between progressive corps music directors and governing American Legion rules committees. Part of the conflict stemmed from the fact that many of these governing veterans had no true musical background; rather they were part of a system that had put them in charge of a multitude of operations, including regulations for flag codes and motorcycle field competitions, as well as drum and bugle corps.

The most significant change for competition bugles occurred in the late sixties, when corps pleaded for rules to allow for a G-F rotor valve. The move would create an almost fully chromatic bugle, and brass instructors could envision student musicians easily transitioning to bugles. Hopefully the move would also garner more support from drum corps-despising band directors. In October of 1967, both the American Legion and VFW approved the rule to permit the G-F bugle for the upcoming season. Intelligent instrument manufactures designed and sold conversion kits for the horns, and most corps quickly made the transition.

With the change in bugles also came the change in the numbers and makeup of horn lines. Those early American Legion drum corps of the twenties and thirties usually consisted of less than two dozen buglers. By the late sixties, many competitive corps had forty plus members playing an assortment of sopranos, mellophones, French horns, baritones, euphoniums, and contrabass bugles.

When Drum Corps International (DCI) was formed in the fall of 1971, it became the major governing body for performance rules. With guidelines and regulations in the hands of the directors, staff, and musically trained judges, changes that would have been considered heresy against doctrine by the military service organizations were now routinely enacted.

By the mid-seventies, most large corps were eager to change out their aging instruments. At that year's 1975 DCI Brass Caucus held before the Rules Congress, instrument designers, along with several directors and instructors, thought corps should make the jump to a truly chromatic three valve G-bugle. Several caucus members had other ideas, and supported by the vocal outcries of old school purists, they argued it was too much of a departure from what made drum corps, a drum corps. Others feared playing "real" instruments would create new obstacles regarding copyright violations, along with breaching performing, broadcasting, and recording rights. Included in the debate was the consideration of manufacturing costs that would add another financial burden for smaller corps. In order to avoid the failure of the proposal, the caucus stuck with the concept of phasing in two-valve bugles over several years.

With their "almost real" instruments, drum corps horn lines continued to grow. It was commonplace for many top DCI corps to have over half of the one hundred and twenty-eight allowable members march in the brass section. Bersag's brass choir concept exploded, and at times their decibel level could become truly dangerous. Weapons indeed!

The evolution of the bugle to its present two-valve design figuratively took corps out of the dark ages into the light of a more accessible musical entertainment activity. It was finally time to let previously hobbled horses run free, and with similar expansion in percussion section's instrumentation and the color guard's rapidly evolving equipment and choreography moves, the mid-seventies showcased a tremendous improvement in the overall show design and performance quality of drum corps across the country. While many of those old school purists were disappointed, it became evident that if drum corps was to survive as an entertainment activity, thoughtful innovations needed to take place to satisfy the sensibilities of a younger generation wanting to disassociate from the constraints and stigma of the classic military tradition.

That cold winter afternoon, the only other soprano worthy of playing the lead part was Dave Bammert. He was a short, muscular, tough-looking high school senior, with a Marine sergeant's chiseled nose and squared off jaw. Informing me that he had been a member since the corps formed in 1965, he was a strong and mechanically proficient bugler.

As a junior high tenderfoot, I was slightly intimidated by his gruff, lunch pail demeanor, but there was also a certain honesty about his affect that I found intriguing. Early in practice he displayed his dominance for the newbies by demonstrating attention, parade rest, and how to properly snap our horns into position. As practice wore on, I realized he was happy to have another lead soprano in the line, and he joked around with me like we were the same age.

We spent the afternoon muddling through two arrangements from the musical *Camelot*. It was fun to just blow your brains out for a couple of hours, even though my chops were becoming sore and chapped from the continuous playing. Feeling the need to keep up, I resorted to pushing the mouthpiece harder and harder into my embouchure and was grateful when Scorpil finally gave us a break.

During our time out, Roger and several of his buddies went out into the bracing cold to sneak some smokes, and I felt more liberated than abandoned by his absence. I wanted to meet some of the other kids in the corps and before practice started, I was surprised to see another band member from my junior high, Tim Daugherty. While I knew him, we really hadn't ever hung out together, and I had no idea he and his two younger brothers were in the corps. Heck, I didn't even know he had brothers. At school, Tim was a talented athlete and musician, with lots of friends, and his presence that afternoon lent some additional credibility to the activity. During the break Tim told me his two older brothers had also been in the corps.

I was envious. Here was a guy with four brothers to share the attention and energy of his parents, and it appeared that being a middle child had cultivated appropriate survival skills; he was gregarious, funny, and easygoing. No wonder he was popular. Getting to know him a little better had me hopeful for the chance to make a new friend, and the possibility of moving up a notch in the pecking order of McKinley Junior High School's social scene.

After introducing me to several of the older kids, we ignored our coats and ran full speed through the biting air into one of the other temporary buildings. Opening the door we were confronted by a thunderous rumble, and I thought that any second the trailer might explode. The room held a collection of mostly high school guys strapped to snare drums, tenors, and bass drums. Playing a variety of rudimental exercises, they looked straight ahead, wearing the expressions of serious concentration. Several college-age instructors were hovering around, with one clicking two drum sticks together for tempo. It was way too loud to talk, and heading back after break, I realized I had no idea how any of this fit together.

That Sunday practice gave me the sensation of discovering a mysterious door that provided a way out of the dark tunnel of eighth-grade self-loathing. It opened to a room I could never have envisioned, full of strange instruments, unique military routines, and a host of new characters from other schools around the city. I tried to take it all in but wasn't exactly quite sure what all of it was. Despite the significant age ranges of the members, they seemed to genuinely enjoy each other and the time spent practicing. I'd instantly felt welcome, and after some reflection, I realized that both members and staff possessed little if any pretense. It was weird how comfortable I felt being there, not at all like the nerve-racking tryouts for the school's sports teams and music groups. I didn't have to audition; rather, it seemed as if I'd been instantly accepted just for showing up.

Riding home, I sensed my presence that afternoon had real value, and that my ability to play the lead part was important to Scorpil, Bammert, and the other older members of the horn line. They seemed to like me, and being at an age where insecurity is profound, and self-esteem is easily derailed, I suddenly felt relevant. Then there was the added bonus of not having to spend a Sunday afternoon bored by bad television or having the constant feeling that the painful solitude of a cold winter day would be broken by something even more painful, like my parents asking me to go shopping or help around the house.

Scorpil told me to take the horn home and practice, and that night I eagerly demonstrated it to my parents. At dinner, to their obvious surprise, I explained as best I could how I thought I wanted to try this Emerald Knight thing for a while.

~ ≈ ~

The gym was filled with the silence of sleeping Blue Stars and I was ready to join them, but just before drifting off, a flashbulb memory triggered a muffled snort: Two years after joining the Knights, word had gotten around that drum corps was finally coming to the national airwaves. Proof was found in the *Gazette*, as small print briefly detailed the program that would air on the frequently-ignored PBS channel.

On a warm late-summer evening, with the first days of high school on my horizon, I sat on a sofa in our comfortably cool basement family room. Stretched out with my stocking feet on the wooden coffee table and holding a large bowl of fresh popcorn in my lap, I yelled for my parents to come down and join me.

The program had been filmed at the famous Boston Common, and started with an introduction to competitive drum corps for the uninformed. It was followed by successive performances from the 27th Lancers, and the Blue Stars, and concluded with a few brief interviews. Several of the Blue Stars indicated they were "aging out," having reached twenty-one.

Until that moment my mom sat tight-lipped, but hearing their ages she again let loose with her patented phrase, "That's ridiculous!" She continued on with a dismissive, "What a ridiculous waste, spending all that time marching in a drum corps."

I responded with, "But Mom, I'll probably march 'til I age-out."

Sufficiently horrified, she retorted, "Don't be ridiculous, you won't be doing that."

Battle lines forming, I defiantly replied, "But it's what I like to do. Why would I quit doing something, if I still liked it?" Program over, I retreated upstairs to my room.

Now, here I was laying on the floor of a high school gym in Allentown, and an actual member of that very same corps I watched on TV four years ago. About to drift off to sleep I thought, *looks like I'm still winning.*

9

OFF IN THE DISTANCE OF my luscious REM sleep came a soft, sonorous Southern accent. "Good mawning ladies and gentlemen, it is time to get up and embrace the challenges of a new day. Breakfast awaits. Please rise, dine, and hopefully you will shine."

Straddling the crease between sleep and wakefulness, I wondered if it was just a lucid dream, or a distant morning bird call. Then I heard the same sweet melody repeated several more times. Diffuse light filtered into the gym. It was just enough to see Moe Latour's short silhouette padding through the maze of sleeping bodies, singing his little song.

While small in stature, Moe Latour played an extra-large role in the consistent success of the Blue Stars. Working closely with corps director David Kampschroer, Moe defined and refined the job description of tour director. Think about it: coordinating the travel, housing, meals, practice and performance schedules, along with overseeing proper health and safety protocols for over one hundred and forty members and staff, required significant proactive planning, attention to detail, and the flexibility to solve issues on the fly. Moe was able to do it all with an affable nature, magnified by his smooth, languid, Southern style.

Moe grew up in drum corps. Joining the New Orleans VFW Cadets with his older sister, he started out as an eleven-year-old bugler, learning the music from a horn instructor who sang the parts to him. While an excellent marcher, he worked hard at playing the soprano. For ten consecutive years he was a member of an organization that progressively moved from a parade unit to a full-fledged competitive drum corps, traveling as far as California to compete in National VFW competitions.

After aging out, Moe was drafted into the army, and luck had him stationed in Germany rather than knee deep (or in Moe's case, thigh deep) in the rice paddies of Vietnam. Tour of duty finished, college completed, Moe decided to follow a career in education, teaching junior high history. It was the perfect profession as Moe had become an inveterate drum corps addict, and now with his summers open, he could continue his passion.

Drum corps in the South were sparse, but there were several neighborhood corps in the parishes of New Orleans. Unfortunately, they were their own worst enemies. Plagued with internal and external conflict, they behaved like bad relatives, stealing members and instructional staff from each other, all while strong personalities played out soap opera-like plots for managerial dominance.

Moe chose to spend his summers working with the largest and most successful corps in the New Orleans area, the Stardusters. However, their size and proficiency did not render them immune from conflict, and after a successful 1971 season, managerial issues divided the corps. Moe and a collection of younger staff left to form the aptly named Bleu Raeders Drum and Bugle Corps. At their first organizational meeting, a surprised Moe Latour found himself appointed corps director by default.

Under Moe's organizational expertise, along with a strong instructional staff led by notable percussion instructor Marty Hurley, the Bleu Raeders got very good, very fast. In months, they put together a program featuring music with a deep southern flair including: "Walk Him Up the Stairs" from the musical Purlie, "Camptown Races," and "Proud Mary." Having only performed in eighteen competitions, they made drum corps history, securing a spot in the first DCI World Championship at Whitewater, Wisconsin.

During an early DCI board of directors meeting in the Fall of 1972, Moe first met the Blue Stars' director, Dr. David Kampschroer. Mutual admiration for their positions in education and drum corps made for an immediate and lasting friendship.

Unfortunately for Moe, nothing in the Big Easy was all that easy, and by 1974, the Bleu Raeders were beginning to realize their own dark forces at work within the organization. Moe had enough and decided to step away. Coincidentally, Dr. Kampschroer had recently advanced his career, becoming the newly appointed Assistant Superintendent of Schools in Germantown, Wisconsin. Located nearly two hundred miles from La Crosse, Kampschroer's new position left him in need of a tour director for the upcoming summer, and a desperate phone call went out to his Southern friend. At the end of May, Moe packed his bags and headed upstream for a new summertime job.

Moe's travel experience and expertise were honed from moving a corps vast distances from the Deep South, and they easily translated to the new extensive touring schedules DCI corps were now programming into their competitive season. With Moe running the day to day corps operations and Kampschroer overseeing the business end of things, like Cinderella's slipper, they were a perfect fit.

Moe blazed a trail from the deep south, and his network of Louisiana drum corps connections provided a direct conduit to La Crosse, eventually leading to a steady stream of talented marching members from Louisiana and Mississippi. By 1975 the La Crosse Blue Stars weren't just made up of "Kids from God's Country," as the dawning of the "Southern Bastards" had arrived.

Moe's scheduling technique had him working backwards from a performance or destination, allowing him to organize time for practice, eating, and sleeping. He had a knack for predicting unforeseen issues that might arise. He sweated the minutiae, allowing staff and members to concentrate solely on their performance responsibilities. Any scheduling disputes between staff, or discipline issues involving members were quickly sorted out by Moe, as he *mitigated common sense final decisions, and people respected his rulings without discord. Moe's logistical prowess was a major factor in how the corps consistently made tremendous improvement throughout the summer.*

My first Blue Star breakfast was a large bowl of Mikey's Life Cereal, supplemented with a banana and a peanut butter sandwich, and I soon found out this would be the menu for every tour breakfast. Unlike our evening dinner, there was no line. We swirled around the morning's offerings scattered on cafeteria tables, like bees in a flower garden, and as we emerged from our torpor, tremendous quantities of food were quickly and quietly scarfed down. Fast, simple, and caloric were critical food requirements to maintain energy throughout a very long day and part of the Blue Stars' standard operating procedure. Not ten minutes into breakfast, drum major John Brown, aka JB, announced that full corps warm-ups would start in fifteen short minutes.

Photo courtesy of the Blue Stars Drum and Bugle Corps

Blue Stars tour director, Moe Latour, happily models his Blue Stars jacket. Note the Heileman's Old Style patch on the sleeve.

Migrating en masse out to the school's athletic fields, tan bodies toted bugles, drums, rifles, and flags. We were clad in an assortment of tops, including drum corps T-shirts, muscle shirts, and halter tops, accompanied by cutoff jeans, loose-fitting army surplus fatigues, or cotton-poly athletic shorts, matched with colorful striped white tube socks and gym shoes.

Thankfully, Cedar Rapids was as far away as it seemed, and my initial trepidation about being accepted into the corps and fleeing the Knights had vanished. While I still felt somewhat anonymous, it wasn't all bad, I would get to know these people eventually. Ready to begin practice in the warm sunshine, amongst a group of strangers that were my new teammates, I was maxed out on the happiness quotient.

JB and the guard captain, Deb Peters, were front and center as we spread out across the field. Today was my first introduction to Deb. She was button nose cute, with blue eyes, short curly dark blonde hair, medium height, and a solid, athletic frame. I smiled to myself listening to her crisp commands tinged with a classic Wiscaaaansin accent.

JB and Deb seemed made for their leadership roles, and their coordination of our morning practice was seamless. Confidence and experience bolstered their authority, and there was obvious evidence of earned respect from members. Together, they led us through a series of light calisthenics and slow yoga-like moves that focused on posture and balance. Still stiff from a night on the gym floor, the welcome morning stretch slowly coaxed my body awake.

JB set the pace for a couple of fast laps around the field, then assembled us into a full corps block to work on marching technique. Eight and eights: forward eight, march time eight, snapping horns up on the first step and back down on the mark time. We repeated the pattern down the field and back, all while covering down our lines and adjusting our rows in perfect unison.

As JB and Deb clapped out a variety of tempos and periodically changed counts and interval structures, we became a single marching entity. Throughout the exercise they reminded everyone of their form and precision of movement, including the attack of initial step, angle of toes and heels, role of foot, height of leg lift, all the while emphasizing posture: posture of head, shoulders, and back.

It felt like I was learning how to march all over again—the Blue Stars' way. Individuals were signaled out by JB and Deb for their errors, improvement, or perfection of technique. Hearing their positive and negative critiques amped my concentration. With the sun rising higher, T-shirts were shed, and our marching block became even more fine-tuned, leaving only their clapping tempo to break the morning silence. Ninety minutes into practice, we took a water break before moving into sectionals.

As horns, drums, and guard dispersed to various areas of the campus, I found a deferential position in the brass line next to the second sopranos, where the short blonde standing next to me introduced herself as Kathy. She demonstrated the set point as to where I should position my horn when not playing. It was much lower on my body than what was done in the Emerald Knights, and I realized that despite our differences in height, the bells of our bugles were now all exactly at the same level. Looking across the arc, I could see how using one of the shortest players to set horn levels provided another layer of uniformity in our appearance. *Huh, go figure.*

Similar to our morning stretch, Hill led us through a protracted and calculated brass warm-up. Breathing exercises were followed by long tones that were separated by equally long pauses. Flexibility, intonation, and articulation etudes were followed by more long tones and tuning. Like musical yoga for the embouchure, it was meditative, and after nearly an hour, my chops were tingling. I got it: we weren't warming up our instruments, we were the instruments being warmed up, and once completed, I felt like I was ready to play anything.

We spent the remainder of the morning working on music. The lead sop parts were well crafted, and the bright, full scoring made every phase exciting to play. I began to add my memorized parts into the full ensemble, carefully choosing the spots where I could blend in unobtrusively.

The repetition of musical phrases, both sung as well as played, allowed for a fast learning curve, and I became more assertive with my playing. Hearing and physically sensing my contribution to the sound of the ensemble gave me a weightless feeling, like being carried by a steady breeze taking me in the direction I wanted to go. I had this, and while perhaps not the player they were hoping for, I was certainly good enough.

Slurping on the dregs of a McDonald's shake, wearing a large Stetson Bridger straw hat, T-shirt, cutoff jeans, and cowboy boots, Don Hill was an anomaly. Medium height and build, he had a head of wavy, thick, reddish brown hair, complimented by a full beard flourishing under an aquiline nose. He possessed penetrating, clear blue eyes that seemed capable of looking well beyond the third dimension. His appearance had affectionately earned him the moniker of "Wolfie," and like *Canis lupus,* he was gifted with sharp ears, and a quick instinctual intelligence to supplement his skills as a horn instructor.

As the caption head, his ability to discern proper intonation, uniformity in phrasing, and timing were pristine. Always emphasizing proper brass technique, he had a plethora of exercises aimed at developing us into stronger brass players and better musicians. He taught us how to breathe, play, and listen. As a music historian, his knowledge ran deep, and he could tell you more than you ever might want to know about how Gustav Theodore Holst's shy personality influenced his compositions, or the complete discography of Willie Nelson. Throughout my experiences in corps and band, I had never been exposed to anyone with his unique combination of teaching talents.

Hill had it all going on, and I quickly learned how to interpret the meaning of his subtle facial expressions. When things weren't quite right, you could watch his brow furl and nostrils flare, then the sharp tone of his clipped critique expertly explained what went awry. The horn lines' quiet concentration matched the seriousness of his approach, and no letup or relief came after a perfect run. For that to happen, it had to be repeated multiple times. Eventually satisfied, he would give us an "Okay, that was good." Like air let out of a tightly stretched balloon, we would pause, recover, and move on.

Growing up in the far western suburbs of Chicago, a young Don Hill attended Dundee Crown High School, where he found himself in the trombone section of the sizable Dundee Scots, a huge, nationally recognized high school marching band. Don excelled in all of his classes, but he was especially fond of music. From classical to jazz, marching to symphonic, folk to rock, he loved it all.

Dundee Township's proximity to Chicago had Hill near the center of the Midwest drum corps scene. Like on the East Coast, numerous VFW and American Legion Posts made it a primary hub of post-World War II junior drum corps, that included the Chicago Cavaliers, Norwood Park Imperials, Chicago Royal Airs, Skokie Indians, and the Des Plaines Vanguard.

During a 1968 summer competition in South Milwaukee, Hill caught his first glimpse of the Des Plaines Vanguard, and he immediately knew he wanted to do that with them. He spent the summers of '71 through '73 marching as a lead baritone with the Vanguard, while majoring in music at Knox College in Galesburg. It was an exciting time in his young life, and drum corps had a profound influence on much more than just his marching arts sensibilities.

Drawing their members from the surrounding white suburbs as well as the housing projects of Chicago, the Vanguard exposed Hill to one of only a handful of the ethnically integrated corps of the times. The Vanguard's creative staff was led by show coordinator James Unrath, whose real job was the program coordinator and announcer for WFMT, Chicago's fine arts station. Unrath was also the technical engineer and producer for the popular Studs Terkel Show. Corps members were fond of Unrath, and his home was a crash pad for many of them. During Hill's time as a member, he learned volumes about classical music from Unrath and the rest of the Vanguard's staff.

A powerhouse corps that came into their own in the late sixties, the Des Plaines Vanguard's innovative programming contributed significantly to the movement of drum corps into the modern DCI era. Their percussion section introduced tuned tympani, and triple tenor drums called timp-toms, along with the use of a variety of mallets for different percussive effects. In the years Don marched, the Vanguard challenged the notion of typical drum corps pro-gramming. While several corps began designing entire shows around thematic music, the Vanguard, like their name implies, took it to an entirely new level. With the assistance of a huge co-ed color guard, they pioneered on-field choreographed drama, acting out scenes during their War and Peace production. Using the music from Holst's The Planets, *and the musicals of* West Side Story *and* Hair, *they staged battlefields and gang warfare on the gridiron, and their general effect-packed program captured seventh place in the finals of the inaugural DCI World Championships in 1972.*

Unfortunately for Hill and his marching companions, the Vanguard's following season saw a significant drop in their perfor-mance quality. Loss of membership due to age-outs, and changes in staff and philosophy created an irreparable decline in morale, making for a challenging 1973 season. The Vanguard limped to twentieth place at the DCI Championships, and sadly made the decision to go inactive for 1974.

Despite being offered spots in the top DCI horn lines of the Racine Kilties and Madison Scouts, a burned out and disenchanted Hill took the summer off. Painting his parents' home in the summer heat gave him plenty of time to ruminate as to where and how he would spend his final year of eligibility, and a late summer road trip to Ithaca, New York for the 1974 DCI World Championship sparked an epiphany.

Watching the Anaheim Kingsmen, aka: "The Blue Machine," with their Bobby Hoffman drill and spotlessly clean and precise performance convinced Hill that California was the place he oughta be. With dreams of a possible World Championship run, he finished his senior year at college, hopped in a car with a couple of Vanguard buddies, and drove due west to what he hoped would truly be, "the happiest place on earth."

The Anaheim Kingsmen did in fact have Disney as one of their major sponsors in the early seventies, but their origin was that of a much more traditional drum corps. Starting from a Boy Scout troop in 1958, they added an all-girl guard into their ranks in 1963, becoming the Anaheim Scouts. Even in laid-back California, the Anaheim drum corps wasn't exempt from the internal strife that plagued many marching organizations, and their decision to return to an all-male color guard created a rift in the corps.

The parents of the ousted girls formed the Velvet Knights Drum and Bugle Corps. That same year, the Anaheim Scouts became the Kingsmen, adopting their cornflower blue West Point-style military uniform and black plumed shako. With the two corps' halls across the street from each other, an intense neighborhood rivalry formed, and for several years they traded state championship victories as well as members. Eventually the Kingsmen began to dominate the competition and ironically reintroduced one of the most extraordinarily clean, and amazingly stalwart, all-girl color guards.

The Kingsmen were the first of the West Coast corps to travel east of the Rocky Mountains for a national competition. Their success in the early seventies was attributed to financial stability, an outstanding staff, and mature members that weren't afraid to outwork their competition. Prior to touring, they endured marathon practice sessions, often exceeding twelve hours a day, seven days a week, and once on the road, they used every free moment to grind out even more. They were so driven they'd work on marching basics while pausing at rest stops along the way. It paid off. At DCI's inaugural world championship nestled in the rolling hills of Whitewater, Wisconsin, the Kingsmen reached drum corps nirvana by entering and remaining in the elusive zone for thirteen straight minutes. Locked in at every level, they overtook the Blue Stars and the Santa Clara Vanguard from prelims, and definitively claimed the title of DCI's first World Champion.

With nothing left to prove, season's end found many exhausted members either burned or aging out. That summer also left them on shaky California ground, not due to fault lines, but rather, diminishing finances. Yet at the '73 and '74 World Championships, they managed sixth and third place respectively. However, the burden of cross-country travel had significantly depleted their financial resources. By the time Hill and his friends arrived, Hoffman was gone, and the corps was now seemingly being run by a transplanted East Coast brass technician, Rocco Oliverio.

Joining fifty plus talented horns and a sizable drumline and guard, Hill thought the first several practices were promising, but something just didn't feel right, and the noticeable absence of proficient instructors left him questioning the solvency of the corps. In short order, Hill was perceptive enough to smell the smoke that was being blown in his face by the loquacious Oliverio, and he quickly realized that if he didn't get out of there, his last year of eligibility might go up in flames.

Making a phone call to one of his Vanguard buddies, who was marching with the Blue Stars, he learned there were still openings in their brass section. He also discovered that the Blue Stars were performing an innovative show with a talented and mature nucleus of members, all complimented by—get this—a Bobby Hoffman drill.

Hill and his two roommates blew out of town and didn't look back. It was the right move, as the Blue Stars maxed out their exciting production with a fifth-place performance at the World Championship in Philadelphia. The Kingsmen didn't compete in a single show that year.

Hill's positive experience with the staff and members of the Blue Stars convinced him he'd found a new drum corps home. Pragmatic about the employment opportunities with an advanced degree in music history, Hill decided to pursue an advanced degree in music education and enrolled in grad school at the University of Wisconsin. Now he was able to study in Madison and practice his craft each summer in nearby La Crosse.

Hill's path was similar to many other drum corps age-outs. Young, unattached, finishing up school, and trying to figure out a direction in life, while still very addicted to the pain/pleasure points that are common to the drum corps experience, they looked for ways to stay connected. While many became instructors, others filled the roles of bus driver, nurse, cook, equipment manager, souvenir salesperson, whatever it takes to spend the summer or at least part of it with "their" corps.

Having numerous dedicated alumni returning to the motherland each summer made it possible for drum corps to maintain their identity and pass down their culture. This at least partially explains why the good corps tended to remain good, and the not-so-good corps, perpetually struggled to find some consistency.

By the seventies, many high schools had developed extensive fine arts programs, and this created a growing population of musicians who wanted to continue to pursue their avocation. The advent of better instruments, show designs, and instruction brought an influx of these talented participants into the activity. Most of drum corps' top brass and percussion lines included some college music education and performance majors. They were in turn reinforced by high school and college musicians, all wanting to expand their portfolio of authentic experiences. The Blue Stars had a substantial number of both, and they arrived with the expectation that the people instructing them would add another dimension to their music education.

Hill's youth, intelligence, broad knowledge base, passion, and communication skills served him well in that capacity. With no tolerance for mediocrity, he expected matching levels of effort from his players. In doling out praise or criticism, Hill could be hilariously caustic one moment, and then completely earnest the next. Hill was a realist, he instantly let everyone know where they stood. He would dress down an individual, "...you aren't in the fuckin' Americanos anymore!" and then build them back up within the same instructional time block. His intensely serious approach to practice and almost unobtainable standard of excellence made it clear to members that when something was acceptable to him, it must be really good. Because of this, brass players quickly recognized he not only rapidly improved the ensemble, he also made significant improvements in their individual skills. With Don Hill and his small staff of disciples, the summer became a musical boot camp on bus wheels for the Blue Stars' brass line.

Hill was genuine. When he was off the clock, he was completely approachable, with a cutting dry wit and willingness to participate in the social aspects of corps. It earned him a deep affinity within the brass line. He was their musical godfather; simultaneously feared, loved, and respected. They wanted nothing more than to please their master and they would willingly chew tinfoil for him.

Sectionals over, we broke for lunch. Corps moms had tables laden with cold cut sandwiches, chips, fruit, and large coolers full of ice cold Kool-Aid and water. Everyday a picnic, most of us took our plates outside. The afternoon sun was blazing, and the Southern Bastards and I searched for a sliver of cool shade.

Lunch completed, our next block of practice had the full corps working through drill moves on a hot dusty field. The equipment truck had been moved near the fifty-yard line, and a ten-foot-tall crow's nest was raised from the roof. Ingenious. That afternoon it was occupied by head marching instructor, Albo, who could observe and adjust drill formations from the elevated vantage point. Albo's real name was Al Timmreck. My newfound Southern friends confirmed he was indeed the talented drum major I had seen leading the Blue Stars in 1975. They also informed me that he was one of the original Southern Bastards who followed Moe from the Bleu Raeders.

I was excited to take my next steps to becoming a Blue Star when Albo told me to get out on the field to learn the drill. Splitting the fifty-yard line, the drill's design was stereoscopic and stereophonic. Each side consisted of half the brass section on side one (stage right,) and side two (stage left.) The "side one and side two" terminology being a holdover from days gone by, when corps had to begin their show from the end zone on side one, and finish their production stepping over the line of the end zone on side two. As with most modern drills, the percussion was primarily staged in various formations up and down the fifty-yard line, and the color guard was either being featured in front, accenting behind, or framing the entire ensemble.

Finding myself on side two, several of my drill responsibilities required me to lead lines of horn players to proper staging points on the field. My fellow sops pushed and pulled me to my spots during which time I realized many of the major marching cues followed the musical phrases making them fairly easy to learn. Similar to learning the music, it was a matter of repetition and understanding my relative position on the field. Trying to play the music while learning the drill was virtually impossible, and I wasn't sure how much of the sweat was from the day's heat, and how much was from the pressure of trying to absorb everything. I felt burdensome, but my mood lightened when several brass players expressed how happy they were to have every spot finally filled on their side.

When the corps performed a final run through, I stepped out of the drill to watch, this time focusing entirely on the little open interval as it moved around the field. Visualizing my cues in the drill, my body moved unconsciously, responding as if I were watching a chase scene in an action flick. As overwhelmed as I was at the beginning of practice, things were starting to make a lot more sense.

Members were silent as they caught their collective breath, and Moe provided a timeline for the remainder of the day. During that down time I got my first real observations of the scope and efficiency that was the Blue Star's touring system. A small, diligent support staff of parents and alumni made it happen. Dinner was sloppy joes, and I now realized the large oven roasters used by the cooks were the only major appliance needed for preparing our meals. They could make a variety of dishes, from tacos to goulash and beyond. The food was decent and filling, and could be dished out efficiently, saving time for practice and preparation before shows.

Marching in the Emerald Knights, it was rare to have meals prepared by parents or staff. Significant amounts of time were spent loading up and driving off to McDonalds, or some other fast food option. Stepping off the buses, we were handed a couple of bucks, and impossibly ordered to be done in a half an hour. Often long lines at the burger joints sent some of us scrambling for nearby alternatives, all resulting in lost time, and occasionally, lost members.

The Blue Stars definitely had an impressive pre-show routine. Gearing up was its own ritual, not unlike actors preparing make-up and costumes for the theater. White bucks and boots were polished, showers taken, and the bottom half of uniforms donned. Guard members wrestled with long strips of red cloth to transform them into turbans. The process was a time consuming ordeal that had the girls carefully putting up their hair, followed by a strip of fabric held at one end in their mouth as they intricately wound and folded the other end around their head.

Asking Pierre Beelendorph about the guard's new look, he explained that before the season started, Albo had learned the turban weave and taught it to the guard. The new guard look matched the period of the pith helmets, and the festive music of the Jewish medley, but for multiple reasons, it was met with tearful disdain by the guard. Occasionally, a turban would come loose during competition, and when it happened, at best they appeared to have red diapers on their heads, and at worst, it could leave a nightmarish eighteen-foot-long bloody streamer dragging across the field. Mixed with sweat from the performance, the dye from the muslin fabric bled onto both hair and skin, and the tight weave tore hair follicles from the scalp. Their removal after a show revealed the dreaded "turban hair," and resulted in mortified girls running for the showers. But the visual staff, along with many others, liked the look that broke the tradition of so many guards wearing the same headgear as the corps proper. The turban's color complimented the crimson plumes in the helmets of the brass and percussion. They also leant a clean appearance, nicely framing their faces and giving the guard members their own identity, while enhancing their ability to communicate facial expressions during the performance.

When it was time to load the buses and head for the stadium, one of Brett's roommates, Perry, the baritone soloist I had only just met, joined me. Carrying his horn, helmet, and corps jacket draped over one arm, he spoke to me in his distinctive Southern-ese, "Michael, you should wear my corps jacket. You're one of us now…you should look like it."

Grabbing him at the shoulders, I made steely eye contact, and quipped, "You know Perry, I don't care what those other guys in the horn line say about you Southern Bastards, you're some of the nicest bastards I've ever met."

Despite the warm night, slipping on the poplin jacket felt good and I was looking forward to having my own before too long. In only one day, I was beginning to sense a growing level of

Photo Jane Boulen.
Used with permission from Sights & Sounds Inc., Publishers of Drum Corps World

1978 Blue Stars color guard member Karen Saugstad strikes a pose.

comfort and acceptance from the collection of "imports" I had befriended. Perhaps having joined the corps only a few months before me, they could empathize with my situation. Whatever the reason, I was thankful for them providing me with an immediate and unconditional friend group.

As I made my way down the aisle, the drummers on board continued their warm-up, pounding out exercises on the armrests and backs of seats. Horn players nervously fingered valves and buzzed mouthpieces. It was impossible not to sympathetically sense the building anticipation—*Almost game time* I thought.

The Blue Stars' distinct culture was developed through the focused mission of its founders. They envisioned the corps as a symbol of excellence, reasoning that instilling a strong work ethic in young people to achieve greatness in something tangible would ultimately give them a template for a successful life outside of the corps. The authentic transformational experiences gained in the Blue Stars would become something they could consistently draw upon throughout their lives, to improve themselves, their families, and society.

The Blue Stars first appeared in public as an all-girl color guard in 1964, but the plan was always to be a drum and bugle corps. The following year they merged with the Apple Arrows Drum and Bugle Corps from across the river in La Crescent, Minnesota, and fielded a parade corps,

By 1966, they were ready to compete, and an August trip to Washington D.C. for the American Legion National Championship found them placing twentieth out of forty-seven corps. On the long bus ride home, the members and staff made it a collective goal to become a national contender.

The following year in New Orleans, they advanced into their first finals at the VFW Nationals, and their mission of competitive excellence provided the foundation for continued success. So, Pierre Beelendorph's sales pitch to prospective members, "We're gonna make finals. We always make finals," was actually the result of a self-fulfilling prophecy. Since 1967, the corps has never missed placing in the finals of any major competition— a remarkable feat that included being one of only two corps to appear in every DCI World Championship. Even their corps button proudly states, "Blue Stars, the Corps of the 70s."

10

RIDING THE BUS TO THE stadium, I thought about just how different pre-show preparations were in the Emerald Knights. The few times we actually made it into several evening competitions during '77, our routines were always more celebratory than serious. Upon learning we'd progressed to the night show our reaction was not unlike that of the awkward little red-headed kid in the back of the classroom, who was amazed and delighted to find out he was invited to the cute girl's birthday party.

Our first such significant achievement came during a five day trip through Michigan and Wisconsin. DCI was always looking to expand the activity's popularity and geographic exposure across the nation, and on August 4, 1977, they were testing the Detroit metro area with a regional championship held at Eastern Michigan University. The Emerald Knights, along with sixteen other corps, were scheduled for the debut, with eight corps advancing to the finals that same evening.

Looking over the slate of competition, I counted five past DCI finalists that were a lock for the night show, leaving only three openings for up-and-coming corps, and I figured we had a decent shot. Fielding our largest corps in Knights' history, including a forty-eight member horn line, our talent level throughout all sections was at its apex, and despite a small three person snare line, the rest of the percussion section was complete, and executing at a very high level. Staff and members all knew a solid performance could carry us into the evening's finals, but I was pretty sure the sixteen other corps competing that day were thinking the very same thing.

Typical for most of the '77 season, we were without a traveling brass instructor, so it was up to me to prep the horn line. In my third season as drum major, I relished my leadership responsibilities, but I was young and inexperienced. At nineteen years of age, I was one of only a dozen or so members who were a year or more out of high school. My strength wasn't in brass technique or music instruction, so I did my best to inspire them to practice and perform with maximum effort, and the relationships I nurtured as their drum major, cheerleader, and unconditionally loving big brother finally had them believing in me and themselves.

That morning's preparation wasn't much different from any other practice, which was followed by a fast food lunch, gearing up, and heading over to the stadium. Our performance time was midafternoon, and the August heat was drenched with Lake Erie's humidity. Once in the stadium parking lot, we warmed up, tuned as best we could, and with twenty minutes to spare before our staging time, I told the brass section to board one of the cool, air-conditioned coach buses.

The somber, compliant faces in front of me acknowledged an acute awareness of our opportunity, and the apprehension coming from each member was palpable. They were ripe and vulnerable for whatever I'd say. My dilemma was just that—what to say, and how to say it?

I wanted to impress upon them that this was our moment, but I didn't want them to pucker up any more than they already had, and I certainly didn't want to pull out the same old tired platitudes and clichés from earlier shows. I wanted—no, needed to do something completely different—something spontaneous, something unique. Then, with my pulse and thoughts racing, it came to me with the ping of countless syncopated neurons. It was time to recognize everyone's value, from the second and third sopranos, to the unassuming kids in the baritone section.

I broke the silence with, "Give me an E!"

The members responded on my directing cue, "E!"

"Give me a V!"

"V!" Now growing in volume.

"Give me an A!"

"A!" in echoing unison, instant awareness, open mouthed smiles appeared. They could tell where this was going.

"What's that spell?"

"Eva."

"I can't hear you!"

"EVA!" They laughed.

I responded in a sing-song drill sergeant manner, "Yes, Eva! E, V, A. Boy, that girl can really play. She plays it loud with perfect pitch. She ain't no hackin', frackin', tickin' bitch."

The bus went up for grabs, and their laughter spurred me on into a new-found, manic flurry. Eva was a shy, blonde veteran second soprano, whom we had luckily acquired from the Nee-Hi's, an all-girl corps from Clinton, Iowa. Tall, and skinny as a ten-speed bike, she blushed magenta. Even her hair seemingly changed color, but I could tell she was digging it, and so was everyone else.

Immediately, I was on to a painfully quiet baritone player. "Repeat after me," I commanded. "Doug, Doug, he's the man!"

They shouted their choral response back.

"Marches with a dedicated plan."

Again, they echoed my call.

"He plays it cool, he plays it mean, he's no fuckin' tick machine."

This time parroting back, they break up on their own obscenity.

"Big Head!" I yell.

"Big Head!" they emphatically reply.

"With his contra he can wake the dead. He plays his part with heart and soul, you can't stop him, he's on a roll."

And so was I, as I danced down the bus aisle singling out members with crazy, simple, spontaneous, and childishly irreverent rhymes that came to me like lightning flashes. Some were spot-on caricatures, based on personalities or nicknames. Others—well, they were a bit of a reach. It didn't matter; they were funny, positive in their intent, and wildly absurd to everyone. Spitting them out so fast, the hits bridged the gaps between the misses, and the bus rocked with laughter. In that one stupid little silly moment, we became loose, we became family—we became one.

I delivered happy high fives to every horn player as they filed off the bus. The earlier pensive atmosphere was gone, now replaced by determined relaxed smiles. Adrenaline had become our ally, as collective fears had been trans-formed into collective energy. We were physically cooled off, fearless, and ready. Verification came in the form of a maxed out performance of brass, per-cussion, and guard. Elation, pride, and complete relief came with hearing our highest score of the year, an even 68.0. We were in seventh place, and with only one more corps left in prelims, we had made the finals, and we celebrated like we'd won a government-sponsored lottery.

It didn't matter that we didn't have any down time before the night show, we were in, and for us that was a great place to be. Completely gassed, our less than stellar evening performance dropped us from seventh to eighth, scoring only a 61.1 before a respectable, but nowhere near capacity crowd.

What did matter was the momentum gained from the experience. The following day we traveled to Whitewater, Wisconsin for the well-established DCI Midwest Championships. There we faced a much more extensive and competitive lineup, including many of our familiar Midwest adversaries, all vying for the last two spots in the final's competition. At least four of them had beaten us earlier in the season, and I knew it would take a lot more than rhyming obscenities to have a chance at slipping into the night show's last spot, and even then, we needed more than a little gris-gris on our side.

Maybe there actually was a lucky horseshoe up our butts, because a variety of factors fell in our favor. We had a day's recovery between our travels from Ypsilanti and Whitewater, leaving us with enough time to relish the success of DCI North, and to realize we wanted more. Staying in one of the gyms on the college campus, we were able to eat in their cafeteria, avoiding time lost from our usual fast food fiascos. Finally we had access to a nearby field, and we combined our extended practice time with a newly realized intensity.

Our last run-through that day had been our best to date, highlighted by an almost flawless percussion performance. Leaving the field, one of our excited tenor players told me, "Piskel, no ticks by the tenors, and the snares only had a couple of breaks."

The color guard had put final touches on their work, cleaned up some timing errors, and with Lilly's creative rifle work, the visual package was finally becoming a contributing element. The horn line didn't require any new tricks to fire themselves up, as their newfound confidence had revealed a comfortable identity that they were eager to put on the field.

The prelim schedule once again had us going on second from last, with our neighboring nemesis, the Colts from Dubuque, finishing out the schedule. In the birthplace of DCI, the afternoon crowd included thousands of fans who probably wouldn't make the trip out to Denver's World Championships, along with hundreds of corps members from the last block of prelims, all anxiously awaiting their scores. It was the largest crowd we had performed for all year.

The best way to describe what took place was a synergistic happening. After twelve years of existence, the Emerald Knights had finally found their way into "the zone." Coming off the backfield line, we played a relentless version of Hindemith's *Symphonic Metamorphosis,* and the opening statement rang through the verdant hills of southern Wisconsin like the bells of Notre Dame on Easter morning. Blazing through the piece with no letup, we transported the audience back to old school "breathe and blow the damn house down" drum corps.

Ecstatic, I was pretty sure that we could be heard echoing off the steps of the capitol in Madison, forty-four miles away. Percussion maintained their clean execution from practice, and our guard was in sync. The experienced crowd could tell that something special was taking place on the field, and at the conclusion of the opener their animated response continued to stoke our inner mounting flame.

Hearing and feeling the raucous roar of the crowd and looking out on the faces of the members taking it in, I could tell we'd reached an entirely new performance level. For the remainder of our program, the corps was at its zenith. Our closer, "Minstrel Boy," featured the impact of a full horn line company front. It was highlighted from behind by the color guard, who fastened their silks together with Velcro. They used the gimmick to create a giant anticipatory undulating wave. Then synchronized with a major chord change, the wall of flags rose up in perfect unison as the front moved toward the crowd. With no dissipation in volume, the sustained closing sound matched the intensity of our show's opening statement. This from a horn line half made up of high school freshmen and sophomores, and a snare line of three. The fully wowed crowd provided us with our first ever spontaneous standing ovation prior to the show's ending. Unbelievable. The only thing that made it better was how much we'd wowed ourselves.

Back in the parking lot, our collective tingle faded to a full corps afterglow. Completely spent, it took a moment for bodies and brains to rebound. Like a startled baby deciding whether to laugh or cry, members and staff finally began to buzz about the experience. We had done our part, and hopefully the judges had experienced what we'd felt.

The final strains of the Colts' closer signaled the end of prelims, and trying to reenter the stadium, we fought a tide of fans heading out. Eventually making it inside the gate by the end zone, we joined a growing crowd of members from other corps, staff, parents, and drum corps groupies, gathering around several large easels where the scores were posted.

When the P.A. system finally clicked on, an excruciating, pregnant pause came to an end. Hearing each score spawned new eruptions of cheers, groans, and profanities, and upon the announcement of our score, numerous Knights went wild, but I wasn't going to believe anything until I saw it posted. Then, watching the show official move the score placards from one easel to the next, I stood in gape-mouthed disbelief as he removed the bottom two positions for the evening's top ten, and replaced them with the Colts in ninth, scoring a 69.55, and the Emerald Knights in the final position with a 69.25.

Besting the Fox Valley Raiders, Spirit of Atlanta, Marquis, Wausau Story, and fourteen others, seemed an impossible feat and I was lost in pure elation. Singularly, it was the happiest moment of my nineteen-year-old life, a Christmas miracle in the August heat. I hugged everyone I could find wearing an ugly green uniform. Navigating my way back through the other corps in the parking lot, I took in the bizarre mixture of magnanimous congratulatory comments, alongside envious disbelieving glares.

A carbon copy of DCI North, we had less than three hours before we got to do it all over again. Second to last to perform in prelims, and first on for the finals, we removed only the top half of our uniforms for our dinner. No time to refresh, we pulled on our sweaty uniforms, and did our best to prepare. With the sun still high in the sky, finals would seem more like another late afternoon show, and many fans were still re-entering the stadium when we went on. Try as we might, we were completely emotionally and physically cashed.

The zone is an elusive place and trying to replicate our prelim performance was futile. I could tell that already-spent adrenaline had robbed us of our concentration. Our hearts were into it, but our minds not so much, as there were numerous music and marching mental errors. While the performance was appreciated by the early eager crowd, it wasn't by the evening's slate of judges.

Our score dropped to a 63.3 and the Colts beat us by four points. Phantom Regiment won the show with an 85.15, reminding us of just how far we still had to go.

THE BLUE STARS CARAVAN PULLED into the small parking lot that was already filling up with buses and equipment trucks. Several corps were scattered about, well into their warm-ups. The show had yet to start, but Whiteley would be pleased, as I could see the stadium was nearly packed. As the first performing corps headed through the entrance gate, they were met with enthusiastic cheers. Warm, still air was suddenly filled with the sights and sounds of pure summertime drum corps.

The guard found empty patches of grass to stretch and rehearse, while the drums retrieved their equipment off the truck and began their organized warm-up. Hill spent the majority of our parking lot prep time tuning and checking the intonation of the full ensemble. No time was lost with speeches or extracurricular hype. Actually, it was quite the opposite, as Hill reminded people of their individual and collective responsibilities, and pointedly told the baritones to hold back on their volume.

If bugles are musical weapons, then the baritones are the heavy artillery, and the Blue Stars had sixteen great big ones. The bari line was full of amusing characters, and it was mostly made up of large guys with large horns. They were thoroughbreds: a tight knit group, whose shenanigans sometimes had them playing the part of jackasses. While the lead baris were musical Clydesdales in their own right, the section's spiritual guru and dominant stallion was third baritone, Jim Schultz— affectionately called Schultzie.

First seeing him at practice, he appeared older than his twenty years. While not as tall as many in his section, he was muscular aside from a slight Buddha paunch. Sporting a butch haircut and sizeable horseshoe mustache, no shirt, cutoff jeans, and combat boots, my initial thought was that the corps had recruited an AWOL Marine, but what impressed me most about Schultzie was the way he practiced. Saying little but doing a lot, he modeled a level of intensity that was hard to match. Always first to our warm-up arc, he'd run back to every drill set, never showing a hint of fatigue or lack of concentration. I'd also later learn that he'd do just about anything to help someone out, from providing housing to helping with dues.

Schultzie and his herd could flat-out honk, and at this point in their lives it seemed that was the sole reason they had been placed on Earth. Hill faced a sizable challenge trying to balance the horn line and still let the wild horses feed their need to run free.

Warmed up, tuned, stretched, and primed, with dusk now in full bloom, the corps prepared to enter the stadium. Members began their own little pre-show rituals, and I watched enviously as they shared spirited words of encouragement, along with energy-transferring hugs and high fives—*Soon,* I kept telling myself.

Once the corps was set on the starting line, the staff climbed the stairs from the field to an aisle in the stands, joining Hoover and me. The evening's brass performance was fairly clean, and the horn line was controlled, but lacked the inspirational edginess of the preliminaries. Hill's emphasis on musicianship and restraint had improved the quality of sound, and the balance issues were noticeably better. While the East Coast crowd's response was appreciative, they didn't let loose until the closing segment of the show.

Behind the stadium, members meticulously arranged horns and drums into a compact parade formation before heading into the back stands to watch the other corps compete. Viewing the performances from the back of the field provided an enlightening perspective, as the crowd's mood clearly conveyed if the performers and design team had got it right. Great shows had a pace that drew the spectators in, and then washed over them with a tsunami of perfectly choreographed sights and sounds.

Only ninety minutes away from Allentown, the Bridgemen had the benefit of being the local favorite and I was given another dose of sympathetic chills as the crowd devoured them.

I also got my first look at the '78 versions of Santa Clara, Phantom, and the Blue Devils, all of whom, at this point in the season seemed to be a step above what we were putting out on the field. It now appeared the Bridgemen wouldn't be able to claim the trophy outright. When the Madison Scouts prepared to take the field, the other corps quietly moved back outside the stadium to set up for the grand finale.

The area behind the stadium was flooded with the participants from eleven corps, but as the Scouts came off the field and joined the ranks, members from each corps systematically aligned themselves in single files next to each other. Marching through the stadium's rear gate, each unit spilled out into their parade formations, filling the field from end zone to end zone.

The stadium lights were surrounded by halos of dancing insects, and the field was filled with vibrant, colorful uniforms, iridescent feathers, and chrome. Over the P.A., drum majors were called front and center to receive their placement and trophies, and the Blue Stars maintained their ninth place position from prelims, but dropped two points, scoring 70.65.

Different judges with different tolerances and different performances always slightly changed scores from show to show. A more telling measurement would be the spreads between scores, and the good news was that the Blue Stars had closed the gap with the eighth place 27th Lancers, along with opening up a bigger spread from the tenth place Boston Crusaders. A tight cluster at the top, the Blue Devils earned an 83.3 hurdling from fourth into first, beating Phantom by a half of a point. Madison Scouts, Santa Clara Vanguard, and Bridgemen were tightly packed into the top five, all with scores above 81 points. Six weeks out from the World Championships in Denver, there was still a lot of jockeying taking place. It was going to be an interesting race.

After the judges' critique, the staff rejoined the corps back at the school. Hill briefly met with the entire brass line and explained that while we were getting better, we should prepare ourselves for coming changes that were needed to improve stamina, balance, power, and overall sound quality. Fueled by an evening snack that looked a lot like our breakfast, the Southern Bastards and I speculated as to what those changes might entail. Then after showering, packing and cleaning the old school better than we found it, we got back on the buses for a midnight ride to Boston—The Blue Stars are coming! The Blue Stars are coming! And just like that, I was on tour.

12

SUMMERTIME IS DRUM CORPS TIME, and I was drenched in it. With my escape secured, and summer reclaimed, I was on tour with the Blue Stars, and I became a stylus floating on grooves in vinyl, carried by the turntable that was our summer caravan. Touring did for me what drum corps does best for anyone who marches, and I was completely lost in an alternate universe. It was a place where I didn't have to spend any time or energy thinking about anything other than becoming a Blue Star. All I had to do was follow the predetermined vibrations, and the music would follow.

Led by Moe's intricate planning, we fell into the simple rhythm of organized movement. Travel, practice, show, travel, practice, show, and the beat goes on. Our swing through the Northeast part of the country crossed national borders, exploring the stadiums of Montreal and Toronto.

JULY 9TH

Traveling silently by night to our next destination, we maximized practice time. Sleeping upright in the bus seat was a learned skill, and now vivid, repetitive dreams had me practicing drill and music both day and night. I could sense the growing comfort with my role as musician and marcher, and the only thing missing was performing in the shows—and what shows they were. Boston found us in the historic CYO Nationals with thirteen other corps, many who'd accompanied us from DCI East. There, we finished in eighth with a score of 74.65 and were now just a point behind the North Star. The Blue Devils were hot again, continuing their winning ways over the Madison Scouts by more than a point.

A full day's practice in Boston provided Hill the opportunity to implement one of his promised changes: a taxing embouchure exercise borrowed from Claude Gordon's Brass Technique Book. Gordon was a trumpet virtuoso, educator, band leader, studio musician, and instrument designer, who correctly tagged brass players as athletes. His technique book included a variety of diabolical exercises to help develop wind-power, range, endurance, and sound projection. They were tailor made for drum corps brass lines.

Hill's adaptation entailed a series of loud, long tones that climbed up a chromatic scale. Each note was held until the last brass member ran out of breath, then, taking a four count, deep, belly-swelling breath, we proceeded back up the scale until the last remaining musician couldn't play any higher. From there we started on high C and went back down the scale. All of this was performed with a slow, low march time. After our first experience with the exercise, we not so affectionately dubbed it "Chop Suey."

While Chop Suey was grueling, there was a certain amount of pride and satisfaction taken in our approach. You wanted to hang in there as best you could, being the last to run out of breath, or play the last high note. While I never won the challenge, endorphins were still released, and it hurt so good. The ritual soon became as routine as brushing teeth, and even after late evening practices and shows, the brass section lined the boundary of nameless gym floors to execute the arduous torture, all while percussion and guard showered, snacked, and prepped for lights out or another midnight bus ride.

I was sure many of us secretly wondered if it would have the desired effect—how soon would we see results? If nothing else, perhaps if we believed it was going to make a difference, we could derive the benefit of a placebo effect. All in all, it didn't really matter what we thought, for there would be no denying Don Hill, or Claude Gordon for that matter.

JULY 11TH

Up early, we left Boston for an eight hour trip to Montreal, arriving with enough time to adequately prepare for our first international show. A crowd of over five thousand seemed quietly lost in the middle of McGill University's huge stadium, until the PA announcer woke them up with French introductions. Suddenly raucous and crazy, they cheered almost to the point of embarrassment. Fired up from the crowd's welcome, the corps' spirited performance was rewarded with a new season high of 75.5, but we were still nearly seven points behind the Crossmen. The drama at the top continued to build as Madison traded blows with the Blue Devils, beating them by over a point.

Compared to sleeping on the buses, a night on a gym floor was a precious gift, made even more delicious by getting to sleep in. We had a light morning practice that began with a wake-up stretch and concluded with the mandatory Chop Suey. Both were the prelude to a free afternoon and evening for corps members. Moe announced that dinner was on our own, and our scheduled departure for Toronto would be another late night drive.

Limited funds, along with a sense of duty and guilt, had me back at our housing after laundry to continue with my personal practice. Most of the corps had already taken off for a day of exploration and celebration in Old Montreal, and there was only a smattering of members left with rest and recovery on their agenda.

I got my horn and went outside. In just five days I had memorized the entire show, but still had a lot left to perfect in terms of playing the actual music. Methodically, I worked through each piece until my tired chops cried uncle. Despite not marching in the shows, I'd been going full speed since my arrival. Finally hitting a wall made me realize I too desperately needed down time.

The best part of drum corps is the people you share it with, and my gregarious nature had me excited and willing to get to know my new family. Memorable nicknames like Promy, Knob, Bubbs, Terr-Terr, Rug Rat, Chink, Rock, Bird Dog, Grunt, Stick, Sev, and little Sev, were now recognizable entities. Getting to know them, I was surprised to learn that only a handful of members were actually from La Crosse. Besides the Southern Bastards, and a contingency of bandies who came from Rock Falls, many members had migrated from smaller corps in Wisconsin, Illinois, and Minnesota. Even more surprising were the number of members that had traveled from as far away as California, Kansas, Pennsylvania, and Canada.

Hearing another horn, I decided to see who else had surrendered their free day for the greater good. Rounding the corner of the school, I observed our youngest lead baritone diligently working through his show. He was an automaton, lost in concentration, mimicking his moves on the field in place with low and high mark time, feigned step offs, horn angles, pausing where he had no part, and playing beautifully through the phrases where he did. At only eighteen years of age he rode on the younger "mixed nuts" bus and I'd yet to meet him.

Soprano in hand, I greeted him, "What's going on?"

"Oh, hey man, keepin' it real." He was dotted with sweat. "I'm on a quest for the perfect show…no ticks. I'm getting there…now I just have to put it on the field."

Everybody has a story—curiously intrigued, I reintroduced myself and he reciprocated, "I'm Ron Collins, but everybody just calls me Ronbo." Another nickname for the memory banks. He paused and added, "I'm from L.A."

If ever there was a poster child for Southern California, he was it. He looked like he'd just rolled off the beach: athletic build, tan, long blonde hair parted down the middle, Dobie Gillis peach fuzz on his chin—dude with a baritone instead of a surfboard.

We sat cross-legged on a patch of shaded grass by the school. "California?" I said, surprised. "How'd you end up in the Blue Stars?"

Leaning back into the sun, he said, "I started marching in the Velvet Knights, but I wanted more. VK was running a little too loose for me, and after seeing the Blue Stars on tour last year, they became one of my favorite corps. I loved the sound of their horn line, their uniform, their disciplined approach, and the clean way they performed." He took his practice gloves off and folded them neatly on his horn. "They always seemed to operate with class, so after last year's season, I got their contact information, and when I found out they had openings, we moved out here right after school. I'm here with my girlfriend, Corky, and the contra who goes by Chink."

"That's amazing that you guys came all the way from California. I don't think my parents would've ever let me do that right out of high school." Stretching out on the grass, I continued, "You're not going to believe this, but when I was in the Emerald Knights, I actually hung out with some Velvet Knights a couple of times. Once they stopped in Cedar Rapids in '73…I think they were on their way to Whitewater. We hosted them for dinner or something. Anyway, they only stayed for a few hours, and played a standstill for us at a youth center downtown. They were pretty good, and pretty good was a lot better than our little corps…I distinctly remember two things from that day. When they tumbled out of the bus, almost the entire horn line was decked out in blue and white pinstripe overalls…you know, the kind a train conductor would wear. A few even had the matching goofy engineer hats. They told us they bought them in Omaha as a joke. I guess coming out to the Midwest they thought it'd help 'em fit in."

Ronbo laughed, replying, "That's pretty funny, I can see them doing that, but that was way before my time."

"The other thing I remember is that a few members were pretty wacked out. A couple of them told us they'd done locker room just before getting off the bus. I was clueless, it was as if they were speaking a foreign language… anyway, what the hell did I know? I was a ninth grader stuck out in the cornfields of Iowa. I was just impressed with how good they were. The following year we took a trip out to Southern California…we were supposed to have a picnic dinner and bonfire with them at Huntington Beach, but the L. A. traffic was so bad, we were hours late. By the time we arrived most of them had left, but a few were still hanging around a bonfire. They were really friendly, and really wasted. I was pretty sure they'd started the party way before we ever got there."

"Oh yeah, I'm sure they were way ahead of you. Who'd a thought a guy from Iowa would be so familiar with my old corps."

"Yeah, small world," I laughed. "One of the guys on the beach gave me a plastic hard hat with a VK sticker on the front. I think I still have it at home." Pausing, I added, "That's all I got for Velvet Knights stories. Have you ever heard of the Emerald Knights before?"

Ronbo picked a dandelion off the lawn and twirled it. "No man, I just remember some scores from *Drum Corps World*. I never saw you guys, but that's pretty funny stuff about VK. Some of them were hard partiers. The whole corps was pretty casual. That's one of the reasons I made the trip out to La Crosse…I think coming here was the best decision I've ever made. I love the people in the Blue Stars, the staff is fantastic, and I'm really into what we're doing and how we're doing it."

Agreeing, I filled him in on the timeline of events with the Emerald Knights leading up to my departure. Telling my history to Ronbo was the first chance I had to articulate what took place with someone who could truly appreciate my situation. A perfect sounding board—if there was any empathy to be had, he could provide it.

Listening intently, he said, "Man, by the time the summer's over, you're going to realize it was the best decision you ever made."

I replied, "Thanks, but I think I already do."

Lost in the bliss of the free day, time also had the chance to slow down. With comfortable ease, Ronbo and I continued our discussion about everything from corps to the perceived complexities in our lives. That was the thing about drum corps people: despite our diversity, there was an instantaneous bond between us, accompanied by a genuine sense of trust. It was one more benefit of having drum corps central to your life. Sharing a common passion that requires sacrifice, work ethic, and heart and soul dedication told you almost everything you needed to know about someone's sensibilities. Awareness of those shared qualities made it all the easier to take the risks that come with putting yourself out there.

In comparison to the Southern Bastards, Ronbo was on a different part of the Blue Stars' continuum. Several years younger than me, he projected a confident yet spacey nature boy vibe. He told me that being from California provided ample heckling fodder for Schultzie and his crew, who regularly dished out clever verbal harassment for the amusement of themselves and others.

The guys in the bari section were the closest thing to a clique in the corps, but while they were tight, they weren't exclusive. Many social ties to the other sections of the corps seemed to radiate from them. They weren't goof-offs, but they were definitely fun-loving goofballs. Experienced and dedicated vets, their pointed gibes were delivered with astutely timed perfection.

I certainly wasn't immune from their antics, and my initiation came after boarding the bus at the CYO Nationals. During one of our frequent "stand around and wait" moments, Schultzie's entourage had apparently observed me chatting it up with several guard members in the parking lot. Upon finding my seat I was suddenly surrounded by a serenading barbershop quartet of baritones harmonizing a bizarre song about water buffalo. The song's inference was that somehow, I'd already glommed on to a collection of the least attractive guard members.

It must've been a popular tune on the guy's bus, because by the chorus the rest of the bus had joined in. Confused, but only slightly embarrassed, I basked in their attention. Hey, at least I was being recognized as one of their own. If this was to be my initiation into the corps, so be it. It was a lot more civil and a lot less painful than the eye-watering twin purple nurples I'd received from Bammert on my first bus trip with the Emerald Knights.

Chilling with the few other Blue Stars who remained at our housing that day, we were treated to a live floor show as the rest of the corps returned from an afternoon of decompressing beer ingestion in Old Montreal. Their comical, boisterous entrance was proof enough that given the chance, the Kids from God's Country could party with the same level of enthusiasm that they practiced, and their good mood vibrated throughout the time spent packing for a sunset bus cruise.

JULY 13TH

Moe's planning provided plenty of time to travel to our Toronto housing site, get some more shuteye, and put in a full day's practice before the show. The small municipal stadium was packed and featured an identical lineup from Montreal. Well-rested, refreshed, and rehearsed, the corps popped a spirited show and yet another consecutive season high score of 77.0.

The Blue Stars were progressing at a remarkable pace, now creeping within five points of the Crossmen. The fab four continued to trade blows, as the Blue Devils were back on top scoring an 86.05, spreading Madison by almost a full point. Phantom took third, and Santa Clara was close behind. Chop Suey'd, showered, snacked, bone weary but content, another day came to an end.

JULY 14TH

After Moe's gentle wake-up, cleaning the school, and the quintessential carb-loaded breakfast, we settled down in the buses for a twelve-hour haul to Whitewater. The long bus ride became even longer as curious U.S. custom officials had us bailing off the bus and opening bay doors at the border. Back on the buses, the hum of the bus engine sang a lullaby for most.

I silently watched the miles roll by. No longer tired, my taciturn bus partner left me alone to contemplate our next destination. Whitewater's DCI Midwest Championship would be our last stop before heading back to La Crosse. Thankfully, it would also be my last competition as merely a spectator, and I was somewhat unsettled by images of running into the Emerald Knights.

The University of Wisconsin at Whitewater was the host site for the first two Drum Corps International World Championships. Most drum corps historians consider Whitewater the birthplace of modern drum and bugle corps; others say it was where the activity's death knell first sounded. Regardless of which it is, in 1972 it was chosen for its prime location to herald a true world champion. With the advent of DCI, elite drum corps began their break from the VFW and American Legion national championships, whose shows were held each August during the organizations' national conventions. Often these conventions took place in areas of the country that proved too remote for many top corps, thus creating a somewhat dubious and arbitrary National Champion.

The fire of creativity is frequently drowned out by the noise and hustle of everyday life, but in the proper environment, a bright spark can occasionally find purchase. In order to fully appreciate the origin of what is considered modern drum corps, one must begin several years before, and twenty-five miles south of that first DCI Championship in Whitewater.

Cue the urinals at the local high school football field restroom in Delavan, Wisconsin.

On August 7, 1970, drum corps icons Don Warren, founder and long-time director of the Chicago Cavaliers, and Jim Jones, his counterpart with the Casper Troopers, serendipitously found them-selves side-by-side during a bathroom break at a local show. Perhaps midstream, Warren suggested to Jones that the only way to break free from the strict program regulations and tight purse strings of the governing veteran service organizations was to unionize. In complete agreement, Jones told Warren to call him after the season.

The actual impetus for DCI's formation started long before that renowned bathroom encounter. From its inception, competitive drum and bugle corps in North America was directly tied to the

American Legion and VFW, and those service organizations were the first to set up the competitive guidelines for the activity.

However, as time and corps marched on, the competition guidelines didn't, and their static rules seriously stifled creativity and overall corps operations. Examples included: having to play the majority of music at a marching tempo of 126 beats per minute, required parade appearances at state and national contests, and subjecting members to scored inspections that included losing points for appearance of hair, uniforms, and equipment. But perhaps the most detrimental impact came from their tight control of performance fees and prize monies, all while banking considerable profits for themselves.

Often, prize money went only to the first and second place corps, leaving the remainder of the field with no compensation for their talent, effort, travel, and growing operational expenses. Making the situation more frustrating were gross inconsistencies in scoring, and the arbitrary way contests were organized. It wasn't uncommon for caption scores to swing wildly from one performance to another, with corps having no recourse other than to suck it up and take what the show organizers and judges doled out.

Constantly lighting the fuse of frustration, it was only a matter of time before something exploded, and in 1966, the VFW Nationals blew up into a total disorganized shit show. With some curiously baffling rules interpretations and reinterpretations of prelim scores, show organizers decided to move the fourteenth-place Madison Scouts ahead of the twelfth-place Racine Scouts and the thirteenth-place Immaculate Conception Reveries. Then, in order to placate the Racine Scouts, the twelve corps finals were adjusted to thirteen. Too bad no one considered placating the I.C. Reveries.

To say the I.C. Reveries were pissed would be a gross understatement. Infuriated, the corps stormed the field at the beginning of the evening's finals, and before show organizers were clued into what was taking place, the Reveries had boldly executed a sit-down protest, demanding to take the field in competition. Ninety minutes after the first corps was scheduled to step off, show organizers reluctantly allowed them to perform, albeit not in the judged competition.

In 1968, the Des Plaines Vanguard fielded their strongest corps to date, capturing first place at the VFW Nationals prelims, then despite another fantastic performance in finals, they inexplicably fell to fourth. Neither were the Blue Stars immune from incompetent show organization. At the 1969 American Legion Nationals in Atlanta, Georgia, seven junior corps were slated to perform in finals, but between prelims and finals, show officials adjusted the number to nine. Too late, by the time they got the news, the ninth-place Blue Stars were already well on their way back to La Crosse.

Due to frequent gaps in judgment, capricious protocols, and indifference for the corps' well-being, each passing year brought a growing sense of distrust in the show organizers and judges of the American Legion and VFW Nationals. Despite the large numbers of competitive junior drum corps popping up across the nation, small minded people were keeping competitive drum corps a small activity. Something had to be done.

For Jones and Warren's plan to work they needed more than just two corps to make their play. Looking for other outstanding corps with strong individual leaders to join their posse, they successfully reached out to Gail Royer of the Santa Clara Vanguard, Bill Howard of the Madison Scouts, and Dr. David Kampschroer of the La Crosse Blue Stars. Calling themselves the Midwest Combine, they were a formidable group, providing show sponsors with a complete high quality performance package, albeit one that now came with guaranteed appearance fees.

Local show organizers didn't balk, and the Combine's summer schedule was easily filled. However, in typical union-busting fashion, the veteran service organizations and regional drum corps circuits told both show sponsors and judges that if they promoted or adjudicated a show with the Combine, they would never be allowed back into the activity. However, having five of the top corps in the country in one show was a popular draw for sponsors, and the empty threats went ignored.

In Wheeling, Illinois, the first Midwest Combine Show took place at a high school stadium with a standing room only crowd of four thousand fans, paying seven dollars a ticket. The gate money not only paid the corps' performance fees, it also produced a $21,000 profit for the show organizers, and the Combine's success spurred seven of the top East Coast corps to create their own collective with the formation of the United Organization of Junior Corps, aka: The Alliance. Drum corps throughout the country were gaining comfort with a newfound autonomy that would lead to significant changes throughout every phase of the activity.

With animosity festering between corps and the VFW, the 1971 National Championships were setting up some interesting histrionics. The season saw both the Madison Scouts and the Cavaliers performing themed shows, each complete with several corps members clad in costumes. During an entire summer of performances, the costumes were a nonissue. Then, at the managers meeting at the VFW National Show in Dallas, the chief judge proclaimed, "Any corps wearing costumes and not proper military uniforms will be penalized two points for each infraction." The penalty would effectively eliminate Madison from competing in the evening's finals. Madison acquiesced.

In contrast, the Cavaliers chose to attend the American Legion Nationals, where they took their circus themed show, complete with ringleader, acrobats, and clowns out on the field without incurring any penalties and earning second place.

The costume incident emphasized the fact that drum corps were still bound to the whims and ineptitude of a governing body that was more about profit, control, and ownership than growth and development. In the fall of 1971, at an American Legion rules session in Indianapolis, the directors from the Combine and five of the corps from the Alliance, along with three other nationally recognized corps, met in a nearby hotel room to devise a plan to form their own independent association.

All thirteen corps had strong directors possessing the authority to make decisions without running to a board for approval. Upon successful and unanimous agreement for their initial protocols, they dubbed the new organization Drum Corps National. After a subtle reminder that there was a Canadian corps present, they quickly augmented the name to Drum Corps International. Voilà, DCI was born.

The Blue Stars' Dr. Kampschroer was voted in as one of two part-time co-executive directors, chosen to oversee their operations for the first year. Shortly thereafter, he was contacted by a Whitewater businessman inquiring about the town hosting a show. Kampschroer realized that the central location and well-appointed campus of the University of Wisconsin, Whitewater, would be a perfect facility to host the World Championship. He was right, as a near sellout of the mid-August show provided the necessary lift for the shiny new organization to take flight, and with DCI now airborne, there was no looking back.

Kampschroer's business acumen and even-handed approach earned him a great deal of respect, and upon the completion of a successful '72 season, he was offered the full-time position as DCI's first executive director. He graciously declined the offer in order to continue directing the Blue Stars and pursue his career in public school administration.

The DCI corps directors then turned to Don Pesceone, whose drum corps vita included extensive and varied participation in the activity. He had been a marching member, instructor, business manager, drill designer, and judge, and it was his reputation as an impartial

marching adjudicator that assured the DCI members that he could
be trusted to head the fledgling organization. Under Pesceone, DCI
prospered, greatly expanding its number of shows, organized tours,
and national exposure. He returned Championships to Whitewater
the following year, and once DCI decided to showcase the World
Championships throughout various parts of the country, Whitewater
became a popular regional site.

As our buses crossed the Wisconsin border, the pastoral countryside reminded me of the giant Grant Wood mural at my elementary school. Rolling hills were blanketed with green corn stalks, pastureland was dotted with grazing black-and-white cows, and the farms were neatly outlined by oak woodlands. They provided a tranquil backdrop to Whitewater's now-famous Warhawks Stadium. Tomorrow, the peaceful town of twelve thousand would be besieged by thirty-one drum corps and an additional twelve thousand fans.

Housed at a small high school in a nearby town, we were blessed with a decent practice field and high-pressure shower heads. Quickly unloading our gear, we were served dinner alfresco in the school's front yard.

Well-rested, and now well-fed, the enthusiasm of the moment was jacked up another notch when Kampschroer arrived. In his late thirties, he bore striking features on a handsome face that included intense blue eyes that relayed a genuine honesty. As he wandered through the groups of staff and members finishing their dinner, his presence radiated a contagious positivity and confidence.

When Kampschroer approached our little dinner party, he cordially greeted us and interestingly, welcomed me by name. Squatting down to join us at eye level, he said, "Hope your tour's been good so far. There's a lot of buzz out there on how much improvement has taken place during these last few weeks. I'm really looking forward to seeing the corps' progress." Then, as he stood to leave, he caught my eyes and said, "Mike, after practice I'd like to have a word with you...nothing to worry about."

Silently, we watched him stroll off to greet others and in a rather concerned tone, Brett asked me, "What do you suppose that's all about?"

"I have absolutely no idea," I said, then nervously added, "but evidently I have nothing to worry about."

Walking out to practice, I couldn't help but think that I might actually have something to worry about, and I considered the possibility that the Emerald Knights had submitted some type of formal protest to DCI. The only thing tempering my anxiety was the fact that if there was a problem, at least I had Dr. K on my side, and if anyone had the pull to resolve that issue, it was him.

A three-hour upbeat practice concluded with a run-through for a sizable and appreciative local crowd. Topping it off were the complimentary goosebumps we received from Dr. K's emotional peroration about how we were without a doubt the most improved corps out there, with even more untapped potential to be realized in the coming weeks. Breaking from our huddle, no one groused about having to do Chop Suey.

Sunset complete, I was heading back to the gym when Dr. K called me over to join Moe and him. Their collective amused expressions definitely piqued my curiosity. Kampschroer said, "Mike, I want you to tell me as best you can how you came to join the corps in the middle of the season."

Here we go—maybe I was right about the Knights. Seared memories were expressed in vivid, but abbreviated detail. Means, motive, and opportunity—I laid it all out for him.

Dr. K nodded his understanding throughout my explanation, and Moe said, "I'm sorry Michael, I didn't know all of that happened...I can't say that I blame you for leaving."

Kampschroer eased me back to the present, saying, "Don't worry about it, Mike. The reason I called you over was that we want to have a little fun with Pierre...it's just too good of an opportunity to pass up." Continuing with a wink and impish grin, he said, "I'm going to infer to him that he is under investigation for unethical recruiting practices, and that he will have to appear in front of a special DCI rules board tomorrow. I'll tell him that you'll be called in to give your version of the incident, so he'll probably want to talk to you to make sure you don't say anything too incriminating." Kampschroer's blue eyes continued to dance with mischief. "I'll set him up, saying my hands are tied on this one, but I'd like you to play along...tell him that you are going to tell it like it is." Smiling at Moe and me, he said, "So what do you think...are you in?"

Unbelievable, here's my first experience with Dr. K, and he's petitioning me to be part of a prank. I had yet to be integrated into the drill but was already being integrated into a comical scheme. I didn't know what to think.

"Sure, I guess," I responded, then added, "but won't he be pissed as hell at me when he finds out I had a part in this?"

"Probably, but knowing Pierre, he'll get over it quick enough. I won't let him stew too long…that'd be cruel. Besides, after we've had our fun, I'll take full responsibility…it'll all be over in a few minutes."

"Okay, I'm in." I said.

"Great. Get ready…this is going to happen pretty fast." Dr. K said, as he left to find Pierre.

A final thin band of light lined the horizon, and I hadn't even made it back into the gym to put my horn away before I saw a flustered Pierre coming my way. It was obvious he had taken the bait like a stunted bluegill, gasping, "Piskel, we need to talk."

Doing my best to look concerned, I replied, "Sure Pierre, what's going on?"

"I just spoke with Doc, he told me I have to meet with some DCI officials regarding how I recruited you." His voice was tight and continued to climb in pitch. "They're meeting in Whitewater, tomorrow morning at 8:00, and we both have to be there."

Facing me, Pierre was oblivious that just yards away, dimly illuminated by the lights of the parking lot, Moe and Dr. K were taking it all in.

I calmly responded, "What do you mean, we?"

Growing more agitated, he exclaimed, "The Emerald Knights are saying I lured you away to join the Blue Stars. Now we have to meet with some DCI officials."

I continued to let him spinout before nodding my understanding.

Anxiously he asked, "Well…what are you going to tell them?"

Putting my horn in its case, I looked up at him and earnestly said, "Pierre, if you think about it, that's almost exactly how it went down…I guess that's what I'll tell them."

"You can't do that!" he cried, and I thought he might get ill.

Behind Pierre, I could see Dr. K and Moe stifling their laughter, and it was all I could do not to crack up myself. Biting my lip, I responded, "Well, what do you want me to say?"

Pierre lamented, "I don't know…maybe you could tell them you asked me for a marching spot to get away from a bad situation, but whatever you do, don't tell them I suggested it. I…I mean, we could be screwed." He was a deer caught directly in the headlights, as he continued pleading, "If they think we did something wrong, they could ban me from instructing, and you could lose your chance at marching for the rest of this year."

Pushing Pierre to the brink, I responded, "Okay, I'll have to think this through, but making up a lie is a lot more difficult than just telling the truth."

Red-faced with laughter, Doc and Moe strolled towards us and I couldn't hold back any longer, before Pierre finally asked, "What's so damn funny?"

Turning around, he saw them, and instantly knew he'd been had. He barked, "You guys are all assholes!"

But even Pierre couldn't deny the combination of humor and relief of the moment. So much so, that he was instantly howling louder than the three of us.

Strolling back to the gym, Doc thanked me for being a good sport, telling me that I'd remember this day a lot more fondly than any of the events leading up to my departure from the Knights.

"Yeah," I said, "as long as Pierre doesn't decide to kill me in my sleep tonight."

With that, it seemed like the entire miserable start to the summer was successfully buried. In fact, it felt like my time with the Blue Stars was the beginning of a whole new year. It didn't matter that I'd yet to march a show. My reception by staff, members, and now management, reminded me that I'd now officially become part of the Blue Star family.

Entering the gym, I felt completely content. A relatively early lights out was dictated by the full day of prelims, finals, and a late night drive back to La Crosse. Surrounded by my newfound sleeping brothers and sisters, I was no longer uneasy about tomorrow's possibility of seeing the Emerald Knights.

SATURDAY, JULY 15ᵀᴴ

Weather is a drum corps show's biggest enemy, but the day's pleasant temps and light winds had joined clear blue skies, providing the perfect conditions for spinning and tossing guard equipment, and the beautiful day had brought out large crowds of multigenerational fans eager to pledge their allegiance. Streaming towards the stadium or stopping to watch their favorites warm up, they were decked out in newly purchased colorful corps T-shirts, buttons and sunburns and the sprawling campus took on a festive atmosphere.

Today's dedicated drum corps nuts would get a twofer, with the biggest and best of the DCI corps slated for morning prelims—done in part to ensure proper rest, recovery, and rehearsal time before the evening's finals. The Blue Stars were scheduled for a mid-morning step-off, and based off of last year's success, the Emerald Knights would take the field soon after the lunch break—I silently wished them luck.

During the gap between prelims and finals, fans would head back to the parking lots to tailgate. With boomboxes blaring bootlegged show recordings, they'd down cold drinks and paper plates of cooler food. Proud parents would brag on their children's marching prowess, while aged out marchers would swap stories of their own glory days and make bold predictions about the evening's results. It was the perfect summer's eve escape.

Dressed in white T-shirt tops and the bottom halves of their uniforms, Blue Star members offloaded in the parking lot and warmed up on one of the adjacent athletic fields. After tuning, brass members finished dressing and gathered around Hill. I hadn't experienced his pregame demeanor before the DCI East prelims, but this morning I sensed a palpable intensity. Hill's voice was strained while spelling out how this show marked the end of the first half of our season. In chronological order, he laid out a list of detailed performance expectations, ending his speech with the importance of not backsliding before a significant break in competition.

Emphasizing how this was our chance to impress some Midwest judges with the meteoric progress we'd made in only two weeks, everyone could easily read between his lines—don't lose your minds and fuck up everything you've worked so hard to gain, just because you hyped out at the second biggest show of the year.

It seemed Hill's exhortations had the desired effect, because it was very apparent no minds were lost during the performance. By now I'd become so familiar with the nuances of the music, I could tell it was a very solid run. Walking out of the stadium, Hill obviously thought so too, as I overheard him tell the rest of the staff that the brass performance was a notch above anything to date.

Uniforms were hung, showers taken, and lunch was eaten before we learned we'd scored a 74.9, down from the 77.0 in Toronto. Initially disheartening, it proved inconsequential. It seemed everyone's score was held back by a couple points. The Blue Devils took the prelims with an 84.0, followed closely by Phantom, Santa Clara, and Madison. More importantly, we continued to close the gap on the fifth place Crossmen, with a strong Spirit of Atlanta corps wedged between us. The Emerald Knights could not repeat the prior year's magical preliminary performance, landing in seventeenth place. Like me, they'd be watching the evening show from the stands.

For our afternoon rehearsal, we worked on drill sets and saved our chops for the night show by singing the music. Afterwards, Pierre happily introduced us to a talented lead soprano who had joined us from St. Louis. He would ably fill the last open spot in a drill written for fifty-four brass members. The Blue Stars had started the season with over a dozen holes in the brass drill, and now would field a full corps for the second tour.

The beautiful day smoothly transitioned into a flawless summer evening. Similar to Allentown, Warhawks Stadium was built into a hill, with the back-side bleachers landscaped with a variety of spruce and arborvitae trees behind them. The stage was set, as a packed house was filled in around the edges with members from the corps that missed making finals.

The Blue Stars entered the gate at the back of the field to the Guardsmen's powerful ending strains of "Greensleeves" and I was mindful to avoid any green Emerald Knights jackets. The stadium lights were beginning to create their refulgent effect on the horns, buckles, and helmet chains of our striking uniforms. Not yet a threat to the crowd favorites, we were warmly received, and as the corps powered through the show, the fans' positive response grew increasingly more energetic inspiring a spontaneous standing ovation upon its completion.

Wisconsin was the corps' home, and while the corps from Madison, Rockford, and Racine were the proximal favorites, the Kids from God's Country weren't far behind. Our performance was every bit as clean and controlled as the morning's preliminaries, but in the clear evening air with the crowd's energy amplifying the programmed impacts. The show sparkled. In Montreal, the guard had shed the heavy drape-like capes from their uniforms, and now unconstrained, they had their best performance of the year. Once again, I was struck by the corps' ability to elevate their show to another level.

The grand finale had a menagerie of twelve colorful corps spread across the field. No backsliding tonight, the show announcer unveiled another season high of 77.1, keeping us firmly in seventh place. What initially had been a six point difference from the Crossmen a week ago, was now whittled to only three and a half points. It would have been even closer except for incurring a point and a half penalties for a bizarre collection of minor infractions and dropped equipment.

However, the evening's competition belonged to the Phantom Regiment, who set their Firebird Suite ablaze and never let up. It seemed the entire citizenry of Rockford had made the fifty mile trek north as the corps garnered multiple standing ovations. Finally breaking free from the pack, Phantom won their first big show of the year, with an 86.85. The Blue Devils fell to second by half a point, followed by the Scouts and Vanguard. Spirit of Atlanta, lifted by their superior horn line, leapfrogged the Crossmen for fifth place. The Guardsmen were a full four points behind us for eighth, and the Freelancers, Garfield Cadets, Cavaliers, and Kilties filled the remaining spots in the evening's competition. Only a few other prominent corps were not in attendance, and I was now almost certain Pierre's prophecy would continue to hold true.

It had been a perfect drum corps day. Buoyed by the excitement from the evening's performance and stimulation from lights, crowd, sights and sounds, we were all on autopilot. Chop Suey'd and cleaned up, we left for La Crosse well past midnight, and by the time we cleared the edge of the small town, only the whir of bus wheels could be heard in the pitch-black bus.

13

THE SILENCE THAT FILLED THE bus cabin provided all the space I needed for new and old memories to crystalize. First tour over, I appreciated its detailed organization. With the help of DCI's master scheduling, connecting the dots on our path to the competitions made perfect sense. Traveling through the night, there was still time between shows for practice and even little breaks to catch our breath. Considering the multitude of components that were packed into each day, revealed the complete logistical brilliance of Moe Latour.

Smaller corps didn't tour, they took trips, and most of my early excursions with the Emerald Knights were spent traversing the cornfields of Iowa, Wisconsin, and Illinois. The Midwest's landscape was sprinkled with rural communities who faithfully filled their high school stadiums to watch small time drum corps, and what they consistently witnessed were the Emerald Knights habitually losing to the Dubuque Colts, Waterloo Chevaliers, Cedar Falls Royals, Osage Precisionnaires, and the all-girl Clinton Nee-Hi's, usually in that order.

Near the end of my first summer, our "big" trip took us to the 1972 American Legion National Championship in Chicago. Mid-August, I was bewildered as to why we had to learn an abbreviated version of our show right before the end of our season, before being told it was just another goofy rule the Legion required to expedite the preliminary competition.

Up early, the corps readied for its first inspection of the year, and we sleepily polished horns, cymbals, and shoes. Hair nets were passed out to all of the girls in the guard and any guys with long hair, as we were told no hair could touch the raised collars of our heavy black wool uniforms.

The Sunday morning prelims took place in Evanston, Illinois, at Northwestern University's Dyche Stadium. It was an old football cathedral, and while it was nowhere near the size of Iowa City's Kinnick Stadium, it was much larger than anyplace I'd ever performed. Silently we lined up in a dark perspiring catacomb under the stadium, where we encountered a little old man with a face deeply lined from too many cigarettes. He wore a military uniform topped with a garrison cap, and was closely shadowed by our drum major, Jim Mason.

Clipboard in hand, he slowly moved down the file of members, giving each of us a critical, somber once over. We'd been told not to make eye contact. "Just look directly through him," Mason cautioned, and I held my breath when the diminutive judge stood in front of me. Relief came when he finally moved on. The entire time all I could think about was the A.A. Milne poem, turned into the song by Max Bygrave, "They're Changing Guard at Buckingham Palace." As a little kid, it had been a regular feature on *Captain Kangaroo* and every time it came on, I'd march around in my PJs, copying the unflinching Queen's Guard in their red coats and black furry busbies.

Entering the field in the vast, empty stadium, our thin, brassy sound bounced off the empty seats, and our show seemed to end almost before it began. Many of us were ignorantly impressed by our highest score of the year, a whopping 56.3. (Amazing what cutting out five minutes of marching and playing could do for execution scores.) Reality kicked in when we discovered that we were once again trounced by every other Iowa corps, but our frustration was slightly tempered when we realized we weren't last, finishing thirty-seventh out of the forty-seven competing corps.

For our consolation prize, we were bused into the heart of the Second City to attend the evening's finals inside the grandiose-columned Soldier Field. An immense crowd of enthusiastic Legionnaires and their families were joined by the other thirty-eight junior corps that didn't make it past prelims. The free seats weren't optimal, so I spent most of my time striving to impress the older girls in our corps.

The most memorable experience I took from the show was hearing the exceptional horn line of the Argonne Rebels, from Great Bend, Kansas. Their sublime intonation, phrasing, and execution provided them with enough of a boost to successfully defend their title over the hometown favorite Cavaliers. This was my initial exposure to a show with a lineup of top corps from around the country, and while distracted by percolating hormones, I subconsciously took note of the diversity in uniforms, and interesting program styles.

Thinking the show was over, things became more curious when several additional corps extended the competition, and what followed were crashing waves of sound emanating from the performances of the Rochester Crusaders, Hawthorne Caballeros, and Yankee Rebels. Their sheer volume squelched any attempt at junior high verbal foreplay. Even bad seats didn't diminish the impact of recognizable songs like "El Gato Montes," "Sabre Dance," "Battle Hymn of the Republic," "76 Trombones," and "When Johnny Comes Marching Home."

What the heck was this? Mason informed me that these were powerful East Coast senior corps, and I was simultaneously amazed and amused to find out that adults were actively engaged in what I'd thought was a young person's game. Their drills featured a variety of repetitive power formations that were interspersed with "park and bark" moments from their colossal horn and percussion sections.

The brass sections of fifty or more fully grown men were capable of putting out a sustained sound that was loud enough to create a sympathetic resonance in my bones. The stimulating buzz painfully pushed the limits of human tolerance, but like spicy food, I wanted more, and at the conclusion of each corps' performance, they willingly obliged. While not sloppy, a peculiar aspect of their programs was an apparent loose indifference to execution, although it didn't seem to matter, as mature performance levels and intense volume overwhelmed the noticeable marching and musical errors.

My initial exposure to a national competition was so mind boggling that I couldn't entirely grasp it, and I felt like I was witnessing an alien arrival. So disparate was it from the other summer contests I had performed in, my puberty-addled brain wasn't able to extrapolate how it might factor into my future drum corps experiences. What I did know was, the season was complete, and I still wanted more.

Sadly, high hopes for a better version of the Emerald Knights were thoroughly dashed throughout a dismal 1973 season. We plodded along with our insignificant trips through the narrow band of small towns and cities in the Midwest. Shampoo, rinse, repeat, and unfortunately the best part of the '73 season was when it ended.

What followed was a family road trip to Milwaukee to see my godparents, Uncle Joe and Auntie Em. Once there my dad saw an ad in the *Milwaukee Journal* for DCI's World Championship, and he suggested the two of us could escape tedious family dynamics and take the hour-long jaunt to Whitewater.

Once again, the flashbulb exposure to nationally competitive drum corps at summer's end had me entirely flummoxed. What the hell was it about the sound of drums and bugles that ignited in me some predisposition to become completely beguiled? Every finalist seemed amazing, and now, having a more defined picture of major league drum corps, I felt a quixotic obsession welling up inside of me, and after that show, I was continuously plagued with visions of the Emerald Knights somehow making a miraculous jump to at least modest respectability.

Proof that miracles can happen came the following year with a trip to California. It was just what we needed to pull us out of the rut that had us trapped in small town drum corps. The tempting promise of travels to sunny southern California worked well as a recruiting ploy, and over the winter our membership grew from the mid-fifties to nearly a hundred. Modest respectability was almost close enough to grasp, and the reason for the miracle was that the Emerald Knights had finally procured a strong new director, and the first one who wasn't a parent.

In January of 1927, a drum corps savior was born in Cedar Rapids, Iowa. Enter James N. Bishop, armed forces veteran, and now California-based aerospace engineer with the Northrop Corporation. Forty-six years after that cold day in January, his job serendipitously took him back to Cedar Rapids. There, he would oversee a subcontract with Collins Radio to build high-tech radios for an advanced generation of military aircraft.

Back in his hometown for an extended period, he was searching for something to fill his free time and happened upon an Emerald Knights practice. Having marched in the Cedar Rapids Musketeers Drum and Bugle Corps as a young teenager, Bishop knew first-hand the collective value and benefits a drum corps experience could bring to young people. With no children of his own, his wife supported his decision to take on the role of executive director for the corps.

Bishop's marching experience was restricted to the old ways of pre-World War II drum corps, and while out of touch with the myriad of transformations that had taken place, he clearly understood what it took to make an organization successful, and it didn't take him long to realize that within the Knights there was a foreboding sense of despair. If he was to have any chance at success, he'd have to act quickly.

When autumn arrives, the biorhythms of drum corps members have them placing any thoughts of marching into a nondescript box in the darkest corner of their minds. The fatigue and habituation associated with a long summer of drum corps cries out for a major palate cleansing. School, jobs, and getting back to real responsibilities now take priority over even occasional reminiscing about a successful season. For members of the Emerald Knights, the uneventful summer and dismal competition results definitely had them purging any memories of their season.

The corps was like a worn-out placemat, with edges that were visibly starting to fray, and attrition had already started to take place during that summer. At a contest in Marshalltown, Iowa, the corps spent a long afternoon learning a tag ending to the show, with a reprise of the dreadful but appropriate opener for a little corps, "Spoonful of Sugar" from Mary Poppins. That evening, the only horn player to boldly enter on cue was Roger Dickinson. Playing so loud he rattled the soldering off his horn, he made several unsuccessful attempts to coax the remaining twenty-two terror-stricken young horn players to join him. After the show, Roger was so infuriated with their cowardice, he loudly proclaimed, "I quit this baby-ass corps!"

Now at season's end, many of the members were visualizing their summers without the distraction of performing in an impotent little kiddie corps. Members, staff, and parents knew the organization was at a tenuous tipping point. So, on a sunny Sunday afternoon in late September, Bishop convened an all-corps meeting in the basement armory of Veterans Memorial Coliseum.

Perched on May's Island in the middle of the Cedar River, the massive old gray building was located in the heart of Cedar Rapids, where it shared limited space on the little sandbar with the Linn County Courthouse and City Hall. It was also the home of the Emerald Knights. The coliseum's basement provided both a central practice facility for the corps during frigid winter months and storage rooms for the corps' possessions. While the armory basement no longer held any weapons, that autumn day, it did hold the remaining members of the Emerald Knights, their staff and some dedicated parents.

Smooth-skinned, with Cary Grant hair, black square framed glasses, a button down shirt with a striped power tie, and dark knit slacks, Bishop looked every bit the part of a respectable aviation engineer, but how would he fare as a corps director? The initial Bishop experience came with strong, sympathetic eyes making direct contact with his young audience, and that day he did something many members had yet to experience: he spoke directly to them. His intellect and positive persona easily penetrated the poor acoustics of the cement basement floor. Members sensed a fresh energy swirling around him as he outlined a comprehensive plan of action that included new uniforms and instruments, experienced instructors with well-organized practices, a streamlined rehearsal schedule, and most importantly, a chance to recruit members with the promise of travel outside of the Midwest. No one's bullshit detectors went off, and in that moment, he charismatically galvanized the remaining nucleus of Emerald Knights.

Money makes the world go around, and also gets the corps out of town. Bishop realized that if there was to be a new and improved Emerald Knights, ample resources would be required. Funding for most drum corps was usually derived from a multitude of sources, which included sponsorship from clubs or service organizations, appearance fees for parades and contests, ticket receipts from home shows, membership dues, profits from a variety of imaginative fundraising projects, along with outright begging in the streets during designated tag days (the key location being right outside of the state-run liquor stores.) Many of the well-established corps had strong revenue streams from loyal alumni, souvenir sales, and successful bingo operations. By the end of the '73 season, the Emerald Knights were just beginning their foray into the bizarre world of bingo gaming.

Initially, the corps was paid a modest sum by the local American Legion to help sell special game sheets at the weekly bingo game, held in a large room off the noisy Legion Lanes Bowling Alley. This soon evolved to renting supplies for their own game, held in a ballroom in the Montrose Hotel. The historic hotel was a mammoth old seven story brick building on a downtown corner, and it was adorned by Grant Wood murals, corn cob chandeliers, and a signature odor. The smell was procured from over sixty-six years of socialites' tobacco smoke, perfume, and banquet food, all thoroughly seasoned in the thick carpeting and dark, heavy ballroom curtains. Eventually, the Knights bought their own gaming equipment and hired good ol' Roger Dickinson's father to expertly call the numbers painted on the bright golf-ball-sized wooden balls that tumbled out of a revolving wire basket.

A large part of the game's success came from Dickinson's über-relaxed style, as his edgy voice clearly enunciated and then slowly repeated the numbers between drags from extra-long brown cigarettes. His languid delivery and proletarian sensibilities were favored by an eclectic and loyal collection of "high rolling" gamers who attended every event. Always arriving early to lay claim to their favorite seats, they came loaded down with colorful daubers, assorted lucky charms, Lucky Strikes, and dreams of waving their flaccid arms in the air while shouting, "Bingo!"

Running three nights a week, the games were staffed by parents, members, and their siblings. For their efforts they were rewarded with vouchers for corps dues and additional spending money for their summer travels. They should have also requested an option to

128

purchase additional health insurance, as the cigarette smoke emanating from the bingo patrons hung like a thick San Francisco fog.

The well-run games were a cash machine and Bishop wasn't afraid to spend it. True to his word, promises were kept, and tangible purchases were made with the regularity of a twenty-two and a half-inch roll step, and a driven Bishop was only getting started. Working long weeknights and even harder on the weekends, he oversaw every aspect of the corps' operations.

That fall, he attended a Central States Judging Association Conference in Chicago to get recommendations for instructors. There he listened as the keynote speaker, marching judge Hank Grana, lamented the lack of experienced instructors and alumni stepping up to assist with the development of smaller corps, stating their indifference was tantamount to treason and a portent to the death of the activity. A smitten Bishop intercepted Grana after his address with a nice cash offer to put his words into action. He willingly agreed.

With the money streaming in, each week was like Christmas, with someone or something new showing up to get members excited. Along with Grana's hiring, additional experienced arrangers and staff came on board. Kids couldn't wait to see what was going to happen next, and one cold Sunday what happened was the announcement of a ten-day trip to California.

The trip out West would be remarkable in that there were no competitions. Instead, Bishop frugally persuaded the entirety of Iowa Jaycees chapters to cover the corps' travel expenses in exchange for a few appearances. The trip became a recruiting tool, and his plan had the Emerald Knights traveling to San Diego under the guise of representing Iowa's young business persons at their national convention: Join the Emerald Knights and experience the fun-filled sights and sounds of sunny California. It worked, and the corps doubled in size from the prior season.

Late winter, rookie and veteran corps members sat mute as Bishop proudly unveiled large sketches of their new uniforms. They featured a black satin blouse with red satin cummerbund and matching ascot, along with light cream-colored vests and bell bottom pants and guard skirts. The pants and skirts were accented by red pleats and, along with the vests, were festooned with brown leather rosettes. The ensemble was capped by a black felt gaucho hat that was adorned with a heavy metal badge.

Resembling a prairie version of the iconic Hawthorne Caballeros' uniform, no reference to Emerald or Knight could be found, and one could easily envision befuddled fans rechecking their programs to see if the announcer had committed a gross lineup error. At least the Spanish themed costume would complement a portion of the corps' repertoire, as they reprised two drum corps standards, "Jezebel" and "Malagueña."

What members didn't fully understand was that Bishop had originally intended to change the corps' name to something that would align with their new look, but upon realizing the scope of the logistics involved, he decided to keep the Emerald Knights' name for the upcoming season. After the uniform reveal, one enterprising member created a red T-shirt with white lettering, proudly proclaiming, "The New Emerald Knights Drum and Bugle Corps."

In due time, most members began to embrace the incongruous look and accepted it as just one more of the many rapid changes that were taking place. That spring, the corps convened for several overnight weekend-long marching and music camps held at the fairgrounds on the edge of town. The extended practices with their out-of-town instructors had their skills and confidence rapidly progressing, and by the beginning of June they were bigger, and definitely better. Bishop's "New Emerald Knights" were ready to take the field in competition.

The Blue Stars' bus rolled on into the black of night, and with it, so did my musings on the Emerald Knights' travels. The June trip out to California was preceded by our season opener on June 9th in Cedar Falls, Iowa. In our excitement to unveil our new look and show off our vast improvement, we were raw, noisy, nervous, and extraordinarily sloppy with Grana's drill and the new musical selections. High expectations were replaced by a clinical case of depressing déjà vu. Mustering only 39.35 points, we tied for last place in a field of just five corps.

Envisioning finally beating the plaid-clad, all-girl Clinton Nee-Hi's had powered me through the cold winter, yet here we were nightmarishly losing to them by more than five points. Back in our familiar role of leaving the field first in the not-so-grand finale, we knew we were an improved corps, but one of the pains of our rapid growth included a sizable collection of inexperienced thirteen and fourteen-year-old kids. They needed time to mature, bond with us, and get comfortable performing the show—just what a ten-day trip out West could provide.

Mid-June had two charter coach buses dividing the girls from the guys. We loaded up and followed the sun down Interstate 80. Having no experience with interstate travel, the guys' bus quickly improvised ways to pass the time. Our main distractions were gambling, followed by storytelling, dirty jokes, and teaching our rookies ribald drum corps songs, the subject matter of which included imaginary horny girlfriends, copious amounts of masturbation, and north-and-south-of-the-border whores. All of this was done while feasting on stashes of assorted junk food and waiting for the next rest stop.

Our first destination was Vegas, and on our way we paid non-stop homage with a simple three card game of chance, Acey-Deucey, otherwise known as In-between. Several seats on the bus were rearranged to face one another, and makeshift dealing tables were erected. By the time we reached Nebraska, my now best friend, Tim Daugherty, had turned into a regular Brett Maverick. I stood watching from the aisle as he waited for a sizable pot to form before implementing the toe tapping scheme he and his coconspirator, drum major Greg Greaser, had devised. With a deft hand, twos and threes were dealt from the bottom of the deck, breaking young members' hearts and their small bank-rolls. It was great to witness his unbridled joy as he tutored little rookies on the evils of gambling.

During my first two seasons, Tim (Dode, as everyone called him) and I had become best buds both in corps and in school. The middle son of five boys, he came from a very musical family and drum corps had played a part in all of their formative years. Lucky to share extended time in corps, we also shared a variety of classes at our junior high. Making a sports magazine for our ninth grade English class, we wrote about our heroes, Connie Hawkins and Joe Namath; we got an A on the project, not for our English prowess, but because our class voted that we had the best cover design. We started a brown bag lunch company selling PB & J and ham sandwiches that, after impacting cafeteria sales, was quickly shut down by the administration. Tim arranged Stevie Wonder's "My Cherie Amour," for our junior high jazz band and he added a little trumpet solo for me to close out the piece. At our winter all-school assembly, I caught a tremendous case of stage fright and proceeded to end the song like a lost whooping crane calling for its mate. A true friend, Dode abstained from giving me any shit, telling me it wasn't all that bad.

Not only was Tim talented on the piano and French horn, he also was a gifted athlete. Tall and fit, he was a starting forward on our ninth-grade basketball team, as well as the number one singles player in tennis—an amazing feat in and of itself, as he was basically self-taught. Quick-fire muscles and great hand and eye coordination were demonstrated one morning in the passing halls of McKinley Jr. High, when with one swing of his racquet, he took down a frenetic rogue bat in mid-air.

In deference to him, I decided to take on some risks of my own, joining the junior high basketball and tennis teams. It wasn't pretty, and I barely survived in either, while he starred in both. It didn't matter; I now had a friend I could count on and going to school seemed all that much more tolerable.

During our eighth-grade human reproduction unit, our tennis coach and P.E. teacher turned health instructor, the snide but strangely likeable Mr. May, sat on the front of his desk and told twenty-five boys, "You can ask me any questions about sex that you want. It doesn't matter if you don't have the vocabulary." Coach May had an annoying habit of sniffing, and I imagined that he was always testing the air for pheromones of prepubescent fear. He continued, "I don't even care if you have questions about girls' pussies, or questions about cocks, dicks...sniff...anything at all...sniff...even questions about masturbation."

Silence filled the room as we held our breath. The class was almost over, and now it couldn't end fast enough. Yet there was Dode's hand anxiously waving, and fearing May's sniffer I closed my eyes, sank lower in my desk, undoubtedly giving off the scent of dire apprehension. Other boys bowed their heads and nervously snickered.

May looked out across the room, sniffed again, and snidely called out, "Daugherty."

Tim, in childlike innocence, asked, "Coach, what's masturbation?"

Oh brother, I thought, *he's really going there?* Promptly, Bill Steel, the biggest, oldest (I think he was held back a year or three) and scariest-looking kid in the class, leaned over the aisle, lewdly tossed out his upward fist, shaking it waist level at Dode, and loudly proclaimed, "Jackin' off, Man!"

Outright whoops erupted. May just sniffled and sneered, and thankfully the passing bell rang. I couldn't leave the room fast enough, wondering if Dode was truly clueless or just putting us on. Despite having two older brothers, and years in drum corps, he later told me he had never fully understood the word.

That was Dode: innocent, fun loving, sympathetic, talented, athletic, and willing to take risks if the right occasion arose. Our friendship was honest and without pretense, something we both cherished and desperately needed while locked in junior high purgatory.

Then, after our tough '73 drum corps season, he quietly told me that his days as an Emerald Knight were over. While his two younger brothers and Dad were committed to the corps, no amount of wheedling from

Photograph courtesy of the Emerald Knights Drum and Bugle Corps

Dode (left) and me, crashed after three Fourth of July parades. Note the first of many Emerald Knight uniforms worn during my time in the corps.

them or anyone else could change his mind. Heading off to senior high, staying in the Emerald Knights would only compromise his chance at athletic stardom and interfere with his involvement in the school's outstanding fine arts programs.

I understood. He had a lot on his mind. His mom had become seriously ill, and he didn't need me trying to dictate any of his future. As a loyal friend, I didn't berate him for his calculated decision. Hell, I couldn't blame him for not wanting to march anymore. His natural talents as an athlete and musician allowed him to travel in high school's expanding social network of cool kids, and the majority of my popularity at school hinged on being his ever present sidekick. We remained tight, but I sensed we were starting to head in different directions. As Dode's high school life spread out before him, my focus narrowed as I immersed myself into all things Emerald Knights.

Bishop's appointment as director completely rejuvenated the attitudes of many veteran Knights, and I was one of them. My passionate verve for corps completely dumbfounded my mother. She had erroneously predicted that once I moved on to senior high school, I would also move on from the Emerald Knights. When she realized it wasn't happening, domestic battles ensued. My grades started to suffer, and Mom forced Dad to play the strict parent card, telling me I could no longer attend practices and to turn in my horn.

Angry, yet motivated, I kept abreast of the corps' progress through Dode's younger brothers. I studied harder, thinking my parents would abrogate my sentence if I improved scholastically. When report cards came out in early November, I happily showed them two As and four Bs. Now I thought, I could finally get back to the business of drum corps—sadly, I was wrong.

With my brother off at military school, Anita Piskel wasn't about to lose her last child to the lowly Emerald Knights. To her our drum corps was a cult, and a rinky-dink one at that. Her plan to free me from its grasp was complete abstinence. My rehab in full swing, the dynamics in our home became painfully somber, and I was determined to do nothing to lighten the mood. With no allies in the house, discussions at family dinner existed only between Mom,

Dad, and my grandmother. I had nothing to say to them; as far as I was concerned their parenting style made absolutely no sense, and I couldn't tolerate any reasoning that didn't agree with my spot-on sense of propriety.

I was completely confused as to why my Mom wanted to snuff out my one authentic passion. *What the hell was so bad about wanting to be in a drum corps? Was it some demented and manipulative power play? Was she embarrassed by my participation in the mostly working class organization? Did she somehow think our corps reflected poorly on her?* Maybe she was just afraid the corps was accelerating my growing independence, while simultaneously emphasizing her descent into middle age.

Concomitantly frustrated, we were quick with spiteful words, and conversations frequently morphed into shouting matches where I challenged her to demonstrate why I shouldn't be allowed to participate in something that was so important to me. She had nothing, and I knew it. After every duel, the room would fill with an icy silence. The problem was, I was still only fifteen, and despite my argumentation skills, that wasn't nearly old enough to purchase any sense of control. After school I robotically worked my neighborhood paper route, stoically ate dinner, and sulked off to my room, where I slogged through homework, practiced trumpet, and blasted drum corps albums on my little stereo. Saturdays and Sundays were worse.

The week after report cards came out, I'd had enough. That Sunday afternoon in November, I told my parents I was going over to Dode's house and hopped on my brother's old ten-speed Schwinn, furiously peddling the four miles to May's Island to watch practice.

I couldn't believe how much had taken place in just two months. New members, new instructors, new energy. I had to find a way back in. Pleading my case with Bishop, he agreed to intervene on my behalf. The following evening, I came clean about attending practice. Bishop spoke with my dad at work, and before the weekend arrived my father called a meeting for our fractured little family.

Under the conditions that I kept up my grades, showed some respect to Mom, and understood that I would be going with my high school band on the two-week trip to Europe in the heart of drum corps season, I'd be allowed to attend practice. No discussion, a true compromise, and as such, no one was particularly happy, especially my mom, but at least now I felt like I could get through another cold Iowa winter.

Unfortunately, the winter of '74 had been more than just cold and gray for the Daugherty family. Tim and four brothers, along with his dad, Willis, and their extended family and friends, painfully watched as the family matriarch, Evelyn, withered away and disappeared. School almost over, Willis and Mr. Bishop told Tim that a summer of drum corps with his two younger siblings might help the family heal, along with providing a solid distraction from the emptiness that permeated their home. Steadfast resolve now lost, Tim either agreed, or didn't have the emotional energy to argue. Whichever it was, I was elated when Dode showed up at our last spring camp. Now a month later, here he was on his way to California, happily stuffing ill-gotten singles into short pockets, and for the moment, gloriously distracted from grief.

The miles flew by as we ignored the scenery, until losing the bus's air conditioning in the desert made us much more aware of our surroundings. The temperature registered one hundred and ten when we hit Sin City, but we easily adjusted to our rolling sauna by stripping down to our underwear. Too bad the dimly-lit Vegas Strip had not fared quite as well in adapting to the ongoing energy crisis. Unloading at the downtown YMCA, the boys were partitioned in two handball courts, while the girls occupied a small gym. Cleaned up, with clothes back on, Bishop took our little traveling carnival to Circus Circus, the largest permanent big top in the world, and the only family-oriented casino in town.

Joining me in the noisy, colorful casino, were some of the older members and my summer girlfriend, Dawn, a taut, reticent redheaded rifle in the guard. She was even more serious about corps than I was, and I think that was partly why I found her so damn cool. From the blue-collar side of town, she was an experienced corps vet. She and her younger sister led by example with skill and discipline. Drum corps and the military ran in her family. Her father, active in the VFW, had written the Emerald Knights' antiquated platoon drills before Grana's arrival.

Restricted to the second-floor mezzanine, we observed brightly illuminated, sequined trapeze acrobats performing daring tricks above us, while below, strangers, chaperones, and staff willingly donated money to help relight the

136

Strip. Younger corps members were gamblers in training, playing the pinging arcade games as parents gambled away their college funds.

Several Knights quickly learned casino protocol after making their way to the main floor, only to have the film stripped from cameras and be escorted back upstairs by extra-large, extra-stern-faced security agents. Soon bored by the bright lights and loud sounds of the casino, our conversations focused on the fact that tomorrow we'd start our second day on the road without any practice. How were we ever supposed to beat the Nee-Hi's if we spent our entire time as bus-riding tourists?

Early the next morning, it was breakfast at a large diner, where third baritone, thirteen-year-old, five-foot-nothing, Mike McGuire, was desperate to earn back the money he'd lost on the bus. Frantically stuffing quarters into a one-armed bandit in the lobby, he was oblivious to the looming shadow of Dode's dad.

Willis Daugherty was an ex-Marine and Korean war veteran. He was also an imposingly large and in charge kind of guy. As such, he was the consummate chaperone for an extended drum corps trip. Despite his strong character and outer strength, he probably needed a season's worth of drum corps distractions even more than his sons. Still, I wasn't sure he considered the possibility of having to deal with the mischievous little munchkin that was Mike McGuire.

Towering over the diminutive baritone player, Willis looked like he could finish him off with one bite, but upon his booming order to cease and desist, Mike bravely pleaded his case. Whining and begging to let him play his last quarter, Willis finally acquiesced, but only to teach Mike the hard lesson that gambling never pays. The fruits, bells, and bars spun, and in Willis's complete disbelief, and Mike's sheer delight, they magically fell into place. The joyous sound of ringing bells mixed with gushing coins filled the diner. Pockets bulging with silver, little Mike was once again flush with cash for the six hour ride to Los Angeles.

Upon reaching our destination in Orange County, we were finally in the backyard of the Anaheim Kingsmen and Velvet Knights, yet there was no sign of another drum corps anywhere. After a full hot day of much-needed practice, designs of spending a cooler evening hanging with the Velvet Knights at famous Huntington Beach were derailed by L.A.'s notorious traffic. Three hours later, a huge orange ball hung low on the ocean's horizon. While the VK's bus was still running block for our parking spots, most of our California hosts had gone home. What remained was a handful of somewhat compromised VK beachcombers waiting to share a hotdog dinner. It didn't matter—we were distracted by the beautiful Pacific sunset, soft sand, and thoughts of seeing Micky tomorrow.

Fantasyland, finally. Dawn and I spent the warm sunny day walking the park, and a semi-romantic night taking in the Pirates of the Caribbean ride and sharing tasty but overpriced Monte Cristo sandwiches at the Blue Bayou restaurant. After dinner, the park was ablaze with tiny brilliant twinkling lights, and I could swear I heard Gabriel's trumpet wailing out into the festive evening. We followed the sound to a gazebo in the Plaza Gardens where, along with a collection of other tired Knights, we stood in disbelief of what we'd discovered.

Under the gazebo's canopy, there stood the man himself, Maynard Ferguson. Dressed in all black, he was a hip Canadian trumpeter channeling his inner Johnny Cash, and his bandmates were decked out in some crazy red velour bathrobes, looking like they'd just left the movie set of a San Fernando Valley porno.

Despite their comical look, the band was tight as they soared through "MacArthur Park" and then Maynard closed out the concert with a screaming stratospheric arrangement of "Hey Jude." If that wasn't enough to wake Sleeping Beauty in her castle, nothing would. For those of us Knights lucky enough to witness Maynard in all of his newfound commercial glory, it really was the happiest place on earth.

The following morning, we cruised down the coast to San Diego to earn our keep at the Jaycees national convention. Long after sunset, we put on our new uniforms and headed over to a large resort and convention center. Marching past palm trees, we took up residence on a sprawling pool deck in the center of several tall hotel buildings. The balconies were filled with bawdy Jaycees holding nearly empty handles of various spirits, and they reminded me of tipsy pirates I had witnessed on my ride at Disneyland the night before. Considering their level of intoxication and our Spanish apparel, I'm sure many of them mistook us for some sort of military academy pep band, smuggled over the border from Tijuana.

Dozens of conventioneers waved large signs that bore the single name of HALE. As in David Hale, an apparently popular presidential candidate for their upcoming election, and their drunken vociferous chants carried out into the night, "Hale Yes! Hale Yes! HALE YES!"

Once arranged into a concert formation we added the sound of drums and bugles to their ballyhoo, and I guess it had the desired effect as the music lured more trashed Jaycees out onto the balconies. Upon completion, wild cheers erupted throughout the resort, followed by the repeated swelling refrains for Hale.

As we prepared to make a break for our buses, a Jaycee official intercepted Bishop and pleaded for an encore performance. What the hell, we didn't have anything else to do. This time, drum major Greg Greaser took a position at the end of the pool's diving board and bounced along as he conducted. From there, things got pretty crazy, pretty fast as our drunken audience pressed in around the corps, and during "Malagueña" Dode brazenly added his touch to the madness of the evening by breaking formation to join Greaser on the diving board.

Spinning the chrome, squared-off French horn bugle up to his chops, he improvised a righteous solo, void of melody but full of rips and glissandos, that within the brass line sparked wide-eyed laughter through the bells of our horns. Hilarious—Hale Yes!

The following morning the Felliniesque weirdness continued as we marched in a parade with several thousand of those same but now more subdued and hungover Jaycees. We led the way for the Iowa block, who sported matching T-shirts and khakis representing their various local chapters. The parade was a two mile trek down a straight stretch of empty highway with the distant San Diego skyline in sight.

Who the hell was this parade for? I had absolutely no clue. With only an occasional cactus or roadside fruit stand operator for an audience, we marched and played, Hale won, and I figured we'd given them their money's worth.

We spent the morning of our last full day in California practicing. Even with limited rehearsals, the show was beginning to gel. Maybe starting the year off as tourists was what we needed. Time spent in close quarters encouraged friendships to form, and the inevitable spontaneous, crazy shit that went down provided multiple opportunities for communal laughter and the shared recognition that we were all in this together. Young rookies were starting to feel like they actually had some ownership, and vets were beginning to understand that if we were to have any chance at success, we needed to abandon the role of tormentors and become their nurturing mentors.

Sightseers once more, the afternoon was spent at the acclaimed San Diego Zoo and I soon tired of looking at all the disinterested, large warm fuzzies sleeping in the shade. As the junior herpetologist in me awakened, I convinced Dawn to join me in the reptile house where we saw Gila monsters, coiled giant pythons, Galápagos tortoises, and were completely captivated by a small two-headed rat snake in a little terrarium.

Seeing the two little forked tongues taste the air, I wondered if both brains sensed the same thing. Intrigued, I figured if it could survive not having a singular focus, maybe the Emerald Knights could too. Perhaps the best way to raise the Knights to respectability would be to first have us grow together as a family of tourists—my one fear being that according to the signage on the terrarium, two-headed snakes don't seem to live very long.

The irony that our last stop of the trip was for an actual contest was lost on our rookies. Surrounded by the cornfields of Osage, they could smell home, and were eager to sleep in their own beds, but most of the older vets wanted to see if our trip had been transformational enough to avoid another last place finish. To our utter delight, it had. Much more relaxed, we gave the small crowd a spirited performance, scoring a 46.65, and finishing second. Hallelujah!

Standing at parade rest during the finale, I watched as Greaser returned from the front sideline award ceremony. Sporting a huge smile, he carried our runner-up trophy high above his head. It was the first time since I'd joined that we actually took home some hardware. Proudly standing in parade formation in my Spanish uniform, I was bursting with pride, as I realized the New Emerald Knights had finally arrived.

Changing back into our street clothes, laughing and joking after a show was a new one for all of us, and it was quite the party atmosphere on the guys' side of the small gym. Still in my skivvies, I spotted a mic stand on the adjacent little stage and was amused to switch it on and find it was live to a PA system. Taking the opportunity to apply my veteran leadership, I pulled the mic off the stand, jumped down from the stage, and did my best imitation of a BVD wearing inspirational speaker.

With time running out before boarding the buses, I loudly stated, "All right men, that was pretty good, but pretty good…isn't good enough!" Oz had spoken, and curious eyes scanned the gym before locking on to the source of the interruption, as I boldly continued, "Taking second is only a start. We can do better. We can do a lot better! We need to win a show…That's right, I want to win a show, and I know you do too…and I believe we can, if we continue to stay focused and practice hard. I believe…"

It was working, I was a snake oil salesman in a small town peddling grandiose aspirations. Members stopped changing and slowly gathered around me. Mesmerized for sure, giving me their rapt attention they were in the palm of my hands, and just as I was about to continue, Dode yelled, "Get him!"

Walled in, with nowhere to run, suddenly it was me that was in the palms of their hands. Tens of fists gripped the waistband of my whitey tighties, then to my abject horror, I was lifted off the ground. Any snake oil salesman wouldn't trade his tar and feathers over my fate. Visions of Richard Harris strung up in "A Man Called Horse" flashed before me, and it seemed as if my high-quality underwear would never give. Stretched to the limits, the waistband and my precious privates were terrifyingly at eye level.

Horrified, I screamed, "Let go you fuckers! Oh, for the love of God, please let go!"

Jeers and evil laughter rose in response, and I was lifted higher, until I literally broke on through to the other side. Flossing pain, shock, embarrassment, and finally relief. Thankfully, young skin is surprisingly elastic, and nothing other than my underwear and dignity was ripped or torn.

Abandoned on the floor, raw and half nude, I watched as Dode grabbed the mic, saying, "And we now return you to your regularly scheduled programming."

Surviving a megaton of all atomic wedgies, I was seriously pissed at Dode, Greaser, and half the older kids, but even through tears of pain, I couldn't help but laugh. Perhaps trying to gain attention by being a showboating killjoy wasn't the best tact, but I thought our performance and score was a seminal event. Something we could use to bolster our desire for continued success, something we could rally around. Then again, preaching in my underwear made me the perfect target. What I did know was it was a good thing we were headed home on a high note, as our familiarity with each other was definitely becoming tedious. In just ten days, my old and new friends had become a family of pain-in-the-ass brothers.

Like a host of other small corps in the Midwest, 1975 saw the Emerald Knights continue to grow and mature. With the exception of a handful of kids who moved on, everyone was excited to see what the new year would bring under Bishop's reign. Having mercifully won a show during last year's Fourth of July Chicago pilgrimage, Dode stated he'd done his penance and could now resume his high school sports and fine arts career. Greg Greaser was no longer interested in continuing with the demands of being the DM and returned to the horn line. That fall, in the armory basement, we celebrated the end of the year with our paper plate pot luck banquet, where to my abundant jubilation and my mom's deep chagrin, I was awarded Knight of the Year, and soon after was selected as the corps' new drum major.

Flush with bingo funds, Bishop surmised it best to continue the rebuilding formula with another trip designed to attract new recruits. His new plan would take us from coast to coast in just two years. Smack dab in the middle of July, we were headed to Florida, this time to march down Main Street U.S.A. at the nearly new and always sunny Disney World.

That summer, our circuitous route to Orlando had us stopping in Shreveport, Louisiana, to perform during the half time of a Steamer's World Football League preseason game, and once again, we found ourselves in the land of the bizarre and ludicrous.

Running late to our afternoon engagement, Bishop somehow procured the flashing lights of a parade of police cars to escort us to the stadium. Rushing from the buses, we ran smack into thick hot air that quickly glued uniforms to bodies, only to have to stagnate in the end zone as we waited for the first half to end.

The municipal stadium was packed, and it was too bad they were there for a football game instead of a drum corps show. Sadly, it felt like we were just another marching band, only there to provide an audible stopwatch for the countdown to the second half.

Our show that year was a step up from the previous year's offering, but it was still pretty antiquated, as we played Mancini's medley, "The Great Race March" for the national flag presentation portion of our show. Most corps had given up the historic requirement after DCI members voted to eliminate it. The Emerald Knights, however, were an anachronism, and Bishop thought that it was an important part of what drum corps should do on the field.

The "flag pres" as it was called, originally came with a host of national flag codes that seemed to be included so a steady stream of penalties could be given out. Once eliminated as a required show element, corps could focus on whatever show themes and music they wanted, and program designs greatly expanded with its removal. Steadfastly we held on to it, winning favor with the patriotic fans we played to in our small-town competitions, and it also garnered us a front page photo feature and article in *Drum Corps World*.

The Mancini arrangement was a razzmatazz mashup of "Hail to the Chief," "Columbia Gem of the Ocean," "America the Beautiful," "You're a Grand Old Flag," "The Caissons Go Rolling Along," and others. The climactic ritardando at the end provided the perfect musical backdrop for a dramatic display of Old Glory coming down the fifty-yard line and being hoisted high into the night sky. But on this brutally humid afternoon, we mindlessly went through the motions, performing to strangers in a strange land, who seemed much more concerned with their cold beer concessions and restroom necessities than the misplaced patriotism of a drum corps from Cedar Rapids, Iowa.

Then the unexpected took place, when a short transition in the medley was played by our mellophones. It was a simple riff, but it cut through the din of the crowd like a ruby laser. We'd never given the phrase much consideration but put even a hint of "Dixie" anywhere near thirteen thousand Deep Southerner's ears, and, well...you'd have thought we scored a touchdown for the home team.

The wave of crowd noise shook the field and it took a moment for me to even realize what had happened. When the melody was repeated once more, it was as if we'd just won the Super Bowl. The stadium erupted, and our whole corps was swallowed by the wild cheers from the audience. Too close to a detonated bomb, I couldn't hear one note of music. Thank God we weren't carrying the rebel flag up the fifty-yard line, or the place would've come completely unhinged.

Suddenly, as if condensed from the humid air, the Shreveport Steamers' tiny mascot, Dancing Francis, appeared. He was a little Sammy Davis Junior wannabe, adorned in a sequined, neon green leprechaun suit. Egged on by the crowd, he began wreaking havoc with the guard as he danced through them to his own improvised drill. Instantly he became our own little Emerald talisman, challenging us to stay focused on our task.

Adopted Yankees, it seemed we had usurped the game, and were now the prime entertainment of the day. The fans took on a mob-like entity and we were the tasty main course in their feeding frenzy. Football? Who the hell cares about a July preseason game for a piddling minor league team when there are Spanish "Dixie"-playing Emerald Knights in the house? Leaving the field to our first ever raucous standing ovation, it was one of those moments that instantly sprouts its own dedicated network of cerebral synapses.

Leaving Louisiana, we followed the Gulf Coast to a Kissimmee high school, only fifteen minutes from Disney World. Sun-soaked central Florida provided a smothering blanket of heat, always dancing a fraction of a degree above the dew point during the day and always followed with sticky nighttime battles with parched mosquitoes and cockroaches as big as Kafka's imagination. Taking our turn on Disney World's Main Street, we proudly played and perspired through our fifteen minutes of fame. Unlike the San Diego parade, the truncated route was lined with appreciative "guests" packed eight deep in the bleachers on either side of the cobblestone path. Sadly, that evening, Maynard was nowhere in sight.

The following day, we were off on a grand tour of the Sunshine State. We covered both sides of the coast, tumbling in the surf at Cocoa Beach, touring the Kennedy Space Center, and surprise surprise, actually meeting up for an exhibition of sorts, with the most geographically isolated drum corps in the country.

The Royal Lancers from Cape Coral hosted the pathetic event at the high school where we were housed. The idea of actual judges traveling to southern Florida was too expensive, so the performances were critiqued by a panel of "judges" made up of the competing corps' instructors.

The event was attended by a smattering of family members and friends from the local corps, and there were way more jumbo bugs under the stadium lights than people filling the small stands, so to bolster the crowd, the participating corps watched each other's performance. No announcer, no concessions, no tickets, or finale. Two of the corps didn't even bother to wear uniforms, and the casualness of the event made it seem more like a grade school show-and-tell than an actual competition. Watching the Florida corps perform reminded me of us from just two years ago. They were small, young organizations with marginal talent, and had names like the Leathernecks, and Devil Dogs.

We went on last, but the day of practice in stagnant heat had baked any hype out of our performance. We were still the best thing to take the field that night, and afterwards it felt like the other corps were staring at us with envy and disbelief. Their expression reminded me of the puzzeled dive bar patrons listening to the stranded keyboard player in Billy Joel's "Piano Man."

Under the steady stream of a cold water post-show shower, I thought, *Man, what the hell are we doing here?* While I'd enjoyed the California trip and saw its value as a recruiting tool, I was reminded of the prophetic sign at the San Diego Zoo's reptile house. The life of a two-headed snake was brief, and as far as I was concerned our snake was already dead.

I'd had enough of this year's extended family field trip, and I wanted the Emerald Knights to be focused on real competitions against real corps, all wanting to beat us as badly as we wanted to beat them. We'd been very competitive throughout the first half of the season, winning the state legion show and doing well at our local little Midwestern competitions, only now I felt like a kid with a cool toy that he wasn't allowed to play with. Here we were sweating our asses off, wasting valuable opportunities to be a real drum corps, and for what—to ride Space Mountain, to dance with Francis at a preseason game for a surely doomed football league, to trade shows for the amusement of the marooned Devil Dogs?

Corps across the country were gearing up for major championship shows, and yet here we were, hidden under a blanket of oppressive heat, unable to reveal our progress with anyone that mattered—so I tried to keep my mind's eye on the prize coming at the end of our trip. The Emerald Knights would have their first DCI experience at Whitewater's Midwest regional. After sixteen stifling hot days, boatloads of bugs, four thousand four hundred and fifty-two miles, and thirteen states—it was about fucking time.

Like the California trip, the one good thing about our Florida odyssey was the full corps rehearsal time. While many corps practiced daily during the summer, our custom had us meeting for only two or three evening practices a week, and even then, we were often missing a rotating handful of members with misplaced priorities. Now arriving in Whitewater, two full days before prelims, we had the practice fields to ourselves. Our bodies, playing chops, and minds were in drum corps shape, and the Wisconsin heat was laughable compared to the basting we had received in Florida.

The day of prelims, in a mostly full Warhawks stadium, all segments of the corps were putting it together. Finally, a chance to stretch our competitive wings and show our stuff. Our throwback show had the old timers getting the new timers in the crowd worked up as well. People actually cheered where they were supposed to cheer, and "Dixie" brought no discernible response. It felt good to be back on a Midwestern football field under the eyes of real drum corps fans.

The highlight of my entire trip took place as I was heading back into the stadium after our performance to wait for our score. Passing by some kids wearing their high school band's T-shirts, I caught them mid conversation.

"D'ja see the Emerald Knights?"

"Yeah, they were a gas. They were wild...they were free."

Wild and free? That wasn't exactly how I would describe us, but their colloquial exchange seemed authentic. I was seventeen and easily impressed with any adoration thrown our way, even if it was from prepubescent high school bandies. *Wild and free, huh? That's what they thought of us?* Even though we weren't a DCI corps, we'd finally procured actual fans who weren't even distantly related to us. Unfortunately we only had four more shows for the rest of the season and, having sadly shot our monetary wad traveling to Florida, they wouldn't include a tour out to the DCI World Championships in Philly.

Scoring a 62.15, we ended up in thirteenth place out of the twenty-two competing corps, just five points from advancing on to the evening's finals. Not too bad considering the top seven were DCI finalists. The one big disappointment with our score was that the Dubuque Colt 45's beat us by three points. Our continued improvement had them as this year's reference point for success.

Displacing the Nee-Hi's as our state rival, we were lucky they didn't come to this year's American Legion state competition. They were the Casper Troopers of Iowa, with cowboy hats and fringed western shirts, drum majors sporting six-shooters in low-slung holsters, and yearly repertoires of powerful western standards like, "How the West was Won," "Wild Wild West," "Ghost Riders," et cetera. Traveling the local Iowa circuit, they were usually at the top of the heap, and it would be another year before we caught them.

The 1975 Whitewater prelims marked the only time all season where the mighty Madison Scouts would finish in anything other than first, as Santa Clara Vanguard bested them by just 0.15 points. That rain-soaked evening, under streaming lights and intermittent rain, satin and chrome glistened hypnotically. Now an end zone spectator, I was all in, mesmerized by each performance and amazed by the progression in quality of sight and sound from each subsequent corps.

When Madison took the field, their brass line blew their competition away. The pacing of their show's programed hits in "Slaughter on Tenth Avenue," a Maynard Ferguson version of "MacArthur Park," "Rhapsody in Blue," a drum solo of "Dueling Banjos," and their perfect closer of "The Way We Were" repeatedly brought twelve thousand damp fans to their feet. Now it was my turn to dole out the adoration, as they truly were "wild and free." Back on top by almost a full point, Madison was crowned DCI's Midwest Champion.

Walking back to our buses in the light rain, I was left with the singular fixation of a delusional juvenile drum corps addict, wondering if the Emerald Knights could ever be that good?

PART 3

MY TURN

14

SENSING THE BUS DOWNSHIFT FOR Its descent into the Mississippi River Valley, I kept my eyes closed until I heard the door open. There was only a hint of dawn in the eastern sky, and it took a while to adjust to the lights in the campus parking lot. Sunday morning silence was reverently preserved while we sleepily unloaded ragged luggage from the bus bays. Grabbing our horns off the equipment truck, five of us crammed bodies and gear into Brett's Dodge Monaco. He guided the car through neighborhoods of aging framed houses along streets that were lined with the thick, dark trunks of mature oaks and maples, their dark canopy forming a tunnel that ended at an old two-story duplex.

Twenty-five bucks was my share of two weeks' rent for space in the unfinished basement. It was an offer I couldn't refuse. There was plenty of room, and everything I required was within reach: a single mattress on a wire bed frame, a clean, cool cement floor, sink, stand-alone shower, toilet, and direct access to the kitchen atop the narrow warped wooden steps. After quickly stowing my gear and throwing my sleeping bag on the bed, I pulled the string on a bare light bulb and slept 'til way past noon.

An early morning arrival gave corps members two glorious days to decompress, and while a few of the imports took the opportunity to head for home, most spent a leisurely Sunday wrapped in luscious sleep before restocking barren refrigerators and washing clothes. Monday, however, was entirely reserved for something special. While La Crosse was no Machu Picchu, it did provide the scenic backdrop for a sacred celebration held to mark the midpoint of the season. It was simply called, "The Puker."

Successfully executed in 1977, the event was destined to become an annual tradition, and this year it was planned with the exacting details of a presidential inauguration. In a generous act of solidarity, invitations were mailed out to all of the DCI member corps across the country. Obviously, none of them would attend, but this was indeed the social event of the summer for the majority of Blue Star members, staff, and nearby alumni. Funding was obtained from modestly priced tickets, generous sponsorships from thirsty alumni, and nicely supplemented with profits from the sales of the simple hand-painted Puker shirts. This year's version was a white T-shirt, adorned with the not-so-subtle blotches of green and brown paint, and below them, fire engine-red letters proudly spelled out: "Puker 78."

The Puker wasn't just a party, it was an all-day dramedy in three acts, beginning with members of legal age convening for a morning tour at the designated epicenter of La Crosse, Heileman's Brewery. The now-historic site was first established in 1858, and it was anchored by a tourism-worthy landmark, the world's largest six-pack. Signage indicated the giant cans could hold a total of 22,200 barrels of beer, the equivalent of which could supply one person with a six pack a day for 3,351 years—truly the stuff from which Wisconsin wet dreams are made. After members completed the tour, fresh samples of Old Style, Blatz Light Cream Ale, and Special Export were gratuitously provided. Let the festivities begin!

The unabashed merriment then moved to a sprawling park outside of town, with an afternoon all-ages picnic and softball game. The semi-serious competition pitted "all-stars" from the brass against the percussion. A rules augmentation included the addition of a pony keg adjacent to the on-deck circle and batters up were required to chug a small plastic pitcher of suds amidst cheers and jeers from spectators and the opposing team. While the quality of play and athleticism were marginal, the late inning antics were well worth the price of the free admission.

The final act was staged at a local banquet hall, and members of legal age enjoyed a beer and bratwurst dinner with all the appropriate side dishes. In order to ensure there were no deviations from the celebration's title, a specially concocted hoodlum drink called

Red Stuff was served. The rose-colored drink was made from a sweet fruit punch that was blended with the highly flammable Everclear grain alcohol.

While the evening's entertainment was partially provided by a polka band, it was also supplemented by bobbing for pickles and the antics supplied by corps members enthusiastically embracing the ritual. The highlight of the celebration was the festive coronation of the Puker King and Queen, selected from two members who had early on "passed go" with reckless abandon. In order to graciously accommodate the overserved, the following day's rehearsal did not reconvene until evening.

The Southern Bastards' house had a whole different take on their precious days off, and I was somewhat disappointed that it didn't include any part of Monday's celebration. Brett flew back to Mississippi to reconnect with his girlfriend and the remainder of my teetotaling housemates absorbed as much rest and recovery as they could.

Entering the individual events competition at the World Championships, Perry was deeply immersed in protracted practice sessions, and later that morning, he auditioned his solo for my critique. It was an oboe concerto he'd carefully transcribed for his baritone bugle. Full of demanding thirty second note runs that nearly outpaced the valve action on the horn, it also featured sweet melodies in the upper-upper register. Standing in the living room, he casually performed it from memory. It was jaw dropping, flawless.

Simultaneously humbled and inspired, I spent the remainder of the morning practicing as well. Wanting lunch and a break, I talked Alton into driving me out to the park to take in the picnic and the hilarity of the Puker softball game. A beautiful La Crosse day, it was dinner theater alfresco.

That night we didn't wash down our dinner with any Red Stuff, but afterwards we did gather in the sparsely furnished living room where the featured entertainment was provided by a small stereo. Going through their scant collection of albums, I gave Robbie, Alton, and Perry good-natured grief when I uncovered one by The Carpenters. To me they were bubblegum, not worthy of taking up any aural space when there were a myriad of blues, rock, fusion, jazz, and funk bands to explore. Alton politely stated his case that Karen Carpenter was the best contralto in the pop music business. With a more open ear, her clear, effortlessly pristine voice demanded I withdraw my objection.

Listening to her music, I shared that in '74, I'd played a solo from a Carpenters medley during the Emerald Knights' closer. It was the easy, melodic opening line to their covered top forty hit, "Superstar." Despite my oppressive stage fright, I'd petitioned hard for the opportunity, in part to help me defeat the persistent performance disorder that had plagued me since my fifth grade trumpet debut.

Only a few months into my career with the horn, the elementary instrumental music teacher had me playing simple Christmas carols throughout the school's halls. Feeling woefully unprepared, that day my tongue was a thin, dry stick, and I painfully transformed "Jingle Bells" into a horrendous version of "Jiggle Bells," as cold sweaty fingers slipped on the horn's valves and I nervously shook like a wet dog. To my teacher's dismay, I destroyed every single happy holiday quarter note I encountered, and afterwards I swore I'd never play a solo again for as long as I breathed.

By the age of sixteen, I reasoned I could overcome my acute affliction, simply by focusing on my drum corps devotion. Aided by the distance from the crowd and the anonymity provided by my uniform, it was the perfect prescription, and over time I was able to steadily transfer my tight pucker of looming dread into anticipatory excitement. Repeated performances in front of modest and respectful crowds varied from requisite to sublime, and before summer's end, genuine applause had replaced the usual polite response.

That was the same summer my parents demanded I spend two weeks in Europe traveling with my high school band. My

Photograph courtesy of the Emerald Knights

1974, the "New" Emerald Knights. Saluting the crowd after my solo at the state competition.

guilt for abandoning the corps in the middle of the season was minimized when our part-time horn instructor, Otto, a twenty-year-old trumpet music major from Cedar Rapids' Coe College, agreed to cover for me. At my first practice back, Dode's not-so-little, lead-sop-playing brother, Matt, brought a cassette recording of one of my missed competitions. Listening to Otto's garnished performance reduced any of my best efforts to mere pablum, and the other lead sopranos laughingly suggested that I should go back to Europe and stay there.

The Southern Bastards loved the inflected drama of my self-deprecating anecdotes, and we enthusiastically swapped stories of our fine arts glory days long into the evening. There'd be no Puker hangover for any of us tomorrow.

The down time between first tour and the second half of the season provided more than just a respite for the members and staff, and it was quite the contrary for the latter. Flush with audiotapes from the country's best adjudicators, staff members took careful measure in reevaluating show designs.

The brief pause was used to consider what additional tweaks and flourishes could be added to the shows, along with outlining a triage for cleaning up, watering down, or cutting out any exposed flaws. New guard work was almost always a given, transitions and formations in drill and music were revised, alongside general effect additions to highlight impacts throughout the entire performance package. Most of these changes were superficial and included everything from adjusting horn angles, to visuals like stick tricks in the percussion section, horn flashes, and variations in marching styles to accentuate the music.

In rare instances, some corps deemed it necessary to revise significant segments of drill and music. In dire situations, an entire portion of the show would be rewritten. After Madison won the '75 World Championship, their following year's disco/funk production failed to groove with judges and the fans. Having no chance of defending their title with the likes of the "Theme from Shaft," and Average White Band's "Pick Up the Pieces" they ditched the entire show.

While still competing with the original program during their first tour, members learned the new music as they traveled from show to show. Arriving home in early July, they withdrew from their competitions for the remainder of the month and revamped their entire production. Despite the herculean task, they couldn't overcome the polished professionalism that was the '76 Blue Devils and settled for a distant second place finish at the World Championships in Philadelphia.

Arriving fifteen minutes before the beginning of the evening's rehearsal, I discovered the Blue Stars' main practice location was a massive blanket of asphalt known as the Oktoberfest Grounds. Located near La Crosse's old downtown area, it provided the substrate for beer tents and band stages during the annual autumn invasion of thousands of thirsty pilgrims disguised in dirndls and lederhosen. At the end of September, like migrating birds, they would flock to the river city. Here they would pay homage to the marriage of an obscure Bavarian prince to a Saxon princess by drinking jumbo steins of beer, while simultaneously destroying truckloads of brats and giant, overpriced soft pretzels. Aside from a few municipal vehicles and the Blue Stars' buses, the remainder of the time the lot sat vacant. Without a grass field and stands, it was only an adequate practice location. The one benefit being its distance from residential areas, which helped the corps to remain in good standing with the local populace when practicing way past sunset.

Recovered, refreshed, and enthusiastic Blue Stars piled from cars, gathered equipment off the truck and casually loosened up on their own. The arc of horns formed organically, and after Pierre led us through a lengthy warm-up, Hill greeted us with ten more measures of *fff* music to tag onto the end of our show.

The prior three years, the corps had closed with Bob James' "Soulero." It set the stage for a dramatic conclusion to the show, building just enough tension that when finally resolved, provided a satisfying and exciting climax. The formula worked so well, the staff continued to bring it back almost to the point of achieving trademark status. In '78 the design team decided it was time to move on, and while the new arrangement of "Tiger of San Pedro" provided an appropriate subtle groove that quickly transformed into a full-frontal attack, the judges' consensus was that the show's finale seemed to be too much of a short dive off a spectacular cliff. For Hill it was a relatively easy fix, and his additional forty counts of "pour it on music" would provide plenty of lift to clear the canyon.

The only issue with the addition was its physical demand. By the show's end, brass members are completely gassed, and having to march up tempo while spewing a firehose of sustained sound into the stands was torturous. However, Hill was convinced our thoroughbred baritones could provide the bottom support for the remainder of the brass section to lean on. Besides, wasn't Chop Suey making everyone stronger players by the day? Hell, in three more weeks, we'd all be superheroes.

By the end of the practice, the brass and percussion had learned the new music and accompanying drill moves, and our guard instructors recorded it in order to write the choreography. It was all good, but I was growing increasingly frustrated. There were still a few segments where my marching responsibilities were obscure, and my first performance was imminent. Hoover and I needed repetition with the drill, and other than the new ending, the kid from St. Louis hadn't learned one count of drill. I shared my frustrations with Albo after practice and he assured me I'd be much more comfortable by the end of the week. He was almost right.

Four days later I nervously stood outside DeKalb's Huskie Stadium at Northern Illinois University. Like an astronaut who had repeated dozens of simulations, I anxiously awaited my first authentic launch.

The entire week before heading to Illinois, it had been eat, sleep, and mostly drum corps. Precisely planned, efficient practices started each morning at nine and lasted well past nine each night, after which Chop Suey was always waiting. As Albo promised, my marching role was becoming more coherent. The bulk of our practices were spent on the field, refining drill, and working all aspects of the full ensemble. Numerous visual accents in the brass line were added to our drum solo, including interesting body movements, ripple turns, and head choppers. Wolfie and Pierre also adjusted horn angles throughout the program, magnifying impacts and balancing the ensemble. No stagnation—the add-ons kept engagement levels high. For me, it was a crash course in focusing on the numerous macro and micro drill responsibilities, while fighting off any symptoms of hypervigilance. Hard nights' sleep brought confused, disjointed dreams of Stars, Knights, parents, friends, and vaguely familiar strangers, all mashed together in frustratingly stupid scenarios.

The previous morning we'd left for DeKalb and went straight to the campus athletic fields. After our warm-up, we were allotted an hour of time in a stadium that seemed to have been specifically built for a drum corps show. Even better than Allentown, the stands were steeper and boasted a concert side capacity of fifteen thousand. It was the first football field in the state carpeted with artificial turf, and we were digging it, as smooth ground with no surprises was the perfect marching surface. Pausing after each section of the show, we listened as our staff shared a bullhorn to critique us from high in the stands.

Back at our housing, Wolfie presented the brass section with a new set of D.E.G. Dynasty II soprano bugles. With only ten more shows in the season, the purchase was surprising, but after spending some time with them, we unanimously agreed that they played much more freely than the old horns, and it added one more boost to our growing assertiveness. D.E.G. had included fifty-four red and white striped cotton driver caps with the order, and sporting them in a variety of goofy ways, our brass section resembled a comical fraternity in search of a party. After Wolfie had the nearly naked baritone section put on some T-shirts, we had an impromptu publicity photo shoot for ads in *Drum Corps World* and marching music industry newsletters.

Time on task helped my confidence considerably. I had this. I better have, my first show as a Blue Star was the inaugural Drum Corps Midwest Championships. Since many corps didn't have DCI membership, Drum Corps Midwest was an independent association formed to provide regional support for all competitive Midwestern corps. DCM worked closely with DCI and was careful to coordinate their show schedule so as not to interfere with their competitions. Nineteen corps were competing, with the top ten moving on to the evening's finals. The

Emerald Knights were here, and they had a very good chance of sharing the field with us tonight. This time, there'd be no place to hide.

Filing into the stadium, with my mouthpiece screwed tight into the leadpipe of a brand new horn, polished white bucks double tied, valves oiled, gloves taped tight to my wrists under gauntlets, red plume pushed flush into my helmet, I was strapped in and ready for blastoff. I felt good. I felt ready. I felt strong. I felt excited, and...I felt pretty fucking nervous about messing something up.

Under oddly cool and overcast skies, we were greeted by a sparse morning crowd that was scattered in the center of the steep stands. The fist pumping jog took the brass section out to our starting position, and I couldn't discern any feeling in my legs. Little in our thirteen minute show had yet to become automatic, and as instructed, I sequentially processed the numerous responsibilities in my mind's eye.

"*March first...play second*," I told myself over the thumping of my heart and the announcer's introduction. Then the rocket that was our show took off with the thunderous crack from our percussion section.

Marching in an actual competition was a rush not unlike a high-speed ride. Hang on through every corner, keep it between the ditches, and don't forget to breathe. The performance compressed minutes into a blur of moments. My entire brain was fully lit with instinct, muscle memory, stimulus, response, and complex conscious awareness coached by an active frontal lobe. It was multiple levels of awareness and concentration strategically laminated together. Opener over, crowd responds, turn the page, JB's commands, and on to the drum solo. Recently added moves—*don't mess up, just march, execute, and move on.* The Jewish Medley: *March first, play second. Play proud, damn it, you're finally a Blue Star!*

Confidently projecting my sound, I nervously skipped the exposed parts, letting my teammates cover for me. *March first, play second, turn the page.* Concert formation: *breathe, execute the attacks and releases, play the idioms, add the dynamics, breathe, and bop to the groove.* Closer: Growing fatigue now masked by new waves of adrenaline, *breathe, push through the phrases of consecutive climaxes. Charge!* Only Hill's last forty new counts of sonic sound remained, *pour it on!* Diaphragm squeezing lungs completely dry, horn snapped down, crowd blows up. Show's over—the buzz persists, fully aware, fully alive—*Hell yeah, let's do that again.*

Leaving the field, I critiqued myself. *Not too bad for a first show.* I knew there was plenty of room for improvement, there would always be, but hey, that's the point of the game. I wasn't about to beat myself up about my performance. Hill called it a very good run, and we were anxious to hear our score.

Surprised yet again, the buses detoured from our housing to stop off at the university's student center. Still in damp T-shirts and uniform bottoms, we were herded into a large, open room where the far wall held a monstrous, state-of-the-art rear projection TV. The morning's show had been recorded from the top of the stadium. It would be a rare treat to see our performance only moments after it had taken place. Seated on the floor, we were gathered close enough to smell our collective sweat, and I was jacked to pick myself out of the drill.

One hundred and seventeen gape-mouthed members listened and watched the kaleidoscope of flowing drill formations come alive. I easily found my spot on the field. *Looking good,* I thought…until we hit the intro to the Jewish medley.

There I was, on the very end of an arc facing the front sideline; completely lost in the moment, proudly blowing my brains out to the crowd, demonstrating the Stars' classic high mark time technique. Only one minor issue—the corps was at a standstill for those opening fourteen counts.

Flushed, I felt like a shiny red zit on an otherwise alabaster rear end. *March first play second…yeah right.* I tried to flatten myself into the floor.

Albo stopped the video, saying, "Who's that? Who's that?"

A hundred and sixteen pairs of eyes looked around as I sheepishly raised my hand.

A blank expression on his perpetually serious face. "Man, what are you doing?"

I swallowed hard, then, trying to diffuse the situation, I stammered, "Uh… uh, a mark time solo?"

Deep snow silence. I could feel dozens of eyes boring holes into me. Albo, finally aware of my stark discomfort, cracked a rare half smile, "Don't do that tonight. Okay?"

I nodded sadly, the video was restarted, and I lowered my head, not wanting to watch anymore. It was worse than being stripped bare in front of the entire corps—more like being stark naked and obviously cold. I wanted nothing more than to disappear for a while. Unfortunately, that's something impossible to do during a drum corps season. Thankfully, members followed Albo's lead and let it go. Boarding the bus, everyone seemed cool. With unconditional love comes unconditional forgiveness for those willing to show remorse, and I was relieved that I wasn't going to become the pariah I had feared. Like with the rest of life, shit happens, move on, and everyone seemingly did. After lunch we found out we'd just missed our eighty point goal by a mere three tenths of a point, at least some of which was blatantly my fault.

Pre-show routines engaged, we once again prepared to storm the hill for another shot at eighty points. The score marks a distinct level of excellence, and once breached, typically ensures a spot in the World Championship Finals. Anything over that line is hard-earned and each point becomes more of a slick wall to scale, than a hill to climb, evidence coming in the seven point increase we'd achieved since Allentown, compared with Madison's two point improvement during that same time period.

Only a few miles from Rockford, and close enough to Chicago, Milwaukee, and Madison, finals held a packed house. The Emerald Knights had snuck into the last finals spot with a 57.35. I was happy for them, but mindful of the repercussions it could bring. Earlier performing corps took seats in the small section of stands on the back side of the stadium while waiting for the finale, and I knew there'd be a gauntlet to run.

Finishing third in prelims, our late slot had us entering the stadium fully illuminated under bright lights. I was a dead man walking, moving down the track between the back field fence and the AstroTurf. A few of the Knights lining the fence, called out, "Piskel, you suck!" and "Hey, Mr. Emerald Knight of the Year, don't fuck up."

It was the 1972 American Legion inspection all over again, and trying not to wince, I stoically stared straight ahead. In line behind me, Bret whispered, "Sheesh, they really love you Mike."

With my helmet's chain laying against my chin, I relaxed, smiling only through my eyes. The wound, made what now seemed like a long time ago, had plenty of time to heal and there wasn't even a scab to pick. I focused on my task. In a minute I'd be free falling through the show with fourteen thousand cheering fans. It'd be the perfect distraction.

Phantom won the inaugural DCM Championship with an impressive 86.35. Madison followed a full two points behind. Despite our solid effort, this time with no personal discernable marching errors, we had yet to crest the hill, scoring a 79.5. We'd get another crack tomorrow. The Guardsmen led the best of the rest with a 74.25, beating the struggling Cavaliers by over two points. The Emerald Knights remained in last place, and during retreat, I shuddered as their sloppy screaming sopranos played the corps off the field.

Up early, we headed for Horicon, Wisconsin, a two hour jaunt straight north. It was a throwback local show like the countless competitions I'd marched in before. It featured a lineup of six corps, who had traveled from DeKalb. Sunday's early afternoon parade and evening competition were part of the closing festivities of Horicon Marsh Days; one of many similar small town summer festivals, organized to kill boredom and bring attention and revenue to a town of less than 3,500. That evening, it seemed at least that many were jammed into the high school football stadium.

Wolfie had one more surprise in store for us that weekend, and at the end of a brief practice between the parade and performance, he called the brass line in around him. With his now-familiar pointed delivery, he said, "Hey people, listen up. I want you to max it out tonight…really let it fly." It was like a bolt of electricity went through the horn line. "Jack up the volume on all impacts and push the cheap seats back as far as you can. Have fun out there tonight but be smart…let's see what you got."

Ring a bell, I could swear the baritone section started to salivate. This was going to be a very interesting experiment, and I wondered how it would play into our quest for eighty points.

Suited up and ready, I was beginning to feel much more at ease as I joined the long blue line filing towards the starting line. This was my third date with the field, and it was indeed time to go all the way. Now my new mindset was, *march first, play first,* as I needed to find out just what I had when it came to playing the entire book. The thought sparked a fresh rush of adrenaline.

Directly in line behind me was Dr. K's stunning, blonde, seventeen-year-old daughter, Kimmy, who was admirably filling a spot on third soprano. She began chanting a mantra of, "Super Cool, Super Blue." One by one, the remainder of the side two horn line joined her. Although a little corny, it did keep me locked in the moment, and helped to take some of the edge off my nerves. Lights were just beginning to take effect when we hit the starting line, and like the Big Bad Wolf, we blew the place down.

We were the first of three DCI finalist corps to take the field after the Colts, Wausau Story, and Minnesota's Blue Knights. Our opening statement was an obvious step up in volume and performance quality, and it created a noticeable murmur in the semi-experienced crowd. The intimacy of a small show is far different than that of the anonymous crowds that filled bigger stadiums. Up close, you see them, and they see you. During the shared time, it's easy to measure individual spectators' reactions, and a reciprocity of emotions and mutual engagement forms. The sights and sounds of crowd and corps all merge into one fused happening. By the end of our performance, our sound had blasted away any remaining loose paint on the bleachers, and those extra forty counts easily pulled the now familiar spectators from their seats in a swell of boisterous adoration. There it was, that unique drum corps feeling that makes all the sacrifices and effort worth it. FCO! Basking in the moment of an authentic natural high, it lasted just long enough to stimulate a desire for more.

Three times being the proverbial charm, I had a satisfying show. We all did. If my corps career had to end at that moment I wouldn't have been devastated. While Wolfie had his notes regarding our performance issues, he was upbeat about the quality and balance of sound. Chop Suey anyone? The question still remained, had we climbed the mountain?

Back on the field for finale, JB moved front and center for the awards presentation. Then the horror began. It started out like a silent summer rain on a cool moist evening. Finding purchase on limited bare skin, I felt one, then two bites to the back of my neck before the sky opened up and clouds of mosquitoes came crashing down. Marsh Days was about to conclude in a torturous 4D experience.

One of the Blue Stars' trademarks was our poised, silent, and classy demeanor during the finale, but tonight we collectively broke proscenium. Guard members were beyond themselves as bare legs became the perfect landing strips for the bloodthirsty horde. Deb had them marking time, but it was still a total swat fest, and they were completely outnumbered. Hell, there was a fucking thirty-three thousand acre breeding ground just north of us. Horicon Marsh Days? I rechristened it, "Marsh Madness."

With no place to hide, the finale couldn't end fast enough. The majority of the audience had fled before the scores were announced. Hearing, "In third place, with a score of 82.75, the Blue Stars," provided only a momentary distraction to the carnage taking place on the field. We could celebrate later. Only an hour from Madison, the Scouts were the obvious crowd favorite. Having one of their best shows of the year, they made up the two point deficit from DeKalb, scoring 87.7 and edged Phantom Regiment by a scant five hundredths of a point. Tonight, having to wait their turn to leave the field, their victory would cost them a pound of real flesh.

Finding refuge inside the high school, we tended our wounds, played Chop Suey, and followed S.O.P. to get the hell out of Horicon High. Moving fast, we were on our buses well before the school had shut off their "open for dinner" stadium lights. As the bus ground its way through low gears, Schultzie stood up from his bus seat and looked back at the high school, still flooded with swarms of tiny flying vampires. Then raising a mocking salute, he snidely shouted, "Adiós, mother-suckers!"

15

THE SEASON'S FIRST SCORE OVER eighty had left a great taste in our mouths, triggering sweet cravings for more. With rehearsal not scheduled until Tuesday, the lead soprano section unanimously agreed that a Monday afternoon sectional was in order. Soloist Steve Severance said, "I know the perfect place."

He would. He was the only locally bred lead sop, and the most tenured. Sev first joined the corps at fourteen, back in '74. Now four years later, he could flat-out wail. He played all of the music's upper splits, and regularly won the Chop Suey high note throwdown. He was the alpha player in the collection of strong trumpet and bugle musicians, and while not all that outspoken, when he did say something, it was always worth listening to and today we took him up on his suggestion.

Ten of us jammed into several cars and headed east towards the long line of white, rocky bluffs that pinned La Crosse against the riverbank. Up a steep road, we wound our way through mature hardwoods and switched back at the entrance to Grandad Bluff Park, then continued to drive to the top where we stopped at a pavilion located near the bluff's sheer face. Immediately I appreciated Sev's instincts. I think we all did.

The spot announced the splendor of the city spread across the floodplain below, and Grandad Bluff was—well, the granddaddy bluff of them all. At 590 feet, it offered an inspirational and isolated locale, where ten lead sopranos could push fast air through shiny new horns over the top of the town. Other than the local wildlife, we wouldn't bother a soul.

Now I understood why the Blue Stars were called "The Kids from God's Country." In the distance I could see tiny lines of rust red barges moving up and down the main river channel. They were flanked by miles of maze-like ribbons of backwater sloughs and oxbow lakes that cut through swamp oaks, maples, cottonwoods, and river birch, all the way across to Minnesota. Indeed, it was most heavenly.

The view reminded me of the trips my family would take to the Mississippi River town of Guttenberg, Iowa. Several weekends a summer we'd boat up and down the river in the houseboats and cabin cruisers of my father's colleagues. Midday, we'd beach them on sun-baked sandbar islands for cookouts with charred hot dogs, burgers, mustard-yellow potato salad, and iced-down watermelon. The fond memory was the first time I'd thought about my folks in a while, and I wondered what they were doing at this moment, while appreciating them for helping me with the chance to have mine.

Warmed up, and out of range of Hill's scrutinizing ears, it was time to stop playing the notes and start playing the music. Collectively, we blasted out waves of sound on an endless trip through white billowy clouds and a cobalt sky. Phrase by phrase, we methodically worked through the book, all the time focusing on uniformity of style and inflection. After completing each phrase, we'd pause for group analysis, before repeating it until a unanimous consensus of perfection was reached.

Horns down for a break, we fell under riverscape's magical spell. Time flowed like the Mississippi below us. Heraclitus was spot on: "No man steps into the same river twice." Senses working overtime, the sectional transcended any rehearsal I'd ever been part of, and I realized it was one of those moments that would forever change the way I looked at life. *Yep, Sev was right, it was the perfect spot for just about anything.*

The following day, Hill met me at our rehearsal with rolled-up sheet music in his hand. "Mike, some key parts in the third soprano music aren't being covered well enough during the show. I've highlighted them. It's either you or St. Louis…you up for it?"

St. Louis was a stronger player than me and he still had plenty to learn, so I didn't hesitate, "Sure, I'll take them." Besides, I was glad Hill offered me the option to make a specific contribution.

"Great, thanks. One more thing…I want you to lay out during the swing section in "Malaga", I've noticed in Horicon and in practice you're dragging through that section."

I flushed, stammering, "Uh…Okay." Then thoughts spun: *First the third sop parts, then his appraisal that I wasn't cutting it during one of the more difficult passages. Was I dragging? Why the third sop parts? Do I suck? Stop thinking so much, and just do what you need to do.*

My mood improved as I looked over the new music. It was only sixteen bars, most of which were lower register melodic lines that didn't even interfere with the lead parts. It was easy and interesting music to play. I considered that when the world championship albums came out, I could go, "Hey, hear that? That's me."

The remainder of our week was filled with systematic and arduous nine a.m. to nine p.m. practices, most of which actually didn't end until ten. They focused on cleaning up everything that could be cleaned, and I loved every minute of them. Blue Star excellence meant putting both perfection and passion into every moment of rehearsal. Great performances required hours of great practices, and I quickly learned how to maintain an intense level of consistent concentration. Doing so made time disappear, and we immersed ourselves into perfecting the details of a now most familiar show.

The staff was indefatigable, fighting for every tenth of a point with zero tolerance for any mistakes. They taught with passion, experience, and intelligence, modeling the concentration they wanted from us. They reserved their wrath only for lapses of blatant stupidity, and we did our best to prevent getting singled out. Yet it happened to most of us at various times throughout the long hours of practice, and while embarrassing, we knew it wasn't personal. Drum corps gave you a thick skin, and the best part of you knew their caustic barbs were the result of their own frustration born from the desire to achieve a level of perfection that existed only in their mind's eyes and ears.

During this last push, we were joined on the practice field by a wiry little man whose expressive face reminded me of a hungry baby bird impatiently waiting to feather out. Balding, with an oversized nose and matching ears, he had large, ever-watchful eyes behind rectangular, wire glasses. He was outfitted in a faded white V-neck T-shirt and shorts, completed by sockless, slip-on dress shoes. Upon his arrival I heard whispers throughout our ranks, "Oh boy, Old Man Frank is here. Don't mess up."

His bony hands carried a long, taped interval stick that he used to measure and repair the spacing between bodies in drill sets. Watching him flitter everywhere throughout the field, simultaneously fixing the intervals while berating those responsible for their errors, I thought, *Who the hell is Old Man Frank?*

One move had our section of the horn line marching into a long arc, after which he ran up and repositioned me, pointing out how I was not properly set in the formation. With a cutting, high pitched voice he squawked, "Hey you! You're not in the form. Look at the guy next to you…read the curve."

Foolishly I replied, "I am looking at him…I'm guiding right off his feet."

Caterwauling to the rest of the horns in the drill form, "His feet! His feet! Did you hear that? He's looking at his feet!" Like a little Moses getting ready to part the Red Sea, he walked towards me with his interval stick in hand. "You big dummy, don't look at his feet. Read his body through the form…what shit corps taught you how to march?"

Now everyone was snickering at his latest tirade. Adequately chastened, and working hard not to laugh, I responded, "The Emerald Knights."

"That figures," he cackled sarcastically. "Nobody knows how to march in Iowa."

Trying the move once more, it was better, but evidently still not good enough. He explained, "You feel like you are ahead of the arc because your eyes are in the front of your head. Now do it again and get it right."

Quite the character, Old Man Frank's spatial intelligence and low threshold for marching errors rivaled that of Hill's demands with the music. For the rest of the day, my name became "Iowa," which I figured was a lot better than, "You Big Dummy."

I later learned that Old Man Frank was Frank Van Voorhis, and some staff members quipped that he'd actually been born old. An appliance repairman by day and drum corps marching savant by night, he was wizened, wise, and funny as hell. He was also one of the two original founders of the Blue Stars. It was Frank's idea to create a youth organization that stood as a symbol of excellence, which then became the framework for the corps' philosophy, ultimately resulting in their sustained success. In the corps' early years, he conceived their precise marching style and designed their drill, and while no longer joining the corps on tour, Frank and a host of other staff alumni magically appeared like

Amish neighbors at a barn raising, helping us any way they could before we embarked on our second tour.

The corps was in a good place as we prepared for the last leg of the season, and the past two weeks had disappeared like a coin in a sleight of hand trick. It'd been my good fortune to have bonded with the Southern Bastards, as they made the time in La Crosse seamless and comfortable. They were great guys, and the only pressure I'd felt came from my desire to not let anybody down. Now with the intense rehearsal schedule and several shows worth of experience, that didn't seem likely to happen. Fully integrated into the drill and gaining more and more confidence playing the music, muscle memory was starting to play a positive role in both. I felt fit and ready for the fifteen day tour that would culminate in the end of my drum corps career.

16

AUGUST 15, 1978

HEADING INTO GOLDEN, COLORADO, I was able to stretch out between two seats. Six days into the second tour, my sullen seatmate Dan, had blatantly decided to kick back with a doobie after an exhibition in Little Rock. Without fanfare or forewarning, Moe and Dr. K put him on a plane for home. Despite our extended time together on the bus, the two of us never really clicked, and it seemed that was also true of his relationships within the snare line. The other drummers had repeatedly told him to cool it when it came to his illicit habit, and the remaining eight snares were seriously pissed about losing a decent player and spending half the day adjusting their drill.

Dan was difficult to read from the beginning, and his penchant for self-isolation made him an anomaly in the corps. I surmised that a couple years in the Marines had left him feeling detached from the whole junior drum corps thing, and that he probably regretted his decision to spend the summer marching. I wondered if he even cared about missing the biggest show of the year. What I did know was that I didn't miss Dan's stale, smoky, and sullen presence.

Luckily, that was our only measurable misstep (well, aside from the fire ants on a practice field in Dallas) in an otherwise smooth, double time tour. Marching instead of spectating greatly accelerated the passing of time, and I tried not to think about summer being over in a few days.

Our journey west had started slowly enough with two small shows in Dubuque, Iowa and Mt. Vernon, Illinois. Despite the program changes and the collective efforts of Old Man Frank, staff, and members, we couldn't match our score from Horicon. It left me with an unspoken sense that we might have plateaued.

The last stretch of competitions before the championships often had judges pigeonholing your position relative to the other corps. There was really no chance of catching the top five, but the crowd of corps in the next tight cluster had us hoping that by season's end we could finish in the top half. Jumping a spot or two required noticeable levels of improvement that the judges couldn't deny. Hell, it seemed like it was taking tremendous levels of effort just to maintain our current position. But true to our mission of excellence, we pushed on with urgency and blind dedication, and that's when the tour took on the speed of Casey Jones's train.

During a blazing hot day of practice in Dallas, brass members were handed a plastic tube that later would be slipped into our cummerbunds. The idea was to toss a shower of red, silver, and blue glitter into the air on the ending unison rim shot of our drum solo. A spectacular surprise accent, it seemed like pure general effect genius! We rehearsed the stunt repeatedly, sans glitter, figuring out how to pop off the cap and synchronize the move to reduce timing errors.

The Dallas show was at a high school stadium of tremendous proportions. They took their football seriously down there. Evidently, they took their drum corps seriously as well, as I was amazed to see a huge crowd filling the stadium that held over 12,000 spectators. Competitive Texas high school marching band programs were gaining in popularity, and the show's fan base was composed of throngs of young people who worshiped DCI corps as if they were rock bands. Taking the field, the crowd was as hot as the temperature, and they were going bonkers before we even played our first note. More than okay by me. This was going to be fun. We roared through our program, and the frenetic bandies responded in kind. My only surprise was that our new sparkling rim shot didn't seem to achieve much of a reaction.

Forming our post performance circle outside the stadium, many of the brass members' sweaty faces were still covered with the tiny Blue Star colored flecks. Moe laughingly told us that from the stands, "It looked like y'all were spreadin' the gray ashes of long lost Legionnaires across the field," and subsequently the decision was made that we would no longer be paying homage to them.

The failed experiment reminded me of an experience from the previous year's Emerald Knights' DCI World Championship prelim performance. With nine days between DCI Midwest and the World Championships, we had only one show in Ft. Dodge, Iowa. That performance found us in last place to three of the corps that we had defeated earlier in Whitewater. Searching for something to give us an edge, our visual staff thought adding a splash of color to our concluding company front would make it standing ovation worthy.

Digging through the storage room in the armory, they resurrected the old, sweat-stained red satin ascots from our '74 uniforms. The plan was for the brass members to stash them inside their green tunics until a short drum break in the closer, then quickly fasten them onto the bells of the horns, revealing a shock of contrasting color during the company front. Fundamentally it was a sound general effect concept, but most of us felt the move was clumsy, and up close the ascots had a desperately trashy look. Despite practicing with them for a couple days before prelims, the end result was depressingly pathetic.

The world championship prelims gave the Emerald Knights their first real crack at becoming a top twenty-five DCI Associate Member—a deeply desired and presumably realistic goal. Associate membership came with much more performance money and show opportunities for the following year, and more importantly, their performances were recorded in high fidelity, and etched in vinyl for perpetuity.

From the podium on prelim morning, I (along with everyone else) counted four ascots on the field before the opener ended. Thoughts about the dropped red rags compromised our focus for the remainder of the show, and by the company front even more of them littered the field. I thought they looked like the bloody wounds of brass players taking shots straight through the heart.

Two days earlier the King had died on his throne in Graceland. Now it was the Knights' turn, and our mortal injuries left us with a performance that was flat and crushingly disappointing. The poor showing still resulted in a season high score of 70.15, but we'd only placed thirtieth out of forty-five competing corps. We were four full points down from making the cut to associate member, and the extra cash, better shows, and albums would have to wait.

Two days later, in a rain-soaked mud bowl at the American Legion Nationals prelims, the full reality of the great ascot debacle became apparent. With the staff finally agreeing to ditch them, we performed our most complete show of the year. For some inexplicable reason (other than the fact that it was an American Legion show) many of the prelim scores were grossly inflated in comparison with DCI's prelims. We found ourselves in third place with an improbable 83.8. During finals, the judging panel had settled down and our score was a 77.5, much more indicative of our true potential, which still had us on top of several of the DCI associate corps from two days earlier. If only...

Like an old 1940s dance band crisscrossing the nation and working up new arrangements before evening concerts, the Blue Stars tour gave us ample opportunities to evaluate the different tweaks and decorations added to our program. The glitter would have to go. Our Dallas performance had us stuck at 82.5, and we were still a full point and a half from the static Crossmen. Perhaps they too were reaching that point where talent level, show design, and instruction couldn't take them any further. Madison won the show, a full point over the Bridgemen, with an 87.4.

The path to Denver's World Championship had sixty-two corps marching their way across the western half of the country. Competitions throughout California, Idaho, Wyoming, Kansas, Iowa, Illinois, Nebraska, and Oklahoma slowly funneled corps towards the Mile High City for the ultimate showdown. During the first two weeks in August, DCI purposely divided and shuffled line ups of competing corps, making it difficult to get a good read on just who had the greatest competitive advantage to become an associate member, top twelve finalist, or take the crown.

Leaving Texas, we left the fire ants behind but took searing hot weather with us, and finally, we started to heat up too, with fantastic brass runs in Oklahoma City and Great Bend. The entire horn line was churning out a full robust sound that helped elevate the scoring in other captions. None of us questioned the effectiveness of Claude Gordon's Chop Suey calisthenics, which had now become as routine as brushing teeth. By the time we hit Pueblo, our brass performance was challenging Wolfie to find things we could do any better. Only three days before prelims, we scored an 83.25, narrowly overtaking a very strong Spirit of Atlanta, a corps who had us by almost four and a half points at Whitewater. Blue Devils won the show with an 89.6, just edging out Phantom, and now only days away, the title of World Champion had no definitive frontrunner.

Our housing for DCI's World Championship was twelve miles west of Denver, at Golden Colorado's School of Mines, and we shared the facility with the Madison Scouts. With four straight days of showers boasting significant water pressure and more importantly, four straight nights of horizontal sleep in the dorm's almost real beds, it was a special treat. The two full days of practice before prelims also gave us enough time to acclimate to the thin air, while continuing our quest for excellence.

My Southern Bastard housemate, Perry Dornbusch, and our exquisite mallet player, Tom Nanni, met DCI's first challenge, winning their individual competitions a day before prelims. An excited yet humble Perry told us how after the first few measures of his concerto, awed judges put down their pencils, sat back, and soaked it in. Perry was awarded a perfect score with a one point penalty for playing past the allotted time. An amazing feat, no one else even came close. Nanni also had a nearly perfect score, and we viewed their victories as positive portents to our collective future, and the sense of pride garnered from their success spurred us to more intense levels of concentration during rehearsals. Now we were down to fine-tuning the minutia. There was little letup; we were young, strong, healthy, and willing. While the days were hot, the cool nights, dry air, excellent facilities, and the moms' "home cooking," helped us to rebound.

The evening before prelims, we were bused to the empty parking lot of a brightly lit shopping mall for a practice that wouldn't end until long after the sun sank behind the mountains. Until now, my time spent with the corps seemed like a month-and-a-half-long Rocky Balboa montage, and I was finally ready for the heavyweight championship bout. Amazed by the transformation that had taken place in body, mind, and spirit, that night my embouchure showed no fear. I played with the thrilling recognition of having reached another level. Hell, I felt like I'd jumped several levels. Having performed the show countless times in the last month, our final run-through morphed into an advanced exercise in the confirmation of confidence. The entire rehearsal offered a new understanding of what it meant to be in complete control. The difficult up-tempo sixteenth note runs in "Tiger of San Pedro" were no longer problematic, they were just energetic phrases to play through while focusing on my marching requirements. I savored the feeling. I was ready to show off—I think we all were.

My only lament was that it was almost over, but perhaps that was best. Hit all the high notes, slide through the octave slurs, perfectly time the horn snaps, nail Old Man Frank's intervals, and then march away with no regrets.

17

EIGHT HOURS OF PERFECT SLEEP cleared the path to waking up in a fantastic mood, and I was ready for what I believed would be an epic sunny day. Wolfie crafted a meditative, lip-tingling warm-up that was followed by a tight, spirited run-through, lunch, showers, and boarding the buses for the show. Our prelim slot had us going on mid-afternoon and the temperature had steadily climbed to over ninety degrees. Embracing the arid heat like a warm blanket, my bones and muscles felt loose, heavy, and relaxed. I was sure I couldn't possibly feel any better.

Prelims were taking place in Boulder, and a large crowd filled the concert side of the University of Colorado's Folsom Field. We prepped like always, following the same routine that was part of a prescribed plan to reduce variables and limit distractions. The only one we couldn't control was the weather. Through the access tunnel and onto the field, the parabolic effect of the stadium had turned the synthetic turf into a scorching heat island. Surface temperatures pushed the field to a hundred and thirty degrees, yet still reveling in my newly acquired confidence, I was oblivious to it. I wasn't about to let heat or anything else derail the joy of my last two performances. How stellar was this? My only concern in life was marching a flawless show. I was ready to let it happen, in a way I'd yet to experience.

The show was movement; movement of drill, movement of music, and movement of emotions. Flowing through each phrase of music and marching, they melded into one, and I conquered it and moved on. Moments were experienced, executed, and discarded all while maintaining flow. Each brief break between our music was filled with the conscious recognition of more smooth moving moments to come. Attack, dominate, and move on—flow. Part of me recognized it as an out of body experience, while another part was still very much in contact with heightened senses firing together to create new sensory submodalities. I realized multiple levels of consciousness, an altogether unique experience of time, space, place, and purpose.

173

The hours of practice had transformed me into a marching machine of precision that still maintained the ability to bear authentic emotion. Focused, I shut out the crowd, and my skin joined with my ears to process only the sound of the brass and percussion. Endless available energy, derived from passionate practice, formed the music emanating from my horn. I couldn't see the crowd, only intervals and drill forms. A buzz shook my body from my head to my feet, and it felt like I was swimming effortlessly through water and not getting wet. Show complete, horn snapped down, the move pulled me from the place I had entered just twelve minutes and fifty seconds ago. I'd never get it back. It didn't matter; at least I'd been there.

Had the rest of the corps felt what I did? Sensing the crowd's prodigious response told me they'd been right there with me. My satisfaction from the performance didn't come from soaking in the admiration of the audience. Today it came from the understanding that I was but one part of a complete system, one that provided a connection with thousands of people there to witness our story told on a field of green. Hopefully the plot was compelling enough that they were as lost in it as I was. *If not, oh well—drum corps was more about what it does for the members than what it does for its fans.*

Suddenly our score and placement didn't matter, what mattered were those seamless controlled moments of flow. Locked in the cortex of my cerebrum, I would take the experience with me for the rest of my life. It was a gift I had been able to give myself by paying attention to the random opportunities that chance sometimes provides.

Back at the School of Mines, we soaked in cool showers. During dinner Moe congratulated us, announcing a seventh place prelim score of 85.65, only a half of a point down from the Crossmen and three points from the Bridgemen. As we cheered our accomplishment, Pierre's prophecy whispered once again, "We're going to make finals...we always make finals." *Damn, we sure as hell didn't back into the night show.* In fact we were now only a half a point away from being in the top half of the dozen best corps on Earth.

The 1978 DCI prelim scores had resulted in a tie of 91.5 points between the Phantom Regiment and the Santa Clara Vanguard. The Blue Devils were a half a point behind them, followed by Madison, and the Bridgemen. Clustered in the middle were the Crossmen,

Blue Stars, Spirit of Atlanta, and 27th Lancers, who were all within a slim two points of each other. The next two corps to join the exclusive top-twelve club were the North Star, and Guardsmen, and the last corps to slip into the night show was the Kilties, who after forty-three years as an all-male corps had finally allowed females to fill out their ranks. Undoubtedly the move had made a difference.

Noticeably absent from the finals were the struggling Cavaliers, a storied and historically successful corps, who after placing eighth in '77, had now fallen to sixteenth. Last year they fought with numerous internal demons including drug issues, confused program objectives, turnover in staff and management, and a profound dissent from a large and usually loyal alumni. The year had been a rehabilitation of sorts, and the side effects from exorcising those demons were reflected on the field, and in their score.

Fred Beyer didn't last the summer with the Emerald Knights, and they finished thirty-ninth of the forty-three corps competing in Open Class. A more prudent management decision would have placed them in the Class A Division of the competition.

In 1975, DCI expanded their World Championships to showcase a prelims and finals competition for smaller corps (ninety members or less) along with an All-Girl division. This increased participation and expanded the championship into a four day marching arts festival. In 1976, the Emerald Knights' first venture to DCI's World Championships, had them finishing in sixth place in the class A finals. Based on the Emerald Knights prior competitions throughout the 1978 season, they would have handily made the Class A night show and been in strong contention for medaling with a top three finish.

The 1978 prelims proved to be the last performance of the decade for the Emerald Knights, becoming yet another victim of the many hazards facing marginalized marching organizations during the late seventies. With operational and travel expenses ballooning, along with the growth and expansion of summer high school competitive marching band programs, any flaws in management and instruction magnified the challenge of bringing new members into the activity. At the same time, many veteran members of these compromised smaller corps now had means and motivation to seek out "better options" to complete their marching careers.

While sleeping with visions of sixth place dancing in our heads, a cold front snuck down from the mountains, and we awoke to abnormally cool temperatures and mostly cloudy skies. The sizzling afternoon prelim show was now just a warm memory, and hopefully the numerous performers overcome from yesterday's heat and thin mountain air had fully recovered.

FCO meant our work wasn't quite over, but at least now the season-long pressure to make finals had dissipated like yesterday's heat. It was a comfortable day with an unhurried pre-show routine, and the visual staff even added one more horn flash to replace the glitter toss we'd abandoned in Dallas. Our brief rehearsal complete, I got the feeling that there wasn't anything left to do that would make a difference in our evening's grand performance. We were better served by relaxing, fueling up with a spaghetti dinner, and spending the extra time polishing horns, shoes, wiping down gauntlets, helmets and changing out drum heads.

In our super cool, super blue uniforms for the last time, the closer we got to the stadium, the more pensive my mood became. The bus ride to Mile High had many of us frenetically gesticulating through a variety of displacement activities, and looking down, I caught my leg nervously bouncing to an unknown beat. Without a seatmate for distraction, I was alone with my thoughts. *Here we go, and here I go.* With deep slow breaths I cleared the clutter from my mind and visualized myself as a pure unwavering laser beam—by the time the bus circled the stadium, my leg had stopped bouncing.

Pulling into the parking lot, there was still an hour of dimming gray light left in the day. Now a finals performer rather than a finals fan, I had a new perspective on the venue, and I was awestruck by its enormity. This was no

Horicon High School football stadium out in the middle of a mosquito-laden marsh. Through the gap in the stadium, I caught a glimpse of the three nearly vertical decks of stands filled with people—it was fucking amazing.

We were not the designated halftime entertainment at a semi-pro football game. Thirty thousand plus fans were there for only one reason: to see the twelve best corps in the country. *Who gets to do this?* I wasn't Elton John, or a professional athlete, but tonight I'd feel like both. Leaving the bus to join the brass section in our shoulder to shoulder warm-up arc, I could hear the distant sound of music. It was the Kilties' opener, getting the evening's festivities appropriately started with an up-tempo, rockin' rendition of "My Favorite Things." It couldn't be more perfect.

Standing next to me, Sev seemed calmly poised, leaving a visibly high-strung Hill wondering if he was even cognizant of the moment. Avoiding the word "nervous," Hill asked if our veteran soprano soloist was ready? Sev responded that he was in a very good place, so good that right now, there was no other place in the world he would rather be. The ease of his demeanor and perfect response tempered the anxiety in all of us. Half smiling, Hill became uncharacteristically sentimental, sharing how proud he was of the phenomenal growth we accrued throughout the season and that tonight should be all about enjoying the perfectly ripe fruits of our labor.

The atmosphere around the corps was taking on the feeling of a gala and I was ready to celebrate. Pierre didn't miss his chance to come up and remind me of his indiscreet proposition, and my subsequently prudent decision to come soar into the night sky with the Blue Stars. My choice was indeed one of those forks in the road of life that I wouldn't have to look back on with abject regret. With adrenaline bubbling, I did my best to direct it away from outright spasmodic panic and looking over at Ronbo I could tell he was lost in his dream of achieving his perfect run, and I realized I needed to be right there with him.

Warm-up complete, the entire corps came together holding hands in a tight circle where we hummed the solemn melody from "Jerusalem of Gold." It was far better than any pregame speech, as it quieted busy minds, and unified our focus for the final act. We were one. We were ready.

~ ≈ ~

The crowd of alumni, groupies, support staff, and family that had been hanging around began to move toward the stadium to find their seats. I was disappointed my parents wouldn't be there, but my dad had a year-long job assignment in Yugoslavia and they'd already left at the beginning of the month. After breaking from our huddle, I heard my name being called through the crowd.

"Piskel. Yo, Piskel!" Through the mass of faces, I spotted Brad Erenberger, a longtime snare drummer with the Emerald Knights, yelling over the crowd, "We're going to be roommates this fall…Dode got an R.A. position. He told me I could take the apartment with you."

There I was, in the perfect place, ready to perform in the biggest and last show of my life, when my peace train of radiant well-being was frustratingly derailed. *What the fuck?* Trying to get it back on track, I replied, "Uh…Okay, I'll talk to you when we get back to Iowa City. I gotta go."

Wedging his way through the crowd, he caught up to me and said, "Hey man, you made the right call this summer, none of us blame you one bit…good luck, we'll be cheering for you…call me when you get back."

Flustered, with only a few remaining minutes to refocus, relax and breathe, I found my spot in line. Staff were moving through the ranks, squirting water from plastic bottles into dry mouths and checking on us like expectant fathers doting on their swollen partners. It was obvious they were lost in their own glory days, and I assumed their heightened anxiety was born from the combination of their own recollections and surrendering control over to us.

A sharply barked command from JB, and we were moving through a narrow break in the back stands to enter the field. Closer to the entrance gate I sensed the vibrations of a tremendous eruption from crowd, brass, and percussion. Magnifying the reality of the moment, The Spirit of Atlanta were in the final throngs of their closer, a righteous arrangement of "Let It Be Me." The crowd's response was breaking records in decibels and duration. It seemed as though their standing ovation was destined for perpetuity, and I only hoped it wouldn't leave them too hung over for us.

Emerging out of the entrance to the brightly lit field, there was no letup from the crowd, and looking up at the massive wall of standing spectators, shot an icy shiver through my spine. With Spirit's show finished, and the crowd's ovation waning, our pumped up jog out onto the field was the perfect antidote for my chill. Like that first show in DeKalb, I lost touch with my body's lower half and the corps' collective energy lifted me into position.

Seconds before our introduction, there was a lull in the crowd, and I could hear a smattering of well-rehearsed cheers throughout the stands. From the distant opposite end zone, I faintly caught my own name, with a collective, "Go Piskel" no doubt from Brad's coalition of Emerald Knights. I was grateful for their gesture, it verified that I'd been at least partially forgiven. Loosening the tension in my neck and shoulders, I reestablished contact with my sense of place, my breath, and my resolve. My train back on track, it was time—time to stoke the fire in the engine, time to heat it up one last time for my new brothers and sisters, for Hill and the rest of our staff, for the fans, and for myself.

While I was no Magister Ludi, years of drum corps experience and untold hours of practice had transformed me into a proficient operator of the wooden labyrinth marble game that was our show. For the next thirteen minutes, I would navigate my steel ball along a carefully prescribed path, engineered by drill designers, music arrangers, and instructors. Well-honed techniques, astute progressive observations, and muscle memory would all combine to play their part in the proficiency of my performance, hopefully guiding my shiny chrome sphere through the playing field, without falling into one of the many holes along its path. Each phrase of music and drill had been done perfectly numerous times, now all that was left was to put it together for one final flawless run. Keep the ball moving, the game isn't that long. Relax, and enjoy the challenges and thrills of the journey.

Hearing the opening percussive drum shots, we were all rolling. Lungs full, I was fully on top of our opening statement. Trusting in my abilities, with fresh chops, I played freely throughout the opener. My steel marble expertly avoided the pitfalls, almost as if there were none. Catching my breath during my designated break, I prepped for the push to the end. Sev and Brett wailed confidently through their alternating solos. Jacked with adrenaline, JB and the percussion section upped the opener's tempo to its driving finish. The brass section shot staccato bursts of Spanish accents into the stands, while the guard highlighted every note with spinning silks and rifles in mirrored unison. Finishing with a bull fighter's salute, we brought the enormous crowd back to life. My chrome ball still rolling smoothly, perfect show intact, I felt a brief moment of bliss from the fan's exuberant response. I took in its entirety. Just as Pierre had foretold, this was pretty fucking awesome.

Next up, drum solo. Now I could focus entirely on my marching and drill. From the podium JB shouted, "Remember the horn flash." *Remember? Hell yeah I remembered, and everybody else better fuckin' remember too. We just added it this morning, how could it not be fresh in everyone's mind?* I didn't want or need a reminder, I didn't want to think about it, I was in the zone and with so many holes to avoid right nearby, I was taking things just as they came.

Back on task: Perfectly choreographed head choppers, ripple moves, funky jazz squats, and sequential robotic bows, along with multiple rapid horn flashes, my route was littered with traps. Yet here I was marching with an exacting precision that would even make Old Man Frank proud, and it seemed I wasn't alone. Everyone's steel bearings appeared to be moving as effortlessly as mine. Drum solo almost concluded, JB's warning echoed in my head, and I now consciously considered the new horn flash—perhaps a little too much, and a fraction before the move—I jumped the gun, raising my horn a split second ahead of time, then bringing it back down in unison with everyone.

Shit! There I was, a sad victim of premature horn flash. Down the hole I went, and my chance at a perfect show was lost forever. *Now what?*

We were moving on. With no options for a different version of the game, I sheepishly snuck the now tarnished steelie back on the board and told myself to keep it together. There were more holes to skirt…lots more. *Relax, let it go, let it fly, you aren't going to get to do this again.* There was still a great deal of perfection and subsequent satisfaction to be had, and I was intent on exacting every bit of it.

The Jewish Medley was a thinking fan's production number. Whether in practice or shows, I loved playing it. The four minute arrangement had numerous engaging moments, but they weren't all designed to pull fans from their seats. Rather than a straight up shot of the hard stuff, the music was to be appreciated like a fine wine, hitting a complex series of tasty notes. With multiple idioms, some majestic, others celebratory, somber, or ominous, you had to be all in to have any chance of transmitting those emotions to the tremendous, distant crowd. Tonight, our ensemble reached deep into our collective souls, resulting in teary-eyed, chest swelling pride bursting from all of us. I was thrilled by the feeling of mastering majestic D to high D octave slurs as the drill moved us toward the audience. By the time we hit the climactic impact in Mancini's "Exodus," my chrome ball was once again boldly cruising down the path. Upon its completion, the crowd's sustained applause and genuine buzz acknowledged our efforts to convey images of a proud people through the show's multiple moods. Music, perfectly synchronized with the colorful choreography of precision movement, formed a language all its own, and drum corps done well truly was a unique art form.

JB momentarily let the crowd and corps recover before firing up "Backwoods Sideman." The brass line had only one brief drill move in our concert, providing us with the opportunity to lay back and let it rip.

Once again, JB gently pushed up the tempo of the bright, light, fast, and fun arrangement. Both brass duets were spot on. Nanni cut loose with his mesmerizing xylophone chops, while the guard went to work partnering with their animated umbrellas and silks. JB's newly added waggish physical inflections inflicted a humorous visual that engaged audience and members alike. Then on cue, he joined the guard. Crowning himself with a red and white-paneled umbrella hat from the side of the podium, he continued his amusing dance as he conducted through the conclusion. It was almost too much fun to be legal, and the crowd ate us up with a spoon.

Listening to the last caress of Perry's beautiful solo in our closer, the performance and our season were coming to a poignant end. The holes on my game board had been seemingly filled in, and my shiny ball fearlessly glided unimpeded down the home stretch. The swells of beautifully controlled melodic lines during our stately five and four-point star drill impacts stirred up the warm comfortable feelings of a summer concert in a park, and then the music's decrescendo signaled our transition to the cool groove of "Tiger of San Pedro."

This was it, the last push of my final drum corps performance, and I wanted to leave every last part of my thumping heart on the field. Marching back field at half tempo, I readied myself as the diamond drill set came together centerfield. Then my leading block of sopranos counter-rotated for one last punch in the face. JB drove the tempo like a jockey whipping his horse to the finish line, and we hung on tight. Behind a wall of double-time spinning rifles, the entire brass section was supercharged. With absolutely no letup, we spilled out along the front sideline blasting Hill's hyperbolic conclusion. Backs arched, we projected barrels of rich sound from deep inside our bodies. It was raw, controlled fury, with our high and low voices achieving the superb balance we'd fought for all summer. The brass and percussion's tremendous volume painted the stands in a thick, drenching Spanish fanfare. Like the tail end of a rapidly accelerating stream of sand in an hourglass, I let go with all of the remaining remnants of my rationed energy.

It was true, stars do shine their brightest just before they burn out. Joyously exhilarating and gut wrenching at the same time, the combination of emotions collided into a most magical moment, and I dug my senses deep into it. As my silver marble hit the finish line, I felt as alive as I ever had. Horns snapped down, it was done. FCO!

Photo by Ed Ferguson, from the DCI archives

1978 Blue Stars performing for the DCI faithful at
Mile High Stadium during the World Championship Finals.

Thirty thousand fans rose in unison, engulfing us in a reverberating mixture of cheers, whistles, and applause. The moment left me shuddering in a final spasm of adrenaline—bathing in it. I wasn't cold, I wasn't hot, I just was. And right then, I liked what I was a lot.

Leaving the field, I retraced the entirety of my final's experience, desperately trying to tattoo it into my memory. For half my life I had "played at the trumpet," yet I had never realized a mastery of the horn like I did tonight. It was a level of playing I wouldn't have thought possible only a month earlier. From a marching standpoint, it was almost as exceptional. While the recognition of my mistimed horn flash was disappointing, it did make my performance seem that much more palpable. Hell, even Leonardo da Vinci got it wrong when he chose his paint for the *Last Supper*, and I figured life isn't always about achieving perfection, even when perfection is the ultimate goal. It was about going for it when given the opportunity, and tonight there was no doubt I had. Maybe that's what the Blue Stars' mission of achieving excellence was all about—given the chance, you should reach out with everything you can. It was another one of drum corps' profound lessons on realizing a dream, and something I knew I'd cherish for the rest of my life.

A genuinely ecstatic staff greeted us outside the stadium, professing that tonight's performance was better than prelims, they needn't have bothered, we knew it was a finals-worthy run. It was a given there were some mistakes, there always would be. Perfect runs only existed in drum corps dreams (well…unless you were Ronbo or the '76 Blue Devils).

Almost to the point of tears, one of our French horn players lamented the loss of his helmet's plume during one of the many moves in our drum solo. Members consoled him, and Hill quieted all of us down, stating that this was the time to celebrate our collective effort and its resulting product. We'd come a long way since June, and we'd peaked at the right time. Running the show another hundred times wouldn't achieve any significantly better results. It no longer mattered where tonight's collection of judges would ultimately place us, and Wolfie carried on in precise and proud detail about how we had played beyond our potential. All of us well aware of his transformational talent, energy, and effort, our sweaty faces beamed in reciprocal adoration.

Crossing the finish line of the summer's all-out cross-country race, I found myself sipping a recovery Coke in the end zone stands. Despite maxing out our performance, blank expressions and quiet demeanor betrayed the resulting fatigue from the past two weeks. Adrenaline depleted, I was completely spent, and the strangely cool evening left me comfortably numb.

I fixated. *It's over—I can't believe it's over.* Seven summers of drum corps were now coming to a most appropriate end. While sensory neurons took in the remaining performances, there was a complete disconnect in my brain. My mind raced through a collage of my drum corps experiences, and the music of Madison, Santa Clara, and Phantom provided only a background soundtrack to the thoughts and emotions swimming in my mind.

It was weird. Up until now, my last performance of summer had only signaled the end of the season, not the finale to an obsessive avocation. I was definitely ready for a break, but hesitant about the ramifications of a permanent one. Despite one more year of eligibility, that was the promise I'd made to my parents and myself. In a couple of days, I'd be back in Iowa City, immersed in a schedule of science and education classes, and I wondered if it'd be enough to cleanse my palate from the inevitable drum corps cravings I was sure would eventually reappear. I'd have to purge any such thoughts, as I owed it to my parents for giving me a truly unforgettable season.

After Phantom's last note, Brett nudged me back into the present, and we headed back outside the stadium to line up for the grand finale. Having won last year's championship, the Blue Devils had the honor of performing last, and if they won tonight, they'd be the first corps in DCI's young history to win back to back to back championships. Prior to that, Santa Clara had won in '73 and '74, before being displaced by the Scouts in '75. Now, in the bustle of the moment, I acknowledged my curiosity for the way the scores would shake out.

Behind the stadium, each corps lined up in a single file awaiting the Blue Devils to join our Olympic-style retreat, and there was a lot of standing around before a Canadian corps, the eighteenth-place Offensive Lions, was given the dubious honor of playing us back onto the field. Twelve corps across, we barely squeezed through the back entrance of the stadium. During our "march" out to the field, members of various corps made small talk and cracked jokes like disruptive theater patrons, but as Blue Stars, with silent eyes focused straight ahead, we maintained our classy military bearing.

Placed between Spirit and Crossmen, the long files lurched forward, stopping often as we moved down the fifty, finally picking up speed as we divided the files in half along the front sidelines to follow the perimeter of the field to the back sideline. One by one, corps peeled off to form parade formations across the field. Pageantry at its finest, we sparkled in color and chrome. God Bless America. (And I guess…Canada?) Being part of the sights and sounds, and once again realizing the scope of the crowd from the field's perspective was like taking a whiff of smelling salts, and I was snapped back into the moment.

As was the order in prelims, the Kilties, Guardsmen, and North Star were announced in presumptive fashion. Then, for a second, I thought there was a possibility of a miraculous sixth place, hearing the resonating echo of DCI's public address announcer, Brandt Crocker. "In ninth place…with one tenth of a point in penalties, and a score of 82.45…the Crossmen."

Whoa, clearly enunciated obscenities emanated from the Crossmen camped next to us, as shocked members realized a three place drop from prelims. It had taken all season long to climb above them, but my hope for a dramatic finish was short lived.

"In eighth place, with two tenths of a point in penalties, and a score of 84.6… the Blue Stars."

I was only momentarily disappointed. We'd taken giant steps throughout the year, resulting in the largest seasonal improvement of any of the top twelve corps. Snapping to attention, we had no reason to hang our heads, and in storied Blue Star tradition, we didn't.

The 27th Lancers had nudged us by a scant fifteen hundredths of a point. And in only their second year of existence, Spirit of Atlanta, bolstered by their grandiose brass performance, trounced us by two. The crowd enthusiastically acknowledged their score. Next the Bridgemen and Madison fell into place; both were very talented corps, with engaging and goosebump-generating shows, and I wondered if, after a summer of busting butts, their members were angry, disappointed, or just resigned to find themselves out of contention for the title. Maybe most of them were like me, happy to be there sharing their show and enjoying the rush derived from performing in the atmosphere of the appreciative packed house.

Silence hung over the huge stadium, until Crocker broke it by announcing, "In third place, with one tenth of a point in penalties, and a score of 91.2…the Blue Devils." No three-peat for them, and while they seemed to be well on their way to becoming a drum corps dynasty, they'd have to wait till next year for a chance at regaining the crown.

Four hours after the show began, it was finally time to reveal who won the prelim tiebreaker, and with practiced suspenseful timing, Crocker sounded, "In second place...one tenth of a point in penalties...and a score of 91.45...the Phantom Regiment."

Once again, the Vanguard had bottle danced their way to their third world championship, but the full story of their victory wasn't realized until the final announcement of, "In first place, with no penalties, and a score of 91.55...the Santa Clara Vanguard."

Never in the history of DCI's World Championships had there been such a monumental murmur. Another tie, barring the exception of a supposed rule infraction for the violation of retrieving a dropped piece of equipment. Too far away to see their reaction, I imagined one hundred and twenty-eight crushed Regiment members, as a season's worth of relentless effort came crashing down by a mere tenth of a point. With the exception of Madison's '75 championship, California corps continued to have a stranglehold on the title.

It was well after midnight when we arrived back at the School of Mines. The evening's cold snap was washed away by steaming showers, and afterward we were greeted with piles of pretzels, chips, and stacked cases of cold Coors. Gathered around in the commons area of the dorm, Hill shared a copy of the recaps. Between the beer, snacks, and our brass section's fifth-place execution score we were feeling pretty good, while the percussion's eleventh-place execution score would require a lot more than Colorado's famous suds to lift their mood.

The nearby Scouts were in full blown pity party mode, doing their best to rinse away the taste of what they considered a major hose job by the judges. Tonight's performance had also been their best of the year, and they were left questioning the sizable spread between them and the top three corps they had traded victories with all summer. Since they were taking their placement hard, we were tight-lipped about beating them in brass execution. Seeing their collective bitterness, I could only imagine what was going on at Phantom's housing site.

Despite heavy fatigue, I didn't want to surrender the day, nor did anyone else. Scattered clusters of Blue Stars were seated on sea foam colored pleather couches, chairs, and the carpeted floor of the large dorm foyer, quietly bringing closure to our season. It would have been a perfect time to party, but aside from a limited ration of beer, there wasn't a lot to celebrate with, so along with Brett, Perry and Alton, we absorbed the tranquil buzz of complete exhaustion.

Startled from my relaxed fade, I realized that I hadn't once considered how I was going to get home from La Crosse. I found Larry LeSuer, a subdued, soft-spoken, age-out lead soprano who came to the Stars via Great Bend's Argonne Rebels. He was from Pratt, Kansas, and I convinced him his route home would take us close enough to Cedar Rapids. Graciously, he agreed to make room for me in his car. It was well past three a.m.; in a few hours we'd be loading the buses for La Crosse. I dragged myself to the dorm room and collapsed.

18

I WAS DEAD TO THE world, in a deep dreamless sleep when Little Craig, the youngest kid in the horn line gingerly shook me back to consciousness after someone pounded hard on the hollow metal dorm door. We hurriedly rolled sleeping bags, grabbed some breakfast and loaded the buses. Nesting into my spacious double seat, I embraced the thought of sleeping my way back to La Crosse.

The bus was idling when the door opened, and the short lean frame of Kelly climbed aboard. Kelly was a Madison Scout alum, and I knew him from instructing the Emerald Knights' horn line during the early part of the season. It was my guess he'd spent last night commiserating with his old corps.

Halfway down the aisle of the bus he announced he was heading back to Madison and needed another rider to share the drive. Getting no response, he moved further into the bus and catching my eye, he said, "Piskel, I thought I might find you. I'll be going right by Cedar Rapids, you wanna split the drive with me?"

Doing so would spare Larry from having to detour through CR, and I'd be home a day sooner. It seemed like a win win situation, and without deliberation I agreed. Saying sudden goodbyes while moving up the aisle, I realized I only had a few moments before leaving my surrogate summer family, and I reconsidered my reflexive decision. I shook off the thought, replacing it with the realization that there was no time like the present to move on to the real life that awaited. I opened the bus bay doors and dug out my gear.

Settling into the passenger seat of the Accord, I noticed cassette tapes littered the dash, and the remainder of the car's interior bore the grubby scars of a long road trip. Behind the wheel, Kelly's appearance matched the car. Around the Knights he'd always maintained a distantly cool persona, but at least he seemed friendly and grateful for my company. Heading straight into the mid-morning sun, we uneasily caught up on the main events of our summer, with mutual fatigue quenching any attempt to press for details. Running out of conversation, I hoped the twelve hour trip would pass quickly. At least it was off to a smooth start, until Kelly took the exit to a new suburban shopping mall for "a look around and something to eat."

Two hours later, the error of my rash decision was obvious. I could have been angelically sleeping to bus tires humming a highway lullaby, instead of lamenting the purchase of an Orange Julius and my role as backup driver. The mall's fluorescent lights didn't help to mitigate my mood, and now wandering aimlessly through sterile stores, Kelly seemed to have fallen into a sullen funk, and I considered that maybe he wasn't quite ready for summer to end.

Tossing half the drink into a garbage can, I curtly suggested we get on down the road. Recognizing the frustration in my voice, Kelly suddenly snapped out of it, and agreed. Heading out to the parking lot, there was an uncomfortable silence. Lifting open the trunk to stash his purchases, he asked if I smoked, and opened a small duffle revealing a clear, gallon-sized plastic bag filled with the tight colorful buds of Columbian Gold. It was the perfect remedy to help me calm down as we headed back onto the interstate.

Cruising over the short grass hills of the front range, with a summer sun now high above us and a light buzz in front of me, I sifted through Kelly's dusty cassettes. Avoiding the Brothers Gibb, I slipped in Chicago's Greatest Hits, and amused myself with the thought that it seemed way past "25 or 6 to 4," and while it was indeed Saturday, there wasn't a park in sight. The high from the pot made the stark scenery all the better, but the trip lagged, and I now felt like we'd become the "slow motion riders" Robert Lamm was singing about. When we stopped for gas, most of the day was already gone, and yet we'd only made it to the desolate junction with I-80. Looking at the torn road map, I realized we still had six hundred more miles before the exit to Cedar Rapids. I was completely bummed.

I was glad to finally take over the driving responsibilities, as it gave me something to do, but only a Blood, Sweat & and Tears tape later, Kelly suggested we grab something to eat. Our dinner at North Platte's golden arches complete, Kelly took the keys, and proceeded to drive away from the highway. A quarter-mile down the road, we pulled into a packed, dusty parking lot of a local watering hole.

Using my mom's well-practiced critical tone, I asked, "Hey, what the heck are we doing?"

"Relax, Mike. I just want to get a drink…we won't be long." Pulling into one of the last remaining spots, he added, "The trip's a bore, it'll be easier and faster driving through the night."

With the sun deep on the western horizon, that wasn't going to be a problem, and I realized I wasn't going to be anywhere close to home before tomorrow's sunrise. Getting out of the car, I stiffly informed him, "Hey FYI, this isn't Wisconsin…I'm not legal in there."

Crunching our way over the gravel lot, Kelly said, "They're not likely to card you in this place. You can wait out here or come inside and get a drink. Like I told you, we're not going to be long."

The brick building was a simple rectangular box that wouldn't have challenged an architecture student on academic probation, and the blackened glass door opened directly into the bar's dark interior. Entering through a haze of smoke, the room was lit by a few glowing neon beer signs, and it took a moment for my eyes to adjust. Clacking billiard balls and loud laughter mixed with thumping honky tonk music coming from old rattling speakers on a corner jukebox. Besides the bar and pool tables, there were a few mismatched tables and the perimeter of the room was lined with high-back booths. I took a seat at the bar and ordered a Coke, hoping the extra caffeine would jack me up for our perpetual road trip. Kelly got some kind of mixed drink and disappeared into a room filled with people who appeared to be anything but drum corps fans.

After traveling the country for six weeks as a Blue Star, I had zero desire to be part of a Saturday evening crowd in a country bar on the outskirts of North Platte. Every second seemed a pointlessly painful waste of time, and I ruminated over my hasty decision to hop a ride home. After a visit to the can, my frustration level grew exponentially.

The bar wasn't that big, but Kelly was nowhere around. *Where the hell was he? Did he go out to the car? Had he suddenly realized he wanted to leave as much as I did?* For a paranoid second I imagined my stuff dumped in the parking lot with me standing there, looking stupid. I went outside, but there sat the

Accord, patiently waiting. Relieved, I went back inside, strolled the room, and rechecked the john. *Nope, no Kelly...now what?* With no plan and no car keys, I anxiously took my seat at the bar and nursed my drink.

I lost count of how many brutal, twangy songs I'd endured before Kelly materialized from a shroud of smoke saying, "Okay, let's roll."

In the parking lot, the distant hum of the interstate replaced the bar's din. Curiously, I asked, "Where'd you go? I looked through the bar like three times and couldn't find you?"

Opening the driver's side of the car, he replied, "I was there all the time man...I don't know what you're talking about."

Hunh? Completely flummoxed, I decided it wasn't worth the effort to figure it or him out. Now more than anything, I just wanted to be home with a couple of days to decompress, get my shit together for school, and sleep undisturbed in my own bed.

The sun and any of its ambient light were long gone. Kelly mandated he'd drive, and that I should get some rest before my turn at the wheel. While my body was begging to shut down, my brain was running full speed, bolstered by caffeine, confusion, and contemplation. There was no way I was going to sleep, so I folded my corps jacket into a makeshift pillow, leaned against the window and let highway hypnosis do its thing. Watching mile markers pass in slow motion, my mind rambled through the forest of recent events.

Interstate 80 paralleled the Platte River's floodplain. The wide shallow river was cut by ribbons of sandbars, and periodically meandered under numerous bridges that were all under some level of summertime construction. The changing lane configurations were the only variation we encountered to an otherwise tedious straight shot.

Each bridge had concrete barriers rerouting traffic down to one narrow lane in each direction. Nearing midnight, I was so tired it hurt. Through half-shut eyes, I watched as the taillights of our wagon train funnel into a single east-bound lane. Merging with the traffic, Kelly continued to drift to the right, and instantly I puckered up, but before I could react, he had careened into the guard rail. Metal against metal, scattered sparks splashed outside my window. The Accord pinballed its way between the rail and the cement barriers.

Yelling, "Kelly!" I reached over to grab the wheel. Jolted awake, he gripped the wheel with both hands to regain control. Clearing the end of the bridge, he pulled off the road and rolled to a stop.

"What happened?" he dully exclaimed.

Heart thumping, I shouted, "What happened? What happened! You fucking fell asleep and almost killed us, that's what happened."

Cars and trucks howled by us as we got out of the car. After looking at the shredded sides of the Accord, he flatly said, "You'd better drive."

Consumed by a full blown adrenaline rage, I hollered over the din of passing semis, "Yeah, no shit...another couple of inches and you would've torn the car in two."

Sliding into the driver's seat there was a profound unsettled silence between us, and in less than a minute Kelly had either fallen back asleep or passed out. Looking over at him, I blamed myself for not realizing how chemically compromised he was when we left the bar.

Staring down a dark highway, my mind played out a variety of horrifying scenarios of what ifs and it took a dozen more miles before I began to calm down. The accident had thrown the car's alignment off, requiring me to torque hard on the steering wheel to keep the car moving straight. Experimenting with the accelerator, I found that I couldn't drive much over fifty without it feeling like the car would shake apart, and my hands tingled on the steering wheel. Adrenaline spent, it was replaced by drunken fatigue, and I anxiously scanned a black horizon for a sign to a rest area.

Slowly moving the dial, I searched the night sky for rogue radio waves from a decent FM station—*yeah right, I was in central Nebraska.* Windows down, I finally gave up and groped the dash for the bad Bee Gees cassette, hoping it would restoke enough anger to keep me awake. With one hand firmly gripping the wheel, I used my other to pinch my earlobe to the point of tears, while praying for a rest stop exit. When the blue rectangular sign finally appeared in the distance, I was crushed to see there were fifty-four more miles to go.

Past two a.m. Sunday morning, I should've been home by now, dreaming lush vivid nonsense in my own comfy bed, but instead, I was stuck in the limbo that was a rest stop just west of Lincoln. Pulling into the first open parking space, I dropped the seat back and lost consciousness.

~ ~ ~

I felt sweat trickle down my face before registering the bright sunlight streaming in the car. Wet hair matted on the headrest, I lifted up the seat back bringing Kelly out of his self-induced coma. Looking at me through puffy eyes, he complained, "Aw man, you stopped?"

Leaving the car to take a leak, I sarcastically replied, "Yeah, sorry. I've only had a couple hours of sleep in the past two days, and after you almost killed us, I didn't want to finish the job."

"What are you talking about?" he said, as he followed my lead to the john. Then, looking at the crumpled front panel of the passenger side, he cried, "Jesus Christ, what the hell'd you do to my car?"

"Me!" I really wanted to punch him hard in the face. "Seriously? You don't remember? Last night you fell asleep at the wheel man…you smashed into the side of a guard rail…we could've died, but with my luck, it would've probably just been me. Then you passed out, and I drove another eighty miles before I pulled off to get some sleep."

Walking back to the Accord, he inspected the scraped driver's side of the car, lamenting, "I don't remember any of this. Jesus, I'm sorry…do you think we can make it home?"

"I'm not sure, the alignment is really fucked up." I wasn't convinced he fully grasped what happened, and somehow still wanted to blame me. I figured he probably didn't want to admit to himself that he messed up. With half a day's travel still in front of us, I decided it was best to back off. "We're not far from Lincoln, let's stop there, get some gas and coffee and see how it's going."

Windows down, for the next six hours we hardly shared more than six words, and it felt even longer as we vibrated through the hazy cloudless heartland. The interstate was bordered by endless fields of fading-green corn stalks and scattered pastures dotted by cows taking refuge in the shade of gnarled massive burr oaks. It definitely felt like summer was on the downside.

Pulling into the driveway of my house, Kelly apologized one more time. I offered him the use of the bathroom and a beverage, but he declined, not even getting out of the car to stretch. I grabbed my stuff from the back and instantly he was gone. I thanked God to be home in one piece.

With my parents and brother five thousand miles away, for the first time in months, I was alone. I cherished it. Throwing my stuff in the laundry room, I opened the windows of the stale house, and jacked on the air conditioner. Then I forced myself to take a quick shower before pulling the covers off my bed and stretching out on stiff clean sheets.

Solitude has value, but sometimes you have to pay for it with the inertia of a steady stream of whispered thoughts. Only now they were coming in loud and clear, carrying me to places I wasn't sure I wanted to go, like my first near death encounter. Well, at least the first one that I was aware of, anyway. With the season and my drum corps career now officially over, I lay there staring at the ceiling, thinking about what it all meant. Gradually the spaces in my mind were filled in with the sights and sounds of the people I'd met, and events of my Blue Star summer.

Everything swirled together, and in that moment, I felt completely overwhelmed. Managing to purge most of it, I settled on a bottom line—*I'd made some major choices in the past few months, most of which led to exciting, positive, and life changing moments. Just what impact they'd have, I'd have to wait and see. At the same time, I was beginning to realize that maybe life is entirely too short to deny yourself from doing what you want, to only end up doing the things you feel you must.* Then the hollowness of total exhaustion completely took over, and I figured that was definitely enough deep thinking for now. I could rehash all of it tomorrow, when there'd still be plenty of solitude and a lot more energy to consider all of the consequences and implications of my drum corps addiction. With that, I let go, instantly surrendering to the gentle tyrant of deep unmoving sleep.

PART 4

AGE OUT

19

SATURDAY, MAY 19, 1979

THE ROAD WAS CALLING, BUT even as I packed my dad's sporty little yellow Toyota, I was still in a state of disbelief. I hadn't even considered any of the hypotheticals that might go along with the possibility of one last season of drum corps glory. Honestly, there'd been no plan A or B, and yet here I was repeatedly questioning whether this was actually happening. In a few minutes I'd be meeting four other Emerald Knight buddies and caravanning up to God's Country. Maybe that would shake the feeling.

Until recently, drum corps had been neatly relegated to a pleasant afterthought, mainly because I'd been distracted by a great year at school. After last summer's breakup, Beth had taken the time to test the palatability of those other fish in the water, and based on her enthusiastic response upon my return, she must've realized I was a pretty good catch after all. The time apart only seemed to have strengthened our relationship.

Dode took his job as an RA at Iowa's Hillcrest dormitory, located across the Iowa River from where Brad Erenberger and I had rented a two-bedroom apartment. About a mile from campus, our building was a ten-unit dark red brick complex, sporting an ugly mansard roof. It seemed completely out of place in a shaded neighborhood of older homes. The best things about it were the off-street parking and the low monthly rent, made even lower by our willingness to vacuum weekly and replace the burned-out bulbs in the stairwells and hallways.

Brad wasn't Dode, but we still had plenty in common, including our Midwestern middle class sensibilities, shared time in drum corps, and a mutual love for music and good times. Brad's other upside was he paid his half of the rent on time, and I took solace in the fact that I was finally out of the dorms and not scrambling for a roommate after Dode's sudden change in plans. Brad was a likable guy, and an extremely bright business and computer programming student. He was also keeping up his percussion chops, playing snare in the Hawkeye Marching Band. Pretty laid back, he took everything with a casual ease, and I was jealous of his academic success that required only limited study time. Prior to any major exam, he would squirrel himself away at the library for an all-nighter, then the following afternoon he'd burst back into our apartment, cheerfully popping a beer and lighting a cig all in one motion, while proudly exclaiming how he'd aced it.

My only real issue with Brad was that he was a bonafide P-I-G, pig, and his domestic indifference was magnified by an addiction to the skanky Salem Menthols that he paired with a daily six-pack of Bud. His hobbies left our small living room with overflowing ashtrays and sour smelling aluminum empties to greet me each morning. Brad's idea of housekeeping was not all that different from his approach to studying: letting dishes, laundry, and garbage pile up until tackling them on the weekend. The end result was a total roach fest, and we had a major infestation. The plague had me buying a complex worth of baited sticky cardboard roach motels. ("Roaches check in, but they don't check out.") After placing them throughout the apartment, I fully expected to see tiny "no vacancy" signs by the following day.

So vastly different were our housekeeping habits that they generated more than one or two heated discussions. Sadly, we never truly rectified a compromise, all to the elation of the arthropod population that shared our space.

For spending money, I worked four dinner shifts a week at Burge Residence Hall, aka "The Zoo," which caged over a thousand freshmen, and had the largest all-you-can-eat cafeteria at the University. Having worked there the year before, it took little effort to re-enlist, and I didn't mind the variety of tasks that came with the job. The cafeteria's supervisor was a tall, matronly woman, whose genetics were spawned from a father that'd been a lineman for the Green Bay Packers. Unfortunately, she was not one to ignore student workers having a little too much fun, and despite my punctuality and solid work ethic, I'd been reprimanded for placing an inappropriate message on the lettered menu board:

DESSERT:
CHOCOLATE ECLAIRS,
ACCOMPANIED BY A LIVE SEX SHOW AT 6 P.M.

No doubt it was my own fault for drawing attention to myself. After realizing that I'd been eating meals there sans board plan, like her football playing father, there was no moving her, and she eliminated the only real perk of the job. Making six measly bucks an hour and having to sneak grilled ham-and-cheese sandwiches into the oversized pockets of my white cafeteria smock, I needed something better. A friend of a friend guided me to a job at the University's pharmacy, where for fifteen hours a week, I would sit in a small white cubical looking for any irregularities or visual dust particles in vials of the various products they manufactured. I rarely found anything of note.

Working in the spotless room alongside other students, I made new friends and fourteen bucks an hour. It was a definite upgrade from dealing with the lasting smell of institutional food and the antics of the cafeteria's full-timers, who were either recovering drug addicts, rehabbed convicts, or in most cases, both.

The only major setback that fall had been a week-long feverish dance with a salmonella infection. With my parents in Europe, my godparents had invited me to drive to Milwaukee and share Thanksgiving dinner with them. Aunty Em sadly rushed the turkey's thawing process and all of us got the bug. Unlike the illness, the rest of the first semester passed quickly.

Mixing education classes with my science curriculum, I was rocking great grades and beginning to enthusiastically embrace the idea of my chosen career path. I'd lucked out that the University of Iowa seemed to be an important node for secondary science education. Several of the faculty members were major players with the National Science Education Association, and while most of their efforts seemed focused on their numerous grad students, I'd somehow become the golden child of their undergraduate program.

During winter break, my academic advisor offered me the opportunity to tag along on a trip to the Everglades and Keys. The program was designed for motivated high school students eager to escape the cold, in exchange for the opportunity to learn about the ecology of southern Florida. My role had me obtaining a chauffeur's license and driving a school bus cross country, along with helping prep meals for sixty students and staff.

The two week excursion gave me the chance to meet and talk with college professors, talented high school science teachers, and bright students from across the country. In that short time it became evident that training to be a high school science teacher dovetailed perfectly with my love of the outdoors, natural sciences, and working with people. I was digging it.

Impressed with my Florida performance, my advisor sent me down the road to the Quad Cities with a carousel of color slides promoting next year's excursion at half a dozen high schools. Having Mom, Dad, and my brother over in Europe, I was making the most of my autonomy and enjoying the growing confidence that came from making good moves in and out of school. *Okay*, I thought, *let this "real life" begin.*

So what the hell happened? As far as I could tell the decision to march organically unfolded after a series of influential coincidences, but isn't that what drives a lot of changes in one's life? I guess a more poetic way of looking at it was that towards the end of second semester, the stars in the sky lined up perfectly with the Stars in La Crosse.

Unfortunately, one of those coincidences was the Emerald Knights going inactive after their '78 season. They weren't alone. Gone, or relegated to parade corps status, were the Precisionnaires, Fox Valley Raiders, Marquis, Royal Chevaliers, and many other competitive drum corps throughout the country. Corps budgets had grown well beyond what service organization sponsorship and members' fund raising projects could offer. Many corps couldn't find enough members and/or finances to keep up with the tripling fuel prices and the extensive touring of top DCI corps.

The close of the decade marked the final spasms of an era of traditional drum corps, and the implications meant that corps needed to evolve or perish. Unfortunately, many corps throughout the country succumbed to the latter. However, if marchers from the defunct organizations wanted to continue with their avocation, they still had plenty of options—that is, if they had the means, talent, and desire to pursue them. So after the Emerald Knights folded, a number of their experienced members scattered like leaves on a windy autumn day, heading off to the Guardsmen, Colts, Blue Stars, Scouts, and some even as far away as the Blue Devils and Garfield Cadets.

Head down and focused, I paid scant attention to the changes going on in drum corps until a frigid Friday afternoon in late January. Coming back from classes, I found Brad sitting on our worn-out couch accompanied by his beer, smokes, drum sticks, and practice pad. Between drags, rolls, flams, and chugs, he told me that Sunday he was going to take a road trip to audition for a snare position with the Scouts. Intrigued, I decided to join him.

Arriving at a large Madison public high school, I realized several other Emerald Knights were also trying out. Spending the afternoon listening to the huge horn line and watching a dozen snares mechanically rolling through technique exercises stirred the dying embers of my desire to march. My freshly buried passion was further stoked when Brad boasted about how he'd made their line. During the ride back to Iowa City I wrestled with clear images of my roommate's plans. *If he was going to take advantage of one more go around, why shouldn't I?*

A short month later, walking to classes on a sunny winter day, I ran into an enthusiastic Mark Jordan. A couple years younger than me, we'd met during my senior year of high school. That year the Emerald Knights included about a dozen of my high school's sophomore band members, and after bonding with them in jazz and concert band, Mark came to a spring camp.

At first, I was skeptical about the marching motivations of this tall, lanky, jazz-loving saxophone player with the distinct Greg Brady fro. He seemed more interested in expanding his social network than playing a baritone. Indeed, Mark picked up many of the names and phone numbers of the girls in the corps, but he was also a good musician, and just as quickly picked up playing the horn. A summer of competitions had him hooked, and when the Knights folded, Mark looked to march elsewhere.

During our brief encounter, he informed me that several Knights were now marching with the Blue Stars and their next camp was on the first weekend of spring break. With no plans or cash to hit the Florida beaches, I convinced myself that attending a weekend camp couldn't hurt.

I was glad I went. Seeing things firsthand prioritized ambivalent feelings and reinforced the decision that my marching days were behind me. The camp revealed a sizable guard and percussion section, but I was surprised by the low numbers in the horn line. Gone missing were my last year's roommates, and with the exception of one returning Southern Bastard, the small first soprano section was entirely new. The few other lead players were serviceable, but they weren't standouts like Brett and Sevs. Having not picked up a horn in seven months, I wasn't much help, and I joined a handful of lower sops learning to play through an entirely new book.

The strength of the horn line remained its veteran baritone section, with Schultzie and several other age-outs making one last heroic charge. Interestingly, JB was one of them. Confessing he'd had enough of the stress and responsibilities of being drum major, he wanted nothing more than to spend his final year sharing in the antics of Schultzie's posse. Jordan was joined by a few other Emerald Knights who'd braved the dank March winds to scope out the corps' potential. Hill calmly assured us of a full line come June, telling us that many of the brass members were unable to attend the camp due to school, distance, or both.

Also missing was Pierre, who'd finally surrendered to real life. His absence set the scene for unquestionably the most significant of those influential coincidences. In Pierre's absence, the corps had hired a new assistant horn instructor, Dave Tippett.

Until then, I'd only known Dave from a distance. He was easy to spot, as he commanded a significant visual presence—think NOLA jazz trumpeter, Al Hirt, "The Round Mound of Sound," meets a great Samoan warrior. He had long wavy, brown hair flowing from a large head that was proportionate to his body. His cherubic face showed the beginnings of a beard and featured small, disarming and happy eyes. With a broad flat nose over an infectious, slightly gapped-tooth smile, his appearance made him instantly recognizable. I clearly remembered seeing the clean-shaven version of him in '75 when he was with the World Champion Madison Scouts. A powerful screaming soprano soloist, Dave was a major vertebrae in arguably one of the best brass lines to ever grace a football field.

During the halftime at one of last fall's Hawkeye football games, I'd caught sight of his Madison fleur-de-lis letter jacket as he perused the sidelines of Kinnick Stadium. That day, watching the massive black and gold Hawkeye Marching Band, I was intrigued that most of their traditional Big Ten swagger had been replaced by the roll step of drum corps' style of marching, and I wondered if Tippett was responsible.

What many Blue Stars didn't know was that prior to marching with the Scouts, Dave had been awarded a monetary scholarship to march with Spokane's well-traveled and notable Percussion-Naut Patriots. During that '73 season, he befriended Patriot member and percussion prodigy Steve Smith, and they ended up being roommates at the University of Idaho. Steve was a standout snare drummer and musician who had gone on to march in Blue Stars during their '74 and '75 season. After he aged out, he was promoted to caption head and arranger.

Tippett also left Idaho, following a migrating music professor to the University of Iowa. There, he played lead trumpet in their jazz band, gigged throughout the area, and helped out with the Hawkeye band. His connection to Smith ultimately led to an informal meeting with Don Hill, who offered him summer employment as the Stars' assistant horn instructor.

Lacking Hill's instructional austerity, Tippett was the perfect counterpart. He was a musical guru with an unbound spiritual energy, and an excellent brass technician. There was always a warm, genuine, feel-good essence coming from his broad surface area, and his powerful gravitational force made him a captivating instructor. Multifaceted, he could provide brass players with new insights as to how to approach their instruments, as well as a back cracking bear hug or meditative relaxation response. Blue Star musicians felt an instantaneous bond, and like their alliance to Hill, they wanted nothing more than to please him.

Tippett's instructional style was all about the quality of sound and expression of the musical phrase. He sang the phrase, his body language spoke the phrase, then, horn in hand, he'd masterfully play through the phrase, explaining in detail how it connected to the next one. Like a soulful snake charmer, he guided musicians toward their contribution to the phrase. No longer just brass players, they became vessels of sound, and with the aid of Tippett's unique multi-sensory teaching technique, the music was brought to life.

By the camp's end, Hill and Tippett divided and conquered each section of music, transforming thirty horn players into a brass ensemble that could stumble their way through their entirely new and challenging book.

The weekend also provided me with a chance to reconnect with some friends, but driving back to Iowa City, I considered all the challenges of doing an about face on the vow to my parents. I imagined hearing the coordinated dissent in their pragmatic voices, and the inability to muster any true conviction in mine. There was no doubt that one last hurrah would be a good time, but it would also be just more of the same. And there went the viability of any argument for justifying the time, energy, and money required to spend another summer in marching music's major league. Not much of a tradeoff from the benefits gained from working, taking classes, and hanging out with Beth in Iowa City. Thankfully, attending that camp had provided me with a definitive answer to resolve my conundrum. The Blue Stars would easily go on without me, and it was becoming more clear that it was time for me to go on without drum corps.

Unexpectedly for Brad, the Madison Scouts were also going to have to go on without him, as an emergency appendectomy required him to surrender his snare spot with the Scouts. Now it seemed both of us were destined to miss our age-out summer. Having fully processed the big picture, I only momentarily grieved the loss—then the phone call came.

After a day of classes in early April, a recuperating Brad told me that Tippett had left a message for me. *Here goes* I thought, *time to officially hear myself say, "I'm done."* After a couple rings, Dave's smooth calming voice answered. "Hi Mike, I'm so glad you called…I wanted to follow up and make sure you're coming to the April camp in Rock Falls."

Swallowing hard, I replied, "Yeah, thanks for reaching out, I've thought a lot about it, and I've decided that I'm going to have to pass. I don't know how I can swing it with my parents in Europe…I promised them that after last summer I'd be done. I still have a lot to do for school and need to take care of the house while they're gone. I'll come to some shows and cheer you on…"

Tippett softly interrupted, "I'm so sorry to hear this Mike, we could really use your experience and leadership." Pausing, he added, "Are you sure about this? You only go around once in life…there's no hurry to get anywhere."

"I know man…but going back on my word for one more season as a lower sop wouldn't be a good move. It'd only be more of the same, and I don't think I should do that when they're counting on me."

Dave replied, "Mike, you know JB's back in the horn line." Then, after a beat of silence, he continued, "What if you were our drum major?" More silence, and for a moment I thought the call had dropped, then he said, "Surely that'd be enough of a different experience."

I stammered, "Really…the staff would consider that?"

"Don and I've already talked about it; you have drum major experience with the Emerald Knights…it just makes sense…come to April's camp and we can talk more."

Thanking him for even considering me, I explained I still had a lot to mull over before I could provide an answer. The last thing I wanted to do was to say yes, only to back out after discussing it with my distant parents and nearby girlfriend. After hanging up, I knocked on Brad's bedroom door and shared the gist of Tippett's call. His hoarse response was pointedly short: "You gotta do it, man."

Yeah, considering my infatuation with the activity, he was probably right, but now there were a whole new set of hypotheticals popping into mind. I tried to focus on the clear ones: *Me, the drum major of the Blue Stars, how crazy cool would that be?* And of course, *what am I going to tell my parents?* Sharing the possibility with Beth that night, she was as adamant as Brad. It was "too good of a chance to miss." This from a woman who'd never even seen a show.

The more I thought about it, the more it seemed the right thing to do, and a new sense of resolve came from an understanding of how well it could fit into building a résumé for a new teacher. Genius! Now I knew how I'd spin it with my parents. What better way to distance myself from other prospective candidates than to have the experience of heading up one of the top corps in the country? It'd be a unique talking point in terms of demonstrating leadership abilities, work ethic, dedication, and sacrifice, not to mention the inevitable reference letter and connections Dr. K could provide. My parents just might buy it…well, my dad anyway. After calculating the time difference in Yugoslavia, I called them the following day.

Dad listened silently as I clearly spelled it out. Given the delay in my voice traveling across the Atlantic Ocean, there was a protracted pause before I felt a tingle of déjá vu when he came back with the inevitable question, "What are we going to tell your mother?"

When Mom took the phone, I heard myself confidently telling her about the possibility of a dream coming true. Reprising last summer's "Mother of the Year" performance, she gave her approval. I hoped it signaled that she was finally starting to understand what drum corps meant to me, and what it still had to offer, but after further consideration, I surmised the more likely explanation was that she was so giddy from touring Europe with dad and spending time with her new grandson that she really didn't care what her goofy second son was planning.

Promising them it'd be worth it once I was looking for a steady teaching gig, the conversation ended with Dad asking how much money I'd need to make it all happen. My heart soared. It was all pretty unbelievable. I was heading back onto a lined carpet of green and clear images popped into view. Suddenly I was dressed in white, leading Kampschroer's powerful, super cool, super Blue Stars in competitions across the country.

I guess I shouldn't have been all that surprised by the way it was playing out. Of course I was going to march my age-out year. I'd been born and raised during that span of time when thousands of young people across the country were unknowingly conditioned to spend their free time in a drum corps, as there were a host of motivating factors floating around that could seduce a young teenager into making the commitment to the activity, and considering our family history, I'd probably been touched by most of them.

To fully understand the scope of my predisposition for competitive drum corps requires a running start from 1919, when my dad was born Paul Louis Postigleone/Piskel. (The surname change to Piskel most likely came from the Pennsylvania coal company where his grandfather worked on their railways.) Paul was the first of four children, raised by a poor first-generation Italian coal miner and his immigrant wife.

Growing up in the tiny mining town of Tresckow, located in the scarred hills of eastern Pennsylvania, young Paulie helped out his parents where and when he could. He had to. In the midst of the Great Depression his father had been left disabled from a mining accident that took an arm and almost his life. Most cold winter mornings, Paul would get up before first light and gather with the other town kids to sneak into vast strip pits. There, they would fill small wagons with a day's supply of rich anthracite coal. Back at home he would hammer it into smaller pieces to fuel the stove and furnace of the narrow two-story duplex. Life was tough.

His parents struggled with English literacy, challenging Paul's own prowess for smooth articulation. In high school, he compensated for his verbal deficiency by excelling and relishing in the universal language of mathematics. However, even graduating with math honors wasn't going to get a cash-strapped kid into college. He had to go out and make a living, and in 1937 he found one: putting tar paper roofs on the shacks of low-income housing in the drenching heat of the Carolinas. Intelligent enough to know he had a lot more to offer, he wasn't the least bit happy.

When the war in Europe broke out, Paul figured anything would be better than life on a hot tar roof and hurriedly enlisted in the army. After basic training and a brief stint in the National Guard, he was sent overseas. Landing in England, his military training ramped up. Struggling to find his niche, he fought through pounding headaches triggered from the sound of booming howitzers and clanking tanks.

Paul couldn't believe his misfortune, until one evening a group of officers came through camp asking if anyone knew trigonometry? He spoke up. That night's intelligence test found him eligible for officer's training school, and several days later the noise and his headaches ceased as he was bound for Oklahoma's Fort Sill. While there, he was given the rank of second lieutenant, and learned the skills of a forward observer. School over, it was back to England, and he arrived in time for a dinner of beans and weenies. Nearby was a huge mess hall filled with soldiers eating thick steaks and roasted chicken. Confused, he was informed that it would be their last sit-down meal before the start of Operation Overlord, and those beef-eating soldiers were part of the first wave of troops to invade mainland Europe. Paul got his steak the next day.

Landing on the beaches of Normandy, he joined thousands of other soldiers, all desperately digging foxholes in a shallow layer of sandy beach and praying the Luftwaffe bombs would miss their mark. The following morning, warily advancing through the hedgerows of the French countryside, he spouted more prayers as he dodged mortar shells and small arms fire until his heaven sent appeals ran out. A deafening explosion sent shrapnel through him, tearing up his ankle, hip, and hand. Perhaps roofing shacks on a hot summer day wasn't so bad after all.

Paul's injuries unfortunately didn't buy him a ticket home, but they did send him back to England, where he convalesced for six months. That was just enough time to win an all-expense paid trip to the Battle of the Bulge, complete with a complimentary case of frostbitten toes. For six brutal weeks, he fought perpetual fear, hunger, and cold as artillery blazed and comrades-in-arms fell. When the battle finally ended, his division quickly pushed deep into Deutschland and three months later they joyously celebrated V-E day.

A lot like L. Frank Baum's character, Dorothy Gale, Paul just wanted to click his heels and go home, but it was not to be. When the guns were silenced, the effects of war could now be more easily heard, and a new assignment took him into the heart of Germany. There he spent way too much time liberating the remaining survivors of the Buchenwald concentration camp before finally receiving his orders home. Like so many with him, he came back a changed person.

War brought tragedy, loss, and lasting pain, but it also brought economic relief, prosperity, and opportunity as the country sprung from depression. Putting the war behind him, Paul took advantage of the newly passed G.I. Bill, officially the Servicemen's Readjustment Act of 1944. Now he could go to college and having become enamored with the radios he used during the war, he chose to study electrical engineering, at the Milwaukee School of Engineering. There he became part of the first graduating class of veterans using the benefit.

One lucky weekend, he was set up on a blind date with an attractive young clerical worker from the Boston Store. In a few short weeks they fell fast and hard for each other in the type of love that lasting partnerships require, and it wasn't long before the baby boom would soon sound off exactly at ear level.

My mom, Anita Elain Yahr, was the youngest of three daughters of a second-generation stout German/Polish couple. Arthur Yahr, and his stoic no-nonsense wife, Margret, raised their three daughters in a well-kept, conservative, middle class neighborhood in Milwaukee, Wisconsin. Arthur traversed the hills of southern Wisconsin, first as a cattle buyer and then A.O. Smith's silo salesman, while wife Margret kept a spotless home.

The baby of the family, Anita grew up sheltered from as much of reality as possible, favoring the Shirley Temple costumes and hairdos she received from her doting older sisters. She relished it. Enough of an above-average student, she excelled at all things drama, domestic, and clerical. Her post-high school claim to fame was the well-received lead role in a community theater production of Noel Coward's comedy, *Blithe Spirit*.

Despite her mother's stern warning that Anita had gotten mixed up with an East Coast Italian gangster who'd take her away forever, she was ready to risk it all and follow her handsome new lover wherever life took them. Shortly after Paul graduated, they married in January of 1953, and after the requisite hour-long Catholic wedding and nearly never-ending festive reception, Paul did in fact take her away to the East Coast. Living in East Orange, New Jersey, he was employed not as a mob hit man, but as an apprentice engineer with Western Electric. Ten months later my mom gave birth to my brother, Tommy.

Shortly thereafter, Paul received a call from a college classmate informing him that electronics genius Arthur Collins was looking to expand his avionics and telecommunications company in Cedar Rapids. The Cold War machinery was ramping up, and my dad was presented with an exciting opportunity to merge his engineering talent with new computer technology to build radios for space, military, and commercial applications. So, in 1955, Paul took his young family to Eastern Iowa, and three years later, I was born.

By my fourth birthday, our little nuclear family was joined by my mom's widowed mother, whom we gladly handed off every other year to Aunty Em. Grandma was an imposing sight. With a bun wrapped tightly around a creepy hair rat, she always doubled down on thick nylon stockings over her deeply bowed legs. With black orthopedic shoes tied tight to her feet, she barked out nonstop orders and old-fashioned dictates in a steep German accent. Constantly trying to rein in my brother and me, she wasn't the least bit fun (well, except for the accent) and once the street lights came on, we did our best to pretend we didn't hear her dry, flinty voice calling us home.

We were too busy playing, and playing was all about army—after all, our dad was a war hero and now he was building radios for high tech fighter jets, Huey helicopters, and the Apollo Space Mission.

Although my dad kept most of his war memories private, Tommy and I couldn't get enough, so we let our imagination fill in the blanks. We were fascinated by the various Nazi souvenirs we discovered in an unsupervised visit to our grandparents' attic, and we fought over his medals, pea green army jacket, and tattered parka with the rank insignias on the shoulders. Luckily, we were also equipped with the finest military hardware that Santa and birthday wishes could provide, including spring-loaded bazookas that fired little blue plastic missiles, ricochet-sounding pop guns, cap-blasting grenades, canteens that made the water taste metallic, helmets covered with rubbery camouflage leaves, and the amazing Johnny Seven O.M.A. (One Man Army.) My brother had a unique Dick Tracy combination pump action shotgun that simultaneously spewed a stream of water while firing rolls of red paper caps. While not quite standard military issue, it completed our arsenal, and for endless hours we played outside with dozens of our likewise lightly armed little friends. Terrorizing broad expanses of the neighborhood, our roaming platoons would sporadically ambush each other in noisy firefights, punctuated with shouts of, "I got you!" "No you didn't!" and "Yes I did!"

Each Friday night, my brother and I donned our military gear and pitched camp in front of the family's black and white TV to watch our favorite show, *Combat*, where Vic Morrow as the consummate Sergeant Saunders, led his team of Littlejohn, Cage, Kirby, and Doc through the simulated battlefields of France and Germany. Other shows fed our hungry military fascination. With slack-jawed concentration, we watched *Rat Patrol*, *12 O'Clock High*, *Gomer Pyle*, *McHale's Navy*, *Garrison's Gorillas*, and *Hogan's Heroes*. Then, imitating exaggerated accents, we recreated various scenes for our own amusement. "I see no-ting. I vas not here. I did not even get up dis morning!"

Saturdays, it was off to movies, mindlessly munching popcorn while the *Longest Day, Guns of Navarone, The Dirty Dozen, The Battle of Britain, the*

Devil's Brigade, Where Eagles Dare, and *Von Ryan's Express* spilled endless streams of bullets, blood, and guts out on the big screen.

During the cold winter weekends, we turned our basement into miniature dioramas, hiding our toy soldiers in Lincoln Log bunkers, or handcrafted shoebox forts. One of my best friends painstakingly built an impressive fleet of detailed wooden battleships, complete with toothpick gun barrels glued to moveable turrets. During cold, rainy Saturday afternoons, we'd lay out long two by fours for harbor docks to reconstruct our version of the attack on Pearl Harbor. Other friends had a significant number of G.I. Joes, and for my eighth Christmas, Santa left me the stiff-legged Stony Smith action figure. Stony was steely tough, amazingly life-like, and came complete with a plethora of tiny accessories, all specifically designed to get easily lost in our shag rug, until painfully discovered by my dad's stocking feet. Numerous summer afternoons were spent in the backyard sandboxes and nearby woods, fabricating networks of trenches and forts for our semi-articulated miniature military men.

Between army playtime, my parents strived to balance our development, hoping we might actually gain enough skills and knowledge to eventually join the human race. Early on, I was taught to swim, forced to write my letters and numbers, and during my tenth summer, challenged by the daily assignment to provide my dad with reams of neatly written multiplication tables. Meanwhile my mom's demand for spotless bedrooms, precisely folded clothes, beds made with taut hospital corners, and semi-sincere handcrafted thank you cards for birthday and Christmas gifts gave me plenty of reasons to whine.

When dad discovered that my fourth-grade parochial schoolteacher (a divorcée instructing under a new moniker) was the same woman he claimed responsible for derailing an entire year of my brother's academic progress, he sent me packing to Grant Wood Elementary School. From that moment on, my life spun like one of those non-stop Whiz-z-zers, with my mom enrolling me in the Y swim team, art classes, and Sokol gymnastics training, all of them wedged around peddling the *Cedar Rapids Gazette* in my neighborhood. That same year I started playing the trumpet, and private lessons were added to the mix. By the time I reached junior high, I was proficient enough to be invited to a drum corps practice by good ol' Roger Dickinson.

Witnessing the military regiment, dazzled by the shiny bugles and the pulsing rhythm of snares and bass drums, instantly reawakened my love for all things "army" and it fell perfectly in line with my ingrained desire for precise order that had been regularly prescribed by my mother. With my protracted puberty keeping me on the younger side of fourteen, I was completely captivated.

Here was a mysterious activity where I could play out battle scenes through the relative safety of drum corps competitions. There wasn't a real or plastic hand grenade in sight, yet I could pledge an allegiance of sweat, sunburn, and sacrifice to an organization with the underlying goal of military precision and contrived combat. Wearing uniforms, marching in patriotic parades, and competing in judged contests against hostile neighboring armies, all came at a time when I had been trying to gather enough courage to tell my dad I was done with the trumpet and the hassles of daily practice. Now suddenly given a tangible reason for hanging on—I wouldn't have to face him. What was not to like?

There was no doubt that it was drum corps' whole military aura that first lured me into the activity, but it was also the feeling of relevance that kept me there, and the more I peeled back its various layers, the more I began to appreciate the unique combination of music, competitions, girls, travel, and performances that were contained in the activity. Oh, and did I mention girls?

Subconsciously, I realized what I really needed during this profoundly insecure time in my life was the authentic fellowship and subsequent comfort derived from being with many like-minded individuals. Every Sunday afternoon and Thursday night practice, gathering with fifty other kids, I'd found a home away from home. Instantly, I was no longer an "only child."

Of course, I was destined to march my last year of eligibility. Years of grooming had predisposed me to a drum corps addiction. How could I have even considered not marching? Given the chance to be the drum major of a top DCI corps for my age-out year was like the satisfaction derived from snapping in the last piece of a huge jigsaw puzzle.

I was fired up for the drive to La Crosse. I loved a good road trip and had always been a happy little hyperactive participant while prepping for our family's annual summer camping vacations. Traveling to all sorts of exotic places, we'd explored the Rocky Mountains, Florida Keys, Black Hills, Door County, Expo 67, Colonial Williamsburg, and the Gulf Coast. My dad would plan each trip with exacting detail, marking highway atlases and packing the trunk of our Delta 88 like the engineer he was. Today, I tried hard to mimic his efficiency, arranging my gear while leaving room for the necessities of two of my buddies.

Focusing on loading the car helped distract me from the one overriding concern triggered during the April camp. It was a scenario I should have predicted, but momentarily distracted by delusions of grandeur, I'd failed to see it coming—so much for my scientifically trained mind.

That Easter weekend, our Saturday lunch had me engaged in a round table interview with Moe, Hill, Tippett and Smith. It also included some past Emerald Knight members, who'd been summoned for their experiences with me as their front man. Having their actual testimonials lent significant legitimacy to what I could bring to the position, and afterwards, Moe congratulated me, explaining that sometime during our afternoon block of instruction, he'd make the announcement.

Rare April sunshine had warmed the asphalt parking lot, and Moe gathered the corps around him, telling us to take a seat. With little fanfare or pretense, he delivered the news with his languid straight forward style "Listen up y'all… Mike Piskel has been selected to be this season's drum major. Mike was the Emerald Knights drum major from '75 through '77 and played soprano with us last year. We all know he'll do a great job. Make him feel welcome in his new position. Let's have a good afternoon of practice."

That was it. A brief smattering of applause, but the expressions on many of the vets' faces revealed confusion and complete disbelief. The lukewarm response, coupled with a lack of eye contact and hushed whispers, had me feeling as if I'd been set adrift on a small lifeboat while a fully functional ship sailed away. I was sure many of them had already speculated on who was worthy enough to be tagged for the position, and watching their reactions, I was positive I'd never even made it on their long list; others had probably been expecting auditions.

Either way, I got it—my tenure in the corps only included filling a spot for half a season, and now here I'd been christened with the honor of leading the corps on and off the field. While slightly shaken, I told myself that if I poured heart and soul into my new role, they'd eventually come around.

By Easter Sunday there were few signs of any resurrection in attitude, and it seemed that my commands only garnered reluctant compliance, coming more from a deference to the position than respect, save for our guard captain, Deb Peters. She too, had returned for her age-out year, and her professionalism and classy demeanor provided some shelter from the storm. No doubt Moe had clued her in that I would need some early assistance, and I was grateful to have her as an ally. I felt a genuine empathy from Deb, perhaps coming from the singularity of our positions and our similar transitions, having been the guard captain of a small corps in Park Falls, Wisconsin.

Working together that weekend, it was evident we shared an ingrained awe and reverence for DCI caliber corps. For us, membership was a privilege that required unconditional dedication, and to be named their drum major or guard captain—well, that was tantamount to knighthood, coming with numerous responsibilities, including modeling that reverence for everyone else.

I knew when I made the commitment to be DM there would be some potholes on the road to glory, and following a setting sun back to Iowa City, I spent much of the time figuring out how to dodge them by reflecting on my time as drum major with the Knights, earnestly searching for anything that might ease the transition in the Blue Stars.

During my rookie year in '72, our eighteen-year-old drum major was a captivating guy named Jim Mason. Jim came from a drum corps family and started his marching career as a seven-year-old in the Cadet Bees, then was a charter member of the Emerald Knights after they broke away from the Grenadiers. Musically gifted, by the age of ten he'd already arranged his first drum corps song and by the time he was sixteen, he was penning some of the Knights' competition music.

As a wide-eyed fourteen-year-old, I was impressed by Mason's bold confidence and leadership ability, recalling how during warm-ups before a rainy spring parade, he transformed our tiny young horn line into the little engine that could, just by adding some much needed dynamics and phrasing to a sickly saccharine arrangement of "Sweet Caroline."

Mason left the Knights after he went off to college. Several years later he marched his age-out season with Tippett, playing lead soprano with the World Champion Madison Scouts. From there he went on to be the horn arranger and instructor for the Dubuque Colts, eventually taking complete creative and managerial control as their director in '77. I had no doubt he was primed to make a name for himself in the activity.

What amazed me most during that first year with the Knights was the tremendous energy and unadulterated showmanship Mason poured into his on field performances. His unabashed, hyperbolic conducting style truly was the best part of our little corps, and his intensity inspired me to pour my heart, guts, and soul into my performance. After being named the drum major in '75, I did my best to model his dramatic conducting style, poise, and ringmaster level of enthusiasm.

I'd had a good run as the drum major for the Knights. My induction came on the heels of being awarded '74's "Knight of the Year," and unlike the weekend camp, I was enthusiastically welcomed by members and staff. I loved playing the bugle, but it was the drum major position where I began to discover an entirely new level of affection for our corps, and before long I was adapting the rest of my life around a broader range of responsibilities than that of the typical drum major.

I was all in, and along with conducting, enforcing corps rules, and being the liaison between staff and members, I expanded my role to that of a player-coach. I filled in as a brass and marching instructor, cheerleader, and inspirational speaker. I shuttled members to and from practice, gave group and private lessons for our younger, less experienced sopranos, and to ensure healthy attendance at practice and grow the corps' brass line, I started phone trees, arranged for rides to practice, and formed welcome committees for new members. Eventually, as our corps community became tighter, and more aware of my unconditional commitment, I ad-libbed as a big brother, confidant, and novice relationship counselor for the members dealing with the excess baggage of their whole "coming of age" thing.

After my first year as drum major, I was becoming the face of the corps, both within and outside of the organization. To my mom's chagrin, my time as drum major was now playing a profound influence in the development of my self-image, as I felt a new confidence growing from the demands of the position. This was bolstered by our continuous improvement, taking the best drum major trophy at several shows, along with my second "Knight of the Year" award.

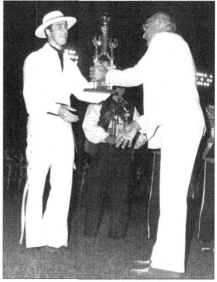

Over time, I'd learned the secret to interpersonal relationships, treating members with the same respect I wanted them to give me, while doing my best to encourage the less focused to buy into our competitive goals, all while disarming them with self-dep-recating humor. Without a regular brass instructor, I fostered leader-ship responsibilities for our best horn players by assigning them to be section

Photograph courtesy of the Emerald Knights

Collecting some second place hardware at the 1976 Tournament of Drums in Cedar Rapids.

leaders. It worked. During my three years on the podium, there was low seasonal turnover, and our steady improvement found us forming critical bonds of trust. We became tighter than TV's most famous family: "Good night, John-Boy."

My one stumble as the Knights' drum major came during our '77 season. Luckily, I still managed to land upright. That spring, back home from college, my dad had insisted I earn some cash by applying for a summer job. Clueless, I went for an interview and dexterity test at the Square D manufacturing plant. To my dismay, I was suddenly a full time tool and die operator and the fol-lowing week I was working the third shift in a noisy and brightly lit factory. A half a football field in size, it held dozens of work spaces, and smelled of fresh plastic and new metal. My job was to place small parts in a specific order into various machines that, after simultaneously pressing two buttons, would bang out a portion of domestic or industrial circuit breakers.

Surrounded by corn-fed middle-aged women, who easily cranked out their hourly quota while sharing ribald stories about their delinquent teenaged kids, I listened, but kept my mouth shut. I was too busy struggling to make my given rate. Monotony magnified by intense concentration made minutes seem like hours, and I was certain I'd been damned to hell for unknown prior transgressions. Home after 7 a.m., I'd collapse into bed, rise midafternoon for dinner, then it was off to practice before heading back to work to do it all over again.

That June, nearby weekend competitions would finish on Sunday evenings. My dad would drive to the small towns to pick me up and race me back to work. During this nonstop madness, I unknowingly collected a tremendous sleep debt. By the time we went on our annual Fourth of July swing to Chicagoland, I was edgy and running on empty.

On that extended weekend, our schedule had us in tight competitions with a collection of other, likewise improved, second-tier corps. It should have been a fun and exciting trip, but I ruminated on a growing complacency within the ranks. Most members seemed content with the second and third place trophies we were accumulating. I wasn't, and I believed we were blowing our chance to take it to the next level.

The final night of our trip had me working way too hard to line up nonchalant members for retreat, and I hit a solid and unforgiving wall of exhaustion. Frustration supplemented my fatigue and in the spirit of Roger Dickinson, I was ready to "quit this baby-ass corps." Walking over to our guard captain, Kim Wyatt, I harshly whispered, "You take them out there, they're not listening to me...I'm through." Leaving the staging area, I broke down. Separated by less than two points from first, we placed fourth, and I was convinced we were a better corps than the three in front of us.

Bewildered members wondered why I refused to take the field. My despair and their confusion only intensified as I ignored everyone on the dark bus ride home. I told the staff that I wasn't coming back until the corps figured out what it wanted to be, and I was fine if they wanted to "quote me, demote me, or fire me." It wasn't the right thing to do, but with no upcoming shows for ten days, it was the perfect time to stage a protest.

Critical relief came from being released from Square D and hopping a car ride with my neighbors to the Lake of the Ozarks. There I was dropped off to visit my junior high girlfriend. Her father's midlife crisis was punctuated by purchasing and running a resort on the huge touristy reservoir, and she had suggested that I come down and check it out. There I experienced the joys of sleeping in, swimming, pleasure boating and water skiing in the summer sun with a beautiful long-haired girl. With no sounds of drums, bugles, or tool and die machines, it was three straight days of blissful rekindled romance. It was also the perfect therapy.

Upon my well-refreshed return, a handful of contrite brass members came by my house to tell me that there had been a significant change in attitude, imploring me to come back and see for myself. Retaking the podium at the following evening's rehearsal revealed a corps that was silent and purposeful. A lot was accomplished, and I credited the success of my improvised hiatus to pure gut instinct. I was fortunate that members and staff were willing to empathize with my distress, realizing that it had been born from fatigue and a heartfelt desire for our corps to reach its potential. By August, it was clear that my sabbatical had played a part in contributing to our success at DCI North and Midwest, along with the American Legion and VFW Nationals.

After the '77 season, there was a persistent sense that it might be the right time to give up the DM/horn instructor position. That same gut was now telling me my shtick and influence had run its course. Our corps was growing older and my forte had always been centered around inspiring younger members. I didn't want to end up like one of those coaches who stayed past an obvious exit point. Besides, if the Emerald Knights were ever going to progress to the next level, they'd need a better brass instructor than a nineteen-year-old secondary science education major.

Now looking back on all that had transpired, I realized if I was to have any success this summer, I'd still need to rely on my drum corps instincts.

Finished packing, it was time to collect my companions for our convoy to La Crosse. Just up the block, I swung into Dave Nelson's driveway and found him ready to go. A couple years younger, he was also a Hawkeye and had just finished his freshman year as a business major. Dave was an enthusiastic musician, longtime neighborhood friend, and all-around great guy. Growing up he was the kind of kid that'd never say a bad thing about anyone. We were as comfortable as cousins, and anytime I asked, he was always eager to hang out, whether it was helping me deliver papers, build snow forts, or play games of five hundred and sandlot football at our neighborhood park. After tempting him and his younger brother with the same chrome-plated noisemakers that hooked me, they joined during the birth of the New Emerald Knights. While his brother only lasted the season, Dave found a second home with the corps.

After five dedicated years in the corps, Dave was an experienced marcher and French horn player. Medium height, medium build, and medium quiet, he could easily go unnoticed, and I sometimes felt guilty for taking him for granted. Before the April camp I suggested he join us, telling him a bunch of Knights were marching, that the Blue Stars always made finals, and that there was a good chance I'd be drum major. Again, eager to march and hang out, it was an easy sell.

Dave and I drove over to rendezvous with the rest of our Blue Star caravan at Frank Gorman's home. Frank was the youngest in our group and was another drum corps convert from Bishop's New Emerald Knights. Joining as a scrawny thirteen-year-old, he'd stoically stand in line, struggling to hold the heavy baritone by jamming boney elbows against skinny ribs. Coke-bottle glasses magnified the look of constant discomfort, but he never bitched once. Now fully grown, he was strong enough physically and musically to hold his own in the powerful Blue Stars' bari section. Yesterday was Frank's high school graduation, which he casually dismissed as an annoying distraction to the important business of drum corps, and pulling into his drive, the thick glasses Frank still relied on now revealed his excitement for the start of our journey. Among his gear was his graduation present and contribution to our summer sublease: a boxed-up stereo, complete with two dishwasher-sized speakers.

Almost immediately we were joined by Mark Jordan, in his little green deathtrap Ford Maverick, and moments later, Dave Lyman pulled into the drive in his coveted electric blue, Chevy stepside pickup. Our convoy was now complete.

Lyman had also graduated with Jordan and Nelson. He joined the Knights in '73, and three short years later, he'd matured into one of the four Emerald Knights' screaming sopranos. Sporting aviator sunglasses and a lit cigarette, he had bad boy good looks that paired well with his cool, soft spoken persona. With a broad disarming smile and a full mane of brown hair parted down the middle, he fit the part of a tough-looking sop, and I knew his presence would be a key addition to our inexperienced lead line. Leaning out of the truck's window, he told us it was time to blow this pop stand, and I was reminded of how glad I was we'd convinced him to join us.

Lyman and Jordan's cars were loosely packed, leaving no room for Frank, so he eagerly sprawled across my back seat. It was time to roll, and roll we did. I slipped in a Boston tape (the band not the corps) and cranked it up. Their eponymous debut album had been on continuous replay in the college dorms my freshman year.

I prided myself in trying to choose music to fit the mood, and it'd been such a long time since playing it, I figured this was the perfect moment for a reprise. Nelson and Frank enthusiastically agreed, as the powerful sensation of summer escape was much more than a feeling. In three weeks we'd be Blue Stars living in competition, but for now, finally on the road with the music jacked, blue skies, and Frank rolling a fat one in the back seat, all we wanted was to have our "Peace of Mind." By the time the road split the cornfields outside of Cedar Rapids, all three of us were there.

The three hour road trip was filled with the sights and smells of a uniquely Eastern Iowa spring day. The scent of freshly turned earth accompanied the greenery of newly cultivated fields and native plant life. Acres of rolling farmland were separated by narrow draws and valleys adorned with robust pink and white flowering crabs, the tail end of redbud blossoms, and giant gnarled oak trees finally starting to leaf out. Senses heightened, we unanimously agreed it looked a lot like Munchkin land.

Cruising along, we frequently slowed for the main streets of small towns like Troy Mills, Elkader, and Lamont. The roads were lined with two story framed houses with wraparound porches supporting wooden swings, and each yard was decorated with lawn ornaments and robust flowering lilac bushes. The residential streets abruptly met simple downtowns of flat glass-faced hardware and clothing stores, diners, and corner bars.

Stopping in Strawberry Point, we gawked at the world's largest fiberglass strawberry while we downed thick handmade milkshakes and delectable greasy burgers. Miles rolled by and we focused on music and spring scenery to distract us from discussions about the sketchy numbers in our horn line and how much work remained before the first show of the season. For now, we were unfettered and free.

Our route had us crossing the Mississippi at McGregor, Iowa. Across the river we'd be in Prairie du Chien, where it had all started. Winding down onto the floodplain, I reminded Dave and Frank of the details from last June, and coming into town, I was interrupted by a detour sign and Jordan's green POS waiting on the roadside.

With the bridge under repair we sadly couldn't cruise the majestic scenic river highway. Instead, we were directed onto a narrow two-lane road that carried us north through miles of Minnesota farmland, before eventually hooking east into La Crescent, where we'd cross the river into Wisconsin.

Cruising along a winding ribbon of asphalt, I kept Jordan in my sights, weaving around slower cars and tractors towing farm implements. Over the Minnesota border, Frank alerted me to a state trooper trailing us. Windows down and our earlier buzz only beginning to fade, I told Frank to make sure he put our stash out of sight, and continued along at the speed limit until he nervously asked, "Hey Mike, aren't you going to pull over?"

Doing a double take in the rear view mirror, I caught the flashing blue and red lights cutting through the sunlight. Behind the wheel, I could see the trooper firmly pointing to the side of the road.

"Shit! Frank, why didn't you tell me he had his lights on?"

"I thought you could see him," he lamented, now sitting up straight in the back seat.

I slowed to the shoulder and watched from the side view mirror as the trooper strapped on his flat brimmed hat while exiting the car.

I fished for my wallet and rolled down my window to await my fate. He leaned over, stating flatly, "Sir, would you follow me back to my car and bring your license and registration with you."

I got in the passenger seat of his rig and sat silently as squawking radio communications provided information on my plates. When they came up clean, he finally broke the silence, "Why'd you take so long to pull over?"

I explained how I initially didn't see his lights, and realizing how lame I sounded, I began conjuring images of him searching the car, before he asked "Do you know why I stopped you?"

Trying my best to play it cool, I responded, "I know I wasn't speeding, so I have absolutely no idea." I rambled on, "We're on our way to La Crosse... we just got out of school, and we're spending the summer marching in the La Crosse Blue Stars Drum Corps." I was babbling, but semi-buzzed and significantly paranoid, I couldn't help myself, telling him about how our little convoy had been detoured at McGregor.

Indifferent to my ad-lib, he interrupted, "The reason I pulled you over is that I watched you pass a car a ways back, but you didn't complete your pass in a passing lane...you know that's against the rules of the road, don't you?"

"Yes sir," I quietly replied, all the time thinking I was sure I had made a good pass, and if I didn't, well at least, I was damn close.

I considered the possibility that he was bored and decided to mess with the guys in the sporty little Celica. Continuing his sobering lecture, he said, "I've been patrolling this road for a long time and I've dealt with more than one head on collision...I don't want you and your friends to be the next." Then he pointed at Mark's car. "If you're trying to stay with your friend up there, and he's doing the speed limit, you'll have to go faster than he is to keep up...so take it easy, I'm letting you off with a warning...drive safely if you want to make it to La Crosse."

After profusely thanking him, I walked back to my car somewhat confused about his physics, but deeply relieved I wouldn't have to inform Moe and Dr. K that three of us had been charged with possession of a controlled substance.

Finally able to breathe, the more I thought about it, the more I realized how lucky I'd been to escape unscathed. There was no doubt that this summer would be filled with a lot more unexpected detours, and if there was any chance of continuing my lucky streak, I reminded myself that I'd need to dial back the initial mania and listen carefully to the Piskel intuition that had served me so well in the Knights.

20

MONDAY, MAY 21ˢᵀ

MOST OF OUR NINE A.M. to nine p.m. rehearsals were held at a high school in West Salem, a small town about a twenty minute drive northwest of La Crosse. While a long way from the Oktoberfest grounds, the school provided limited distractions with a real stadium to learn our drill, but as the morning unfolded, our brass numbers weren't much better than at our last camp.

The low turnout had my Knights buddies and me somewhat anxious. However, Hill, Tippett, and the rest of the line forged ahead, seemingly unconcerned. With only thirty-six brass players, it was pointless to teach a drill that was written for twenty more, so while the percussion section and guard learned drill, the horn line worked hard to catch up from a lackluster winter program.

As the week continued, the fantastic spring weather was made all the more glorious by the regular arrival of handfuls of additional brass members. As cars carrying familiar and not-so-familiar faces pulled into the parking lot, they were greeted by rowdy welcoming cheers. By the following weekend, a car packed with another four unknown Southern faces had arrived, and on Sunday, our morning prayers were answered, as Hill, Tippett, and I stood in front of fifty-five horns that mostly knew their music.

This year's corps would field a percussion section of thirty-three members, featuring nine snares, four quads, five base drummers, five timpani, five cymbals, four keyboards, and one timbale player. The drill was written for fifty-six brass, including twenty-four sopranos, three mellophones, five French horns, eighteen baritones and six contras. Our color guard consisted of thirty-six girls in the flag line, and to the dismay of some, no rifle line, but to the joy of all, no turbans. Counting Deb and I, when our last brass spot was filled, we would take the field only one marcher shy of the maximum one hundred and twenty-eight allowed by DCI.

With nearly everyone in the fold, and tomorrow's scheduled appearance in the town's Memorial Day parade, sections of the corps were rotated through the school cafeteria to be fit for uniforms. I was slightly embarrassed by the fact that my six foot frame had gradually snuck over one-hundred and ninety pounds, requiring a deeper dig into the pants box, and one mom laughingly suggested that I'd better not gain any more weight.

Putting on the polar white drum major uniform made my new role seem all the more palpable. Seeing my reflection in the cafeteria's glass wall reawakened the remaining dormant drum major DNA, including the daunting sense of responsibility that came with it.

No longer a tacit observer, I was relegated to twelve square feet of wooden podium perched four feet off the ground. It was the best seat in the house, but I was still having difficulty getting comfortable. Earlier in the week, I'd successfully petitioned Hill for a conducting lesson. Away from critical eyes, our meeting took place in the early morning light of a quiet staff house. I felt awkward and intrusive standing in a bedroom as a half-hungover Wolfie sat propped up in bed, slurping on some sort of remedy. His lecture focused almost entirely on the value and importance of a sharply defined ictus. I took what I could from his comments, ultimately refining my conducting to his approval, but getting into the car a half hour later, I left for practice still dissatisfied.

I knew I had a good grasp of the meter changes and overall tempo responsibilities, but what I really wanted was guidance in my conducting style. Two years away from my role as the Knights' DM made me realize that my Masonesque conducting approach wouldn't be the best fit for the Blue Stars. What I really wanted was to adopt something equivalent to the uniquely effortless and precisely stylized conducting Albo used during the '75 show. His classy, unobtrusive approach visually personified the corps marching style and their music. I probably should have sought him out for advice, but for now he seemed unapproachable and singularly focused on getting us on the field.

With limited feedback other than Smith's insistence that I was always with the snares, I decided it best to take a mostly unassuming approach. For now, it'd have to be good enough to have spot-on tempos that were locked in with the percussion. Maybe sometime during the season somebody would have some suggestions for the showbiz stuff.

~ ⟋⟍ ~

A completely new Blue Stars program began with "St. Louis Blues," as suggested by Smith and pushed for by Dr. Kampschroer. Kampschroer had a penchant for jazzy old tunes, and during '72 and '73, the corps had performed "South Rampart Street Parade" to great acclaim, while '74's "Tiger Rag" only garnered a modest crowd reaction. Hopefully that wouldn't be the case with the swinging blues march. The enduring song was written back in 1914, by W.C. Handy, the self-proclaimed father of the blues. Since then the tune had a life of its own and was repeatedly covered by such famous artists as Louis Armstrong and Count Basie, and during World War II, Glen Miller's U.S. Army Air Force Band made it a standard.

Our up-tempo adaptation made it a challenge to swing, until an early company front provided a dramatic time change. Emphasizing the move, our guard used telescoping flag poles that were ingeniously repurposed from handles designed to hold brushes for cleaning swimming pools. During the front they were closed down into a swing style flag that the guard spun in a wide open one handed manner. Back to a march tempo, the number accelerated to its fortissimo climax with four booming bass drum beats signaling another ritenuto for the full ensemble's swinging conclusion. Most of us thought the arrangement was decent but didn't generate the energy or suspense of last year's "Malaga."

From the old to the new, we did an abrupt about face with a wildly innovative drum solo based around Weather Report's jazz fusion composition, "Birdland." The piece came off their 1977 *Heavy Weather* album, which had been voted Jazz Album of the Year by *DOWNBEAT* Magazine's listener poll. "Birdland" had been so artistically and commercially successful, it was soon being covered by many other artists, including us.

I thought it was a great choice. It was my kind of music. Where most college students across the country had AC/DC, Allman Brothers, Boston, Eagles, ELO, Floyd, Frampton, Heart, Kansas, Queen, Rush, and Zeppelin coming from their stereos, many young musicians were trending in the jazz fusion genre. My own collection was loaded up with fresh vinyl and dollar cut-outs from Chick Corea, Miles Davis, Herbie Hancock, Jan Hammer, Pat Metheny, Jean Luc Ponty, Mahavishnu Orchestra, and Weather Report.

When the album *Heavy Weather* came out, it didn't leave my turntable for several weeks. In the fall of '77, Beth and I were lucky enough to witness a live performance of it at the University's acoustic wonderland, Hancher Auditorium. That night we let Wayne Shorter's sax, Joe Zawinul's keyboards, and the bass of an amazing young virtuoso, Jaco Pastorius, transport us to another cosmic dimension.

Percussion caption head and arranger Steve Smith was also enamored with Weather Report, and it was their Peruvian-American percussionist, Alex Acuña's deft drumming that first attracted him to their sound. Having a talented, veteran snare and tenor line, Smith wanted to challenge them with the polyrhythmic possibilities "Birdland" offered. The percussion feature included many surprises, including a brass sextet echoing the melodic line first introduced by the keyboards, followed by a full brass and percussion ensemble of its syncopated chorus. From there, an infectious groove was created through multiple percussion voicings that included funky tenor drum rhythms, clapping snare drummers, and coordinated runs throughout the line, after which an up-tempo transition had our nine snares executing a series of stick handling maneuvers that included backsticking and playing on each other's drums. The arrangement ended with the full line executing a unison series of gunshot-like accents. While the syncopation proved to be a constant challenge, it was an undeniably upbeat, subtly complex, and effervescent piece that was bound to revolutionize percussion features.

The drum solo drill also provided a stirring color guard feature down the fifty-yard line, that had our lone spot of rifle work. During the move a dozen of our most talented members threw unison triples, as twelve color guard members on either side tossed their flags through them. As the corps continued to learn the drill, it was apparent that there'd be numerous opportunities to incorporate additional visuals throughout the season.

The percussion feature took us into our concert number, and keeping the jazz fusion vibe going, we threw down Chick Corea's vibrant, "La Fiesta." Corea first performed his composition in the early '70s with Stan Getz, and soon it was also covered by many other jazz artists, including the big bands of Buddy Rich and Woody Herman, and an exaggerated screaming trumpet rendition by Maynard.

During my senior year in high school, our jazz band performed Woody Herman's arrangement, mashing it with Ferguson's ending for our concluding number at the state competition in Des Moines. It was a memorable night of fun, tarnished only by placing a close but heartbreaking second. The arrangement had me enthusiastically playing flugelhorn on a brisk opening duet with our lead alto sax, but the real drama came from placing the four powerful Emerald Knights soprano players we had in our trumpet section into the corners of the auditorium's house. Then after Dode's electrifying electric piano solo, they alternately wailed into the darkness with echoing lip trills and upper register shakes, all while our drummer provided a sizzling snare backdrop that gradually grew in tension until the full force of the entire ensemble recapitulated the melody. Exciting as a train off its tracks, at assemblies and jazz competitions, we'd blow the place apart, leaving judges and audience fully dumbstruck. That night at State, it had been our uniform opinion that we fuckin' should've won.

"La Fiesta" maintained the Blue Stars' affinity for dangerously loud and Latin-inspired pieces, and while most of the Blue Stars' music was penned by their longtime brass arranger, Rick Young, this was Hill's first foray into a full-blown arrangement for the corps. He didn't disappoint. Hill's interpretation was dramatic, complex, and challenging, but to make it really work, it required a lead soprano soloist of significant proportion. This year, Wolfie was counting heavily on our seventeen-year-old Tennessean trumpet savant, Mike Haynes.

Throughout the winter, Mike had been heavily touted by Hill and he was a part of the final wave of brass players to find their way to La Crosse that summer. Haynes had just graduated from Tullahoma High School, one of many high schools across the U.S. that were adopting a drum corps style and venturing into the growing movement of competitive marching bands. Last fall, his talent was revealed to a network of drum corps brass instructors recruiting at marching band competitions, but what eventually brought Mike to La Crosse was yet another example of fortuitous coincidences.

Three times being the proverbial charm, Haynes had first been recruited by the Spirit of Atlanta. However, being cast as the lead in the school play, he missed their audition camp. Next up, the Madison Scouts poked him several times to come to theirs, but a timely bout of mono kept him at home in bed. Finally his talent was brought to Hill's attention by Blue Stars' drill writer Colin Klos, who'd drafted Tullahoma's drill the year before. Haynes accepted Hill's invite to an early winter camp, and once there, Hill laid out images of Mike majestically soloing in front of large appreciative crowds across the country. The part was his if he wanted it, and luckily for us, he did.

Mike's youth and "aw-shucks" attitude instantly endeared him to the entire brass line, and although he only attended one camp, he impressively arrived in May with music memorized and soprano bell a-blazing. Fire alarm loud, he was completely naïve to the nuances of drum corps, and his effortless ability to generate an ear-blinking volume often overpowered an already roaring brass line. Mike's sound didn't pop out of the ensemble, he just completely out-blew it, requiring Hill and Tippett to constantly remind him to hold something back—except for "La Fiesta."

Nearing the number's conclusion, the solo began with a dramatic timpani accompaniment. From there, Mike's melodic statements grew through a series of lip trilling progressions, until, like Maynard and my old jazz band, he was joined by the entire ensemble, after which Mike was free to fully unsheathe his chrome plated Excalibur. No mics necessary, he used his freakishly prodigious power and stratospheric range to soar over the full corps' *fff* closing statement, and the piece finished with him hanging onto a tasty high note.

Musically, it was the most exhilarating moment of the show, and Mike's talent took Hill's festive arrangement to an intense decibel level only rocket ships, blue whales, and G-bugles can generate. Early on, staff and members would get so caught up in his performance, they would lose track of their own. It truly was the Blue Stars' good fortune that Mike had been a mononucleosis-plagued thespian that prior fall.

After "La Fiesta," our production number of Gershwin's "Strike Up the Band" seemed incongruous to the three prior selections. More richly scored than the Emerald Knights' stripped-down jazz version played in '78, it had a Boston Pops kind of vibe. The arrangement included difficult brass licks, a variety of tempo changes, a muted soprano line feature, a Dave Lyman soprano horse whinny, and a bright, up-tempo finish. It also featured our guard performing an unusual flag exchange from a seated position and a visually captivating sit circle, where thirty-six flags formed a tight ring before each gracefully sat back on the guard member's knee behind them. Then their flags opened and swayed in unison to reveal a center stage baritone soloist.

Used with permission from Sights & Sounds Inc.,
Publishers of Drum Corps World
1979 color guard sit circle during
"Strike Up the Band."

It was no Jewish Medley, but it would be an equally onerous performance challenge for Blue Stars' brass line. Summer's rolling music camp 101, Hill, Tippett, and the rest of us would have the difficult charge of striking up an emotional and engaging response from the fans and judges.

Our show concluded with Chuck Mangione's Grammy award winning composition, "Children of Sanchez." Mangione's music was on every drum corps fan's hummable playlist, as his pop jazz compositions appeared to be purposely scored for today's corps. In '76 the Blue Stars used "Bellavia" for their closer, while the Bridgemen played "Land of Make Believe," for their concert number in both '76 and '77.

In '76, the World Champion Blue Devils concert number was once again the "Legend of a One-Eyed Sailor," and it was followed up with "Chase the Clouds Away," for their closer. Those arrangements partially defined the Blue Devils' wide open jazz programs and helped propel them to their first World Championship. Their concert number showcased the genius of brass arranger and instructor, Jim Ott, and also gave Ott's attractive sister Bonnie the opportunity to display her talent at manipulating a mellophone to mimic Mangione's flugelhorn.

Mangione's latest music provided the soundtrack for the 1978 movie, *Children of Sanchez,* and after the album's release, it became vastly more popular than the film. High school and college jazz bands gobbled up various arrangements, and the Blue Stars were no different. The perfect closer, it packed a variety of emotions into phrases backed by a percussive pulse and haunting minor key that ultimately resolved into a hopeful and joyous conclusion.

Our program then segued into another original Don Hill: faster, higher, louder, Spanish flavored finale. The accompanying drill had symmetrical expanding triangles of brass merging into a large centerfield wedge, before it was split down the middle by the advancing percussion section. The guard moved into a huge arc behind the corps, accenting each note with swirling flags while the drum line pushed the brass out across the front sidelines into two horizontal lines. The last counts of the show had five cymbals rippling their crashes directly down the fifty as the entire ensemble laid waste to the crowd with a steady stream of scintillating sound. It was another classic Blue Stars big push ending, designed to leave the audience with ringing ears and drooling for more.

That was our show—now if we could only march it. While Mike Haynes was a tremendous musician, it was too bad he couldn't march even half as well as he played. He wasn't alone. A significant number of our new brass players struggled with their supposed marching technique, and it seemed an almost nonexistent winter of marching basics would handicap us throughout the season. For now it would have to be good enough just to get people to their right spots on the field.

Getting Blue Stars to those right spots on the field was the responsibility of Colin Klos, who'd written their drills since '76. Colin was a homegrown Blue Star, marching as a charter member in '65, then aging out after the summer of '71. As a dedicated fourteen-year-old he rode his bike seven miles to practice, but lacking musical prowess, his marching career was spent as a lower soprano. What Colin didn't lack was a strong work ethic and deep love for the activity. After aging out he followed his strengths, becoming a marching techni-cian, cleaning drill and teaching basics, while being mentored by the corps' initial marching and guard instructors, Frank Van Voorhis and Doc Nelson.

Studying architecture at the University of Wisconsin in Milwaukee allowed Klos to provide drum corps with a more precise and system-atic methodology for drill writing. During the '75 season, the time spent with Bobby Hoffman greatly enhanced Colin's understanding of drill design. Hoffman had innovative ideas for what music should look like on the field, but often delegated the details of precise tran-sitions to others. Colin was saddled with much of the painstaking task of bringing Hoffman's creativity to life, as he positioned the movement of each member on chart paper.

Challenged with providing a seamless transition for spelling out "Chicago" in the '75 show, hours were spent at the drafting table. Upon completion, Hoffman looked at Colin's drill and, half-kid-ding, asked, "Is that the best you can do?" Colin headed back home, staying up the majority of the night perfecting the moves for one of the first scripted words to be incorporated into a drum corps drill set.

"When the student is ready, the teacher will disappear" and after Hoffman's departure, Colin was tagged as the visual caption head. Keeping the remainder of the team intact, he harmoniously switched instructional responsibilities with Doc and Frank, and was fortunate to add '75 drum major Al Timmreck, aka Albo, to the staff. It was a strong team.

Colin's drill writing evolved from there. He was part of a growing collection of talented visual designers taking drills from the old parade formations on a football field to an expressive visual inter-pretation of the music, and his training as an architect provided him with the understanding of measured balance, detail, and design. He had the patience to repeatedly listen to the music until it revealed what it should look like, then used his expertise to create flowing follow-me transitions from set to set for the soft melodic phrases, and angular, forward-moving and/or expanding formations for the most powerful moments.

The advent of the new drill designs meant spectators could now watch the music come alive, not just in the performers' body movements or regimental squads and platoons, but through kaleidoscope-like effects that would synchronize music with a big moving picture. From this point on, drill designs would only continue to get better.

During a seminar for band directors, Klos described writing drill as not all that unlike designing a house, only one that moves. Colin was enamored with balance and symmetry and his drill forms rarely drifted beyond the twenty-yard lines. Within those boundaries, he connected the dots of guard, percussion, and brass, creating eye-pleasing formations that addressed appropriate staging for brass and percussion voices, as well as providing the color guard with featured moments to complement the musical performance.

Klos was a competitive and tireless perfectionist, and his solid interpersonal skills and professionalism made him a desired commodity in the marching arts. Besides the '79 Blue Stars show, that year he wrote the drill for five other corps and twelve competitive marching bands. While the Blue Stars were lucky to have spawned such a talent, they were also fortunate that Colin and Albo had formed a working friendship. With the demands of both architecture and drill writing consuming Colin's time, Albo adeptly took charge of the day to day responsibilities of teaching and cleaning the drill.

The Memorial Day parade was our first public appearance, and warm, sunny skies lit up clean uniforms that were the perfect color palette for a patriotic parade. While our required performance took us away from the practice field, it didn't necessarily interrupt rehearsal, as the corps took a disciplined approach to any public performance, and even the parade became an opportunity for the staff to work in some marching basics. Today's route ended in front of a downtown store, where we gave the locals a standstill performance of our show.

Still getting comfortable with our music, the tempos between brass and percussion ebbed and flowed. Per Wolfie's early morning lesson, I plainly and steadfastly enunciated the ictus. Afterwards, standing in front of the brass section, he rhetorically asked, "Did you feel yourselves starting to lose it in "La Fiesta?" With members nodding, he continued, "Do you know why you didn't...because Piskel wouldn't let it. He kept you from coming totally apart at the seams. This is exactly why it's so vitally important for you to follow him while listening to each other. It's the only way it's going to work."

Boom. There it was. I gave no indication of acknowledging his brief praise, but inside I was busting, and hoped the comments would garner a greater confidence in me and perhaps plow a path to greater acceptance from the vets. At least now there'd been a tangible example for why I'd been chosen for the role.

After the parade, it was grab a bite to eat and head back to West Salem. We went at it non-stop, with a rhythm of eat, sleep, practice, rinse and repeat. Despite the intensity and duration of our rehearsals, they were not without some peripheral personal benefits. During my freshman year at Iowa, my ecology professor once jokingly commented, "The solution to pollution is dilution." His point now seemed to have some validity, as the additional twenty brass members, coupled with full corps run-throughs and Hill's bit of praise, seemed to have watered down much of the brass vets' disdain. Either that, or they were beginning to realize how counterproductive it would be to hang on to a misplaced grudge. Having a collection of Emerald Knights joining this year's corps provided additional support.

Finding cheap housing wasn't difficult with the summer's exodus of UWL college students. Most of our members weren't picky. If it was out of the elements, had a fridge, shower, room for a sleeping bag, and a private dump, it would work.

About a dozen young brass members, mostly from the South, had rented an old, dilapidated foursquare house that wouldn't have raised a sniff from desperate frat boys. They proudly christened their ramshackle domicile "The Horn House," and it became a famous hangout for the eighteen and under crowd. Several of the vets that had moved to La Crosse earlier in the year were now doubling as innkeepers for the last of the migrating members. Moe and his staff had rented a large, old clapboard two story that provided each of them their own bedroom.

Jordan, Lyman, Nelson, and I were lucky enough to sublet an apartment in a newer two story complex that was only a mile away from the Oktoberfest grounds. Our unit was on the second level, with a front door that opened directly into the living room. The apartment was sparsely appointed, with the exception of a kitchen table and chairs and two twin beds in each of the two bedrooms. We'd brought along several well-used bean bag chairs and assembled a makeshift stereo stand from unfinished boards and cinder blocks for Frank's graduation present. Those few furnishings, along with Lyman's ever-growing and morphing geometric design of empty Old Style cans lining the blank living room wall, were the extent of our décor.

Each of us contributed several hundred bucks for the clean, decent air conditioned living space. Because Frank was the youngest, we consigned him to the hallway's narrow walk-in closet for his sleeping quarters and cut his rent in half. He didn't mind one bit. Compared to the housing many members tolerated, our apartment was a palatial retreat, and I was happy it wasn't large enough to facilitate corps parties that would undoubtedly leave it trashed. The members that did stop by after practice were always amused by Frank's tiny bedroom, but impressed by the neat, well-organized digs of our "Iowa House."

Despite the given name of our apartment, we weren't the only Iowans to join the Blue Stars. Five other Emerald Knights chose to lose themselves in a summer of DCI-caliber competition, and I was proud of the experienced, hardworking, and talented representatives from my old corps.

One of the first Emerald Knights to venture north this year was percussionist and University of Iowa music major, Vicky Novak. Back in '74, through relentless diligence and tenacity, she was able to break through the gender barrier as a snare drummer. From then on, she seemingly never went anywhere without her drumsticks. Tough, courageous, and determined, she was at it again, willingly putting up with a constantly overflowing five-gallon bucket of good-natured shit from the eight other guys in the line. Like blaming a nearby friend for your own farts, they'd laughingly berate her for any dirt coming from their music even if it was obviously from the opposite end of the line. While soft-spoken, she was strong-willed, extremely focused, and amazingly positive, and her professional demeanor and work ethic personified a classic example of FCO.

Vicky Novak and the other members of the
1979 Blue Stars snare line practice
at La Crosse's Riverside Park.

Many organizations and activities are blessed by strong legacy families, and after World War II, drum corps parents exemplified the tradition of passing the baton better than most. The Emerald Knights had several families steeped in Cedar Rapids' storied drum corps history, but among them the Wyatts were standouts. This summer, three members of their large family, Kim, Pete, and Barb, had decided to join the Stars for their drum corps fix. In the 1930s, their father Bob had been a Cedar Rapids Musketeer, and after World War II, he joined the local senior corps, before sharing his passion for the activity with his growing family.

Even with seven children to care for, Bob's wife, Bonnie, took on dozens more as a drum corps mom. She chaperoned weekend trips, sewed uniforms and flags, became a member of the Emerald

Knights' board of directors, and somehow found extra time to help organize the annual Tournament of Drums. Meanwhile, Bob worked nights and weekends to design and convert an old moving van into the Emerald Knights' impressive walk through equipment trailer.

The Wyatts' oldest sister had been a member of the Scarlet Knights, a national champion color guard, and their oldest brother was a charter member of the Cedar Rapids Cadet Bees, before marching in the snare line of the Cadets and Grenadiers. Several years later he became a valuable member of the Emerald Knights' percussion staff.

Kim joined the Knights' color guard during Bishop's reign in'74, and her dedication earned her the position of guard captain and assistant drum major from '76 through '78. At the end of that last tough season, she was appropriately honored at their banquet as "Knight of the Year." Now, as an age-out member of the Blue Stars' guard, she brought along her experienced sister Barb, and good friend, Linda Malik, to capably fill the last remaining spots.

Kim's younger brother Pete was a music education student at Iowa. He'd been devastated by the Emerald Knights' breakup. Feeling like he'd lost a significant part of his family, he searched for a surrogate, and joined the corps' percussion section with Vicky, willingly tolerating the weight of a marimba in the line of four talented Blue Star keyboard players. The Wyatt's remaining two younger brothers, who had also marched with the Emerald Knights, were still in high school and didn't make the trek to La Crosse.

With the entire household taking part in the activity, the Wyatts were one of those dedicated families that marching organizations rely heavily upon. Volunteering for a myriad of responsibilities, they'd become so entrenched in the organization that it had become central to their lives. Most drum corps can't exist without at least a few families like them in their organization, and their exemplary hard work, time, and energy, were key in shaming other parents into helping out.

~ ~ ~

The week before our first show we'd finally finished learning the drill; not that we were actually performing it, but for the moment, we could breathe, and an elated staff gave us Saturday evening off. It was time to celebrate, and not letting the well-deserved opportunity to blow off some steam evaporate, there was only one thing to do. TOGA!

The previous year's National Lampoon film *Animal House* featured a riotous toga party that quickly became a national trend at college campuses across the country. The movie featured a wild, four minute sing-a-long dance scene with the fictitious Otis Day and the Knights, covering the Isley Brothers' infectious hit, "Shout."

For the Blue Stars, and our "Finis Coronat Opus" motto, adopting the party theme for our season opener was a no-brainer. So the staff and Schultzie's crew hastily organized the affair. The simple gathering consisted of only the barest of necessities for a quality celebration: beer, bedsheets, and brats.

I couldn't quite bring myself to don a toga, and arriving at the staff house a little late, I was definitely on the outside looking in. Sneaking through the side door that led to the large kitchen, I was met by rocking music and the warm glow of Roman revelers, three deep around a keg. Once spotted by Schultz, I was immediately tried and found guilty for my lack of appropriate apparel. Instantly sentenced, I was confined by a large cardboard "penalty box" that held a wooden kitchen chair. Taking my seat, I was handed the keg hose and instructed to draw from the trigger for thirty seconds. To the synchronized chants of "Thirty seconds! Thirty seconds!" I barely lasted twenty. Foamy beer shot from my nose and mouth, initiating the guffaws and howls I'd easily seen coming.

Having missed last year's Puker, I was impressed with the staff and older members' unrestrained enthusiasm for debauchery and a damn fine time, but even after my stint in the penalty box, I felt more like an observer than participant. As their new drum major, I had a self-imposed reservation about cutting loose in front of the majority of the corps. Maybe that's why JB had wanted out of the job, but I was pretty sure some of my precaution was initiated by a lingering case of paranoia from the Easter camp, compounded by the sense of restraint inspired by my forgiving Minnesota trooper.

236

The party started early and lasted well past midnight, and I was happy to see that Jordan, Lyman, and Nelson were having no problem finding their niche. Hell, even a red-nosed Moe looked like a little Cajun Caesar as he happily held his matching red solo cup in one hand and a corner of the loose-fitting bed sheet in the other.

The party was a welcome break, but more importantly, the celebratory atmosphere provided the right environment to bond at the next level. The house and yard were packed with members from around the country, and the formation of our '79 summer Blue Star family had officially begun.

While our party didn't have John Belushi, we did have Schultzie, which in my opinion, was way better. As the evening progressed, inhibitions were stripped away as easily as the sheets from beds, and the snow white butts of Schultzie and four others streaked through the crowded living room. Their entrance was lightning quick, but their exit, uh...not so much. Falling like dominoes, they piled on top of each other before recovering to make their escape. The crowd in the living room exploded in a roar of laughter. Thankfully, I didn't have a clear view of their shenanigans. However, I was quite certain I saw the back of Jordan's fro, along with his skinny ass bringing up the rear.

After their departure, it was loudly brought to everyone's attention that in the throngs of their bold, intoxicated dash one of them had lost the only provision they'd taken to insure a modicum of modesty. Apparently, before entering the room, they'd taped large promotional beer buttons over their privates. The buttons sported an, "Open Your Big Mouth" slogan, off a newly designed Schmidt's beer bottle from Heileman's Brewery. The entire episode was a sight that months later would still be very hard to unsee, and after the initial shock and subsequent din of the crowd had died, staff members said it might be prudent to announce last call.

Mercifully, Sunday's practice wasn't scheduled until noon, and we spent the day and the remaining last week of preseason getting used to playing while marching the new drill, working on tempo changes, adding guard work, and searching for some elusive continuity.

21

SUNDAY, JUNE 10TH

WHILE I THOUGHT WE WERE ready enough for our first show of the season, our charter buses weren't, so we relied on leased yellow buckboards to take us to Oshkosh, Wisconsin. The contest featured some of the Midwest's best: Madison, Phantom, the Cavies, and us. The prior week's numerous run-throughs had put me enough at ease that I wasn't freaking out. I had too many responsibilities to even consider nerves, and that was a good thing, because unlike the marching members getting ticked for a small error, any mistake on my part could create a much more catastrophic chain reaction.

I was determined to make sure that our show would hang together, and I thanked God that for the most part, it did. During practice, I'd ingeniously resolved Hill and Smith's cadence concerns by using the second hand on my watch to precisely set tempos before starting each number. It worked well enough that for our first shows, I placed the watch to the inside of my cummerbund. Facing away from the crowd I could discreetly take a peek before clapping out the tempo and giving the "Corps...resume, march command.

Between hearing my name announced on the PA system and our closing notes, the time went scary fast, making for a wild ride. Forming our post-performance circle outside the high school stadium, we listened to mostly ambivalent reactions from the staff. Hill and Tippet acknowledged our effort but also said there was more than a summer's worth of work ahead of us. Not a word was spoken to me, and I took the lack of feedback as a sign that, at least for now, I'd been good enough.

With some down time before the finale, I wondered just how good we might actually be? Listening to Phantom's powerful performance, I became acutely aware of the growing jitters I'd earlier ignored. Back on the field for retreat, the other three drum majors and myself were called front and center for our scores. Hearing a score of 61.45, followed by The Blue Stars, I internally winced before acknowledging our placement with a salute. I winced again when I heard the

Cavies had beaten us by almost three full points, but what stung the most was hearing that both Phantom and Madison were twelve points ahead of us. Madison topped Phantom by a half a point, and their scores, along with the Cavies' apparent rebound from last year's difficulties, had us in a place we didn't want to be.

Scores announced, the Cavaliers' new drum major sported a goofy grin as he shook my hand. Introducing himself as Jeff, he continued going down the line and shaking all of the other DMs' hands, talking about what a fantastic summer this was going to be, and blah, blah, blah. *Oh brother, all I could think about was that he'd better enjoy it for now, cuz we'd be coming.*

Summer drum corps season had finally blossomed. FCO, no one was going to outwork us. A brief break on Monday was followed by a long evening rehearsal, and full-day practices for the remainder of the week. Intelligent staff paired well with motivated members and we began to reap results. The weekend after Oshkosh, the now-familiar school buses took us on a three-day swing from Dubuque through Northern Illinois. In that time we realized a six point jump in our score and had cut the gap between us and Madison to less than eight. Cavies were still almost three points ahead of us, and surprisingly, we barely topped the Guardsmen on Saturday and Sunday.

I wasn't so worried about the Cavies, I felt confident we'd eventually catch them, but we were bummed out hearing they had also chosen "Children of Sanchez" for their closer. Although their arrangement didn't quite match the complexity and demand of ours, it did seem to distract from the originality of our program. The G-men, however, were vastly improved. They'd smartly commissioned Klos to write the drill, and their talented color guard was coming off of an outstanding winter guard season.

Corps mingled in the parking lot as we loaded equipment and waited for the staff to get back from the critique, and it was then we realized the Guardsmen had also benefited from the recent demise of nearby corps. Their brass, guard, and percussion consisted of many Fox Valley Raiders and some key Emerald Knights, including two lead sops, who now traded screaming licks during their concert. Depending on just how good the East and West Coast corps were, we were in for a tough season of competition.

~ ∾ ~

During the following evening's rehearsal, while Tippett warmed up the brass section, Hill took me aside. Working closely with him for over a month, I felt like we were forming a more comfortable professional and personal relationship. Hill was very good at separating the two, and somewhat guarded in his approach to both. As we strolled away from the arc of horns, I could tell from the tone of his voice there was something significant he wanted to discuss. Instantly I went on point.

"Mike, I wanted to let you know we're going to be making JB the assistant drum major. Are you going to be okay with that?"

Like an out of body experience, I heard myself flatly respond, "Sure, whatever you think's best for the corps." Reflexively, I went right down the rabbit hole. I couldn't help it, my mind reeled with images of sharing the position or worse, being relegated to a back field or peripheral conductor while JB reclaimed the podium. *What the fuck? Was I doing a shitty job? If so, where was the remediation?* The only smart thing I did was keeping my mouth shut, but I was pretty sure my expression betrayed my discomfort.

"Thanks, I figured you'd understand, I just didn't want to make the move before checking with you." Out of ear shot from the brass line, we stopped walking. Clearing his throat, he continued, "Little Massey contacted Moe and wants to march. He's a much better horn player than JB, and frankly there are quite a few spots in the drill where we could use three conductors. I've already spoken with JB…you're still the drum major. He won't be doing any conducting from the podium…he doesn't even want to, and he's really not all that happy with making the switch, but like you, he's willing to do what's best for us."

I felt myself starting to relax, "So, when's this all going down?"

"Massey will be up from Louisiana before the end of the week. So we're going to move JB today." I was sure Hill sensed my trepidation, adding, "It'll be alright Mike. This is a good move for the entire corps…you'll see."

I appreciated him giving me the heads up before telling everyone else. I couldn't disagree that another field conductor would help, but heading back to the semicircle of brass players, I heard the voice inside my head whispering that the vets might see it as an opportunity for something more. It spurred more uncomfortable visions of being replaced, and I wondered how I'd respond if it came to that. Not much I could do now. I had to trust Hill, while acknowledging the change as just one more of those inevitable detours.

When the announcement was made, there was a ripple of cheers in the line, and I felt the definite pang of jealousy. JB seemed a little embarrassed and almost apologetic about it, but more importantly, there wasn't any indication that he wanted something more from the move. Deb seemed happy to have him back by her side, and that night, during our final run through, as Hill had foretold, I spent less time running around on the field, and the side to side phasing issues already began to improve.

Having missed the start of last year's Blue Star season, I was surprised by the early pace of our summer. It was frenetic. With the exception of our toga party there'd been virtually no time off, and I craved even a small pause to collect my thoughts and reload. Later that week, a guardian angel came to my rescue. During a transition in the evening's practice, one of the corps' moms who regularly cooked on tour, showed up at the Oktoberfest grounds with an unexpected gift for the Iowa house. At her car she handed over a huge foil covered pan of lasagna. Still warm, it must have weighed in at over ten pounds, and even tightly wrapped, it smelled heavenly.

"Whoa," I exclaimed, "what's this for?"

"It's just to get you off to a good start, my guess is you probably need it, and in a couple of weeks, you'll be more desperate for a good meal than you realize. This should last you a couple of days."

"We're already desperate," I laughed, adding, "it might not last as long as you think."

I couldn't believe her premeditated generosity. "Thanks to you, tonight we're gonna dine like kings." I popped the trunk and nestled the pan in a blanket to keep it warm. I couldn't wait to tell my roommates about our revised dinner plans.

Before the season had even started, we'd consumed all of the food we'd carefully packed for our trip. Now with little time or inclination to cook, we'd grown tired of the cold cereal, sandwiches, SpaghettiOs, beans and weenies, and frozen pizzas. Any groceries purchased instantly and mysteriously disappeared, and for kicks, I'd always blame Frank.

The only prior deviation in our diet had been on the free Monday after our first show. Lyman and I were big into fishing and had brought some of our gear from home. Hearing there was good shore action below the La Crosse River spillway in West Salem, we'd driven out there that sunny morning, and expertly creeled a mixed bag of panfish along with a bonus northern pike. With no time to clean them before the evening's scheduled rehearsal, we threw them in a half-filled bathtub.

By the time practice ended, I was headache hungry, but with this being Wisconsin, of course I had to take the time to make us a late night shore lunch, so I sent Jordan and Nelson off to the grocery store for supplies and beer. Back in the apartment Lyman and I cracked up after discovering our fish were still swimming nervous circles in the tub.

While the meal was better than delicious, we'd trashed the kitchen, and it was after midnight before we finally hit the sack. Agreeing it was worth the trouble, the short night and the next couple days of lingering odors of fried fish made us realize this was a one-time deal. It'd been back to cold cereal and cold sandwiches ever since.

Now walking over to the reassembling brass arc, Lyman and Frank stated they had other plans and surprisingly chose to opt out, so I asked Hill and Tippett to join us at Chez Iowa. Instantly in, they even agreed to bring the beer to ensure the authenticity of a well-balanced Wisconsin meal.

Back at the apartment I took the foil off the heavy pan and slid it into the oven to toast up the cheese. When Hill and Tippett arrived, we fortified the beer's low alcohol content with some high quality herb, and it wasn't long before illegal smiles accompanied fast growing appetites. Taking the bubbling lasagna from the oven I cut it into humongous, gooey slabs that bordered on the size of absolute stupidity. In daydream-silence, we ate like German police dogs before entering a collective, slack-jawed coma.

For our after-dinner mint, Jordan broke out a cassette tape of the '77 Emerald Knights, and with no regard for the neighbors, we indoctrinated our unsuspecting brass staff to our Emerald Knight roots. Hill and Tippett seemed both bemused and amused by the sound of our old corps' eclectic mix of arrangements. During our version of Quincy Jones's "Theme from Sandford and Son" there was an unexpected baroque segment where the lead sops screamed away with no apparent regard for balance or intonation, causing Hill to sit upright and exclaim, "Good grief! Who the hell was your brass instructor?"

Cherry-red eyes darted between the three of us, until Nelson and Jordan both sheepishly pointed my way.

"Well that explains a lot," Hill laughed.

Everyone cracked up, after which I boisterously retorted, "Hey, you do the best you can with what you got…think how good we'd have been if we'd had an actual brass instructor?"

I couldn't imagine what Hill and Tippett actually thought of the Knights' brass line or my initial foray as a horn instructor, but with senses and emotions working overtime, the three of us reverently described the history behind the sad fate of the Emerald Knights and other neighboring corps, while lamenting that we'd let two of the best EK sops escape to the likes of the Guardsmen.

FRIDAY, JUNE 29TH

Our home show marked the last competition before leaving on our first tour. Done with practice by noon, Moe asked Deb, JB, and me to drive out to the town's small airport and pick up Santa Clara's director, Gail Royer, and George Zengali, the 27th Lancers' drill writer and color guard choreographer. Royer was here to check out the competition, while Zengali was just trying to catch up with his corps. Coming from opposite ends of the country, they'd met up on the connecting flight from Chicago to La Crosse.

Our small welcome party greeted them at the gate, gathered their luggage, and walked them back to my little yellow car. Royer sat in front, while Zengali, Deb, and JB jammed themselves into the back seat. Thankfully, Zengali was a slight guy. A charismatic extrovert, he instantly put us at ease with his flamboyant sense of humor and infectious laugh, commenting, "If I knew I was going to have to sit on the laps of such good looking people, I'd have dressed up."

Having Gail Royer sitting next to me was every bit as surreal as tooling around Allentown in Whiteley's Lincoln a year ago. Royer was the most successful director of the DCI era. An original member of the Midwest Combine, his Vanguard were the only corps other than us to have made the World Championship finals every year, the one difference being that Santa Clara had won it three times, and never placed lower than third. It was well understood by everyone who followed the activity that their consistent excellence was due to Royer's passionate genius. Not just a director, Royer penned creative brass arrangements, taught the brass section, and gathered a staff of strong caption heads to coordinate innovative shows. But their identity came from more than just great show designs and execution. Formed from the remnants of another California corps in the late sixties, they quickly established a distinct sense of tradition and mystique. These qualities came from their ability to add a touch of class to everything they did, and there was no doubt that the Vanguard's unique persona emanated from Royer's conception of drum corps as a newly evolving medium in the performing arts.

Dressed comfortably in shorts and T-shirt Royer was unathletic, middle-aged, with tired, sympathetic eyes. He looked a lot more like his alter ego of a junior high band teacher than a world-class drum corps director. Chancing my luck, I played the one card I had, "Hey Gail...Don and Trudy wanted me to tell you, hi."

"You know Don and Trudy Hughes," he said excitedly. "How do you know them?"

"Well I grew up in Cedar Rapids...I was their paperboy for five years, and Mr. Hughes was a math teacher at my high school. One day he saw me wearing my corps jacket and asked me if I'd ever heard of the Santa Clara Vanguard? He told me how you'd both taught in a small town in Iowa, before they moved to Cedar Rapids."

Suddenly we were in full blown conversation about his old friends, his experiences in the Gowrie Iowa Gauchos, the Emerald Knights, and my career choice as science educator. To the amazement of JB and Deb, there I was sharing a friendly conversation with THE Gail Royer, and all he wanted to do was ask about his friends and my backstory. The brief encounter made it obvious why his corps was so successful. He was a master at connecting with people, because he actually took the time to listen.

That night, Royer and the La Crosse faithful listened as Madison scored a 74.05 to beat Phantom by five hundredths of a point. They also heard the North Star, playing yet one more rendition of "Children of Sanchez." Formed only a few years earlier from an amalgamation of smaller drum corps from the northern suburbs of Boston, North Star had quickly joined the DCI elite. With black Aussie hats, old-school red satin tops, black pants, and white-trimmed uniforms, they had a very fun East Coast style of show that featured another soaring soprano soloist. He was so good they took almost thirty seconds in the middle of their show to shut down everything but him, and he didn't disappoint. Beating us by over a point, they were one more vastly improved corps that'd be pushing us all the season. Our disappointing 65.15 points had us avoiding last place, barely edging out the 27th Lancers, who in only their second show, were struggling with Zengali's difficult close order drill.

SATURDAY MORNING, JULY 13TH

Drum corps is a hard religion.

The easiest way to summarize our western tour would be the good, the bad, and the most definitely ugly. Yesterday we'd experienced our third bus breakdown and made do with an unscheduled day of practice in Des Moines. Now way behind schedule, we were still looking at a five-hour road trip to Whitewater before an afternoon step off for DCI Midwest's prelims. On the road at first light, we were cruising down the all-too-familiar Interstate 80. Fortunately, I was distracted from the horrors of last year's trip home from Denver. Unfortunately, it was because I was in the midst of making some equally horrific new ones.

Directly behind the bus driver, Moe sat holding an open road atlas. Stating loudly and to no one in particular, "Look here, we can drop that Lyman character right off at the I-380 intersection and he can walk his sorry ass back to Cedar Rapids from there." I knew he was serious, having seen him in action when my last year's seatmate suddenly disappeared.

Moe was still fuming about a towel snapping skirmish that took place after the Denver show. Beginning as innocent fun, it had escalated into something a little rowdier, with partially dressed guard members sporting telltale red marks on exposed arms and legs. Unfortunately, Lyman had been caught in the middle, which happened to be in the girl's shower room. While no one's modesty had been totally compromised, Moe had zero tolerance for shit like that. Now, two days later, he seemed to be reliving the scenario all over again, though I was fairly certain he was trying to displace the frustration generated by our troublesome buses.

With a chorus of snoring guys behind me, I was doing my best to walk him back from the edge. "Moe, I had a long talk with Lyman. No harm was really done. He understands that it was a mistake...he gave me his word that it'd never happen again, and I know it won't. I think we should give him another chance...I'll take personal responsibility for him for the rest of the summer." (Actually, Lyman had promised no such thing. Indignant and dismissive after the event, he was now sacked out like everyone else, but there was no way I wanted one of my Emerald Knight buddies walking home in the middle of our season.)

Moe didn't acknowledge my plea, but he finally closed the map and dozed off, and I held my breath until we passed the interchange outside of Iowa City. At least for now, Lyman would live to march another day.

That was just one of many ugly examples from our first tour. Here I'd been worried about the metaphorical detours that came with being a drum major, when what I should have really been concerned with was literally getting the corps down the road.

The tone of despair had been set early on with the arrival of our summer tour transportation. True, they were coach buses, but they were also musty, nasty, and so depressing that the buckboards might have been the preferred option. Somehow one coach had made its way to La Crosse from Puyallup, Washington, boasting a fading scripted logo, "The Sounds of the Pentecost," however, none of us could ever imagine anything heavenly coming from it.

Thankfully it wasn't my ride as it was designated as our "mixed nuts" bus. Only three days into the tour, while heading into the thick heat of Arkansas, their spavined chariot lost its feeble air conditioning compressor, and the young riders instantly and unceremoniously rechristened it, "The Sounds of the Holocaust."

How hot was Little Rock? Pulling into the asphalt parking lot of our housing at a local high school, the girls' bus sank down to the lug nuts of the double axle rear tires. It took half the corps to rock the bus from the soft tar pit, and the incident provided the perfect excuse for the guys' bus to start up with the water buffalo song, along with teasing jeers about the "Heifer Hauler," and the Arkansas Razorbacks' "Woo, Pig Sooie."

Photo courtesy of Penny Reedy

The girls' coach trapped in an Arkansas tar pit

I felt for the guard. They were anything but overweight and unattractive, yet since I'd joined the corps last year, they were constantly maligned by pathetic attempts at humor from a collection of vets in the brass and percussion sections. I never quite got it, and figured the hazing provided a convenient distraction from their own raging hormones.

The guard didn't need any additional grief. They were dealing with their own issues. The corps' new guard instructor was a recent Madison Scout alum. He was good, wrote solid work, and was well liked, but his inexperience left him slow to finish the choreography. Halfway through the tour, we were still missing chunks of much-needed visual support, and it was definitely impacting the GE scores. Compounding the problem, members of our guard came from across the country, including a contingency of Southern belles, who would curiously rise extra early each day to do their hair and makeup, only to have it badly blow up in the morning's heat and humidity. The differences in the guard's regional decorum only accentuated their variations in marching and equipment handling foundations. Like the brass section, they had significant work ahead of them.

Evidently, I needed my own work. Three shows into the tour, we'd lost to the streaking Guardsmen by three points, and finished in a sixty-seven point tie with the North Star. Frustrated by slow progress, my on-the-field body language betrayed me, and after the show, I was cornered by several vets from the guard and brass line. The discussion was entirely one-sided, challenging me to stand proud, and better represent the corps in uniform. Agreeing with them, I put up a good front, but inside I was mortified. Here I was trying hard to gain their respect, and I'd blown it—shit, forget respect, now I was wondering what it'd take to at least earn their acceptance.

While the whole episode left a bad taste in my mouth, it wasn't nearly as bad as the one left in Mike Haynes. After a brutally hot afternoon practice, Mike entered a darkened gym and reflexively mistook a jug of poorly-placed diesel fuel for a gallon of Southern sweet tea. I was sure its careless location had some-thing to do with our needy buses. One chug in, Mike sourly realized his mis-take. Moe hurriedly made some calls to the nearby hospital, and somehow Mike survived the episode. To everyone's amazement, he was even able to get through the show that evening, only to dry heave his way through our night drive to Colorado.

Relieved that he was feeling better by the next day's equally hot practice, we jokingly piled on, telling him that in this heat he had to be extra careful, as he might still be combustible, and because his solo was "such a gas" tonight he'd be "spittin' fire."

So other than Haynes' remark-able recovery, what was actually good about the trip? For one, the huge drum corps-hungry crowds, and the Dallas fans were every bit as enthusiastic as last year. Coming off the field, I had my first encounter with teenage drum major groupies, as JB and I (well, mostly JB) were tracked to the parking lot by a flock of high school girls, decked out in full Big D platinum-blonde makeup and attire.

Timing is everything, and sometimes

Used with permission from Sights & Sounds Inc., Publishers of Drum Corps World

1979, Mike Haynes air mails his solo during La Fiesta.

when the Stars line up, you get lucky. The evening's fans included a former Iowa Hawkeye food service colleague. Attending the show, and hearing my name announced at the start of our performance, she'd found me in the parking lot afterwards to see if it was indeed me, then offered to take me out for a Tex-Mex lunch on our off day in Dallas. Moe's approval came with the Cinderella dictate that I be back at our housing by six, and the following day she swung by the high school in a sweet red Camaro convertible.

Having a relaxing afternoon away from the corps, touring shiny Dallas in a shiny car, and ending up at a sleek modern cantina, where a spicy mountain of fully-loaded nachos was washed down with ice cold beer was exactly what I needed, and I appreciated the effort she'd taken to make it happen.

Dutifully back in time, I got to witness the corps' sloppy return. The day off had provided most members with the usual options of laundry, food court dinners, movies, snack food and souvenir shopping, but the corps grapevine told me that there'd also been a free-day farce performed by some of the corps' age-outs.

As mandated by the dry county's liquor laws, Schultzie's stage crew had to pool their tour money to purchase a single club membership at a private drinking establishment—whatever that was? Their purchase was not in vain, as a single membership could now entertain a contingency of "guests," and they heartily consumed two dozen pitchers of Lone Star hops. The suds fueled the antics for a dramatic final curtain call, as a conspicuously-compromised 6'4" lead baritone player was wheeled back to the buses in a grocery cart. Momentarily unattended by his equally-intoxicated entourage, the gravity in a sloping parking lot did the rest. To the horror of sober Blue Stars waiting on the buses, he accelerated down the hill, narrowly avoiding what was sure to be a disastrous collision with oncoming traffic. Timing was indeed everything.

Accident avoided, the day off had the positive desired effect; now fully rejuvenated, with fresh stories to tell, we plowed straight ahead. The Blue Stars were nothing if not resilient. Searing temps, bus breakdowns, beer-induced hangovers, poisonous diesel tea, and our scores fluctuating like water levels on the Mississippi didn't dissuade us. Like the summer's heat, we never let up. Sure, we had our share of rookies, but we also had the deeply ingrained culture of FCO, and we made incremental progress. At Little Rock, the corps finally crested seventy points, and the percussion section took high drums over the Scouts and North Star's superb chrome wall.

A cruel hundred-plus degree rehearsal in Pueblo had Hill and Tippett inducing mass-brass hysteria, as four brutal hours were singularly focused on "Strike Up the Band." When the torture subsided, Tippett mitigated our pain with his soothing voice taking us through a relaxing meditation in a cool, dimly lit gym. The yin and yang of the day's work had the most difficult part of our show finally starting to take on a more musically recognizable shape. That evening we summoned enough remaining energy to score a 73.25 and beat North Star by over two points.

Then there was Deb. All season she'd been a steadfast and trusty confidant, and her calming presence helped me to keep my sanity and maintain my resolve. With Beth back in Iowa City and Deb madly in love with the corps' tenor tech, there weren't any romantic under-or-overtones. She was comfortable in her position, taking things as they came, and I followed her and JB's experienced lead with the off the field responsibilities of checking out new facilities, supervising the housing cleanup and departure, setting up the field, and the other tedious necessities of transitioning the corps throughout its daily schedule. With twenty years of drum corps experience between the three of us, Moe had a competent and reliable leadership team.

Now standing much straighter, the performances were the best part of my summer. Despite all the snafus of our tour, when we took the field in competition, I was in my element. It was my time to make things happen, and from the podium, it felt like I was on the top of the world. Standing at the focal point of point of nearly ninety musicians armed with instruments designed for maximum sound projection was a thrilling place to be. As the conduit between corps and crowd, I made eye contact with members and audience at every opportunity, and with virtually no negative feedback from the staff, I knew I was making things happen as they were intended. Throughout the remainder of the tour I sensed an ever growing confidence as I continued to refine my unassuming straightforward style.

Our late arrival in Whitewater left us with barely enough time for the brass section to warm up and tune before step off, it also left us fairly anxious, as we were without our percussion section and a dozen guard members. A little over two hours from Whitewater, the "Sounds" broke down yet again. Crunched for time, Moe had us in our uniforms and rearranged bus assignments, with the percussion section and some guard members riding on the "Sounds" once it was repaired. Moe's accommodation would allow the brass to have time to tune, while the drums could use armrests and seat backs to loosen up on their way. The guy was always thinking.

Outside the stadium, we were in the on-deck circle, when our repaired bus finally limped into the lot with the last-minute heroics of reinforcements showing up for a fort under siege. *Here comes the awkward cavalry.* I rejoiced, as I watched tenors, timps, and mallets bobbing on the harnesses of our drummers quickly waddling over to join us. The combined heroics and relief were inspirational enough for us to crank out our best performance of the tour, and returning to the parking lot, we finally got to experience that same after-show vibe I'd witnessed in Allentown a year ago. It was about time.

When our post-show circle was dismissed, I turned around to see the friendly smile of Beth standing by the side of a bus. It was one of those overwhelming and humbling moments, sadly diminished by too many watchful eyes. With no car, she must have worked hard to convince several of her friends to give up a day to drive four hours to a drum corps show. Different worlds unexpectedly collided, and the continuity of my season was instantly broken.

Beth's unexpected presence made for a clumsy reunion. It was the first show she'd ever witnessed, and I could tell she was still trying to process it, as I uncomfortably hugged her in my sweaty uniform. She wanted to talk about how amazing we were, and how completely different it'd been from what she'd envisioned. Me, I just wanted to be in street clothes and have the chance to go on a long walk. I was grateful she'd been able to see the corps, but caught completely off guard, my drum corps life was now messing with my personal one.

We needed a moment alone, where I could have time to tell her how much I missed her, find out how her summer was going, and reconnect with the one person I knew was genuinely happy to see me, but with only a sliver of time before departing the stadium, our conversation was clunky and disjointed. She'd be heading back to Iowa City as soon as we packed up our equipment. Despite the promise of a long follow-up phone call, I felt cheated having to get on the bus so soon after seeing her. It was as if our meeting hadn't even happened, and for the first time all summer, I questioned my decision to march.

Arriving in La Crosse Sunday afternoon, we were given a much needed day and a half to reset. While it was left unspoken, everyone knew the remainder of the season would be a full-bore, non-stop push to August's World Championships. A solid prelim run at Whitewater had us in sixth place with a 74.55, but with one step forward there were two steps back and we were once again a half a point behind the North Star. Our disappointment was momentarily tempered by having narrowly edged the Crossmen, Bridgemen, 27th, and Cavies, but fifth through tenth place were packed within a narrow two-point spread. Madison, seemingly stuck in a July rut, was in fourth, having narrowly lost to the upstart Guardsmen. Even more improved than the Guardsmen, the Spirit of Atlanta took prelims with an 81.65, a half a point better than Phantom.

Prelim scores were always fickle, and Saturday evening's finals provided a more telling picture of relative rankings. Even with a decent performance to a packed house, we'd dropped to ninth place, barely beating the Cavies. Back on their home turf, Madison had pulled themselves up by their spats to overtake the Guardsmen for third place. Phantom's 85.9 performance destroyed Spirit by three points and kept DCI's Midwest Championship tightly in the grips of a Midwestern corps. Their victory proved once again they'd be serious contenders for August's World Championship.

Without any of the Western corps in the mix, we were in a rather tenuous position. In four weeks we'd be heading into Birmingham, Alabama for DCI's World Championships, and as far away as it was, we had a much longer way to go with our show. With GE and execution scores lagging, I contemplated how the staff would address the inherent issues in our show design.

IN SPACE NO ONE CAN hear you scream, but in La Crosse, just about everyone can.

By late afternoon on Monday I'd finished my domestic chores. Immediately my mind began swirling with racing drum corps thoughts, motivating me to considered a host of ways to slow them down. A few members had talked about going to see the new sci-fi flick, *Alien*, but I'd been abandoned by my Iowa buddies, who were hanging out with their newfound friends, so I called Deb. With her boyfriend working a night shift, and me earnestly convincing her this wasn't a date, we drove to the downtown theater and discovered a long ticket line forming out front. *On a Monday night?* Closer examination revealed they were almost all Blue Stars with the same diversion in mind.

What fun. It was like we'd rented out the theater for a private screening. Having just come off tour, there'd been no spoilers as to the nature of the flick, and the end result was nearly a hundred thoroughly terrified Blue Stars. When the toothy little sperm-shaped extraterrestrial exploded out of the dude's chest, we jumped like startled babies, and from the rear of the theater, Tippett shrieked like an abducted four-year-old. Catching our collective breaths, just like the poor space traveler playing host to the incubating alien, the entire house busted their guts.

The flick had Deb scared shitless—alright, I was too—and she left deep red nail marks in my arm, and me questioning my choice for a movie partner. However it was the perfect distraction, as drum corps thoughts were now light years away, and afterwards all we could talk about was the beautiful simplicity of the horror house plot, Sigourney Weaver's incredible performance as Ripley, and the completely terrifying monster that she'd expertly dispatched.

Thankfully, no sci-fi nightmares disturbed my sleep, and Tuesday morning broke with high pressure, light breezes, dew-topped lawns, and a royal-blue sky, all complimented by those well-defined, puffy, white clouds. Cool enough to require my army surplus pants, I completed my practice wardrobe with a white Old Style T-shirt and tennies, slammed a toasted PB&J, and joyfully drove Frank and Nelson out to practice.

The daytime rehearsals were scheduled at the local high school across the river in La Crescent, Minnesota. It was a much better facility than the Oktoberfest grounds, and the stadium's elevated press box provided the staff with a decent view for cleaning drill and music.

Fully recovered from our tour, I was ready to climb back into drum corps mode. How could I not be? On a day like today, how could anyone not be? All we had to do for the next two weeks was practice our butts off and get better. But not everyone was in my same great mood. Arriving early, a few members were getting their equipment off of the truck and milling about, and as I headed over to the truck to get the podium, I was intercepted by a visibly distraught Ronbo.

"Um, Mike, can I talk to you for a second?" Nervously he scratched the light blonde stubble on his face. "Man, I can't believe what I did…I don't have my horn. Yesterday, I got it out to practice, and when I finished, I forgot to put it back on the truck. Wolfie's going to kill me…is there any chance you could run over to corps hall and get it?"

"Ronbo, Ronbo, Ronbo," I chided, trying to lighten the mood, "I'll ask him, but realize you just volunteered for luggage loading duty to start second tour." After seeing him starting to relax, I joked, "It's probably too much of that good California weed…you know what that does to short-term memory."

Not watching his reaction, I went over to Hill and asked if I could leave during warm-ups. He was pretty easygoing about the whole thing—sunshine will do that, plus it's hard to get mad at a kid who'd never seemed to stop practicing.

Jumping into my little yellow car, I dialed up some oldies on the radio, and took off. Windows down, Beach Boys turned up, blue skies and sunshine above, and nothing to concern myself with other than drum corps for the rest of the summer—yep, I was definitely cresting the arc of some good, good vibrations.

Cruising back over the river to La Crosse, the route took me through the serene backwater lakes and sloughs of the floodplain, and eventually crossed two bridges on the main river channel that was severed by Baron Island. The island was filled with swamp white oaks and blooming wild flowers on either side of the road, and the lush vegetation added more colorful layers to the gorgeous day. I cranked up the radio another notch.

Over the music, my peripheral senses detected a faint 'tick' on the side view mirror and a dark streak that flashed off to my left. I glanced around the driver's side of the interior. Nothing unusual, I went back to mindlessly tapping out rhythms on the steering wheel. Back in town, I headed north along the east side of the river to corps hall, then parked the car across the street from the old brick building in one of the many spots facing Riverside Park.

Taking only a few steps into the street, I was smacked hard by a searing burn on the calf of my left leg. So hot was the pain, I scrambled to pull up my pants' leg, revealing a huge red welt that looked like I'd taken a direct hit from a ninety mile an hour fastball. Borderline hysteria instantly set in, and I made a dash to the corps hall for water, or ice, or even…Moe. Three paces more and WHAM, it happened again. This time on my inner thigh. *Aaargh! What the fuck?* Beside myself, I pulled down my army fatigues right in the middle of the road, discovering a second giant welt. Confusion joined the pain and panic, and thoughts of being entirely consumed by invisible flames flashed through my mind.

Hiking up my pants, I made it as far as the building's entryway before a third blast—*are you kidding me?* This time it was in a place no guy (not even your worst enemy) should ever have to take a hit. Crazy with searing pain, my mind whirled: *Was I mortally wounded? Was I going to be left sterile, or worse…impotent?* Once again, I dropped trou and found my own little horrific sci-fi movie playing out between my legs. Right there in the front row was the mother of all furry yellow and black aliens probing my underwear, angrily discharging her venom into my left one!

I flicked the bumble hard onto the floor, where she wildly buzzed in tight circles. Stomping once, I raced up the steps to the corps' office, yelling for help. "Moe, where are you…Moe? A huge bee flew up my pants and stung me forty times, and it stung me in my nuts!" (Okay, so I exaggerated the number of stings a bit.)

A baffled Moe scurried around the corner from his office to find me hopping around holding my jewels. Realizing it was no joke, his slow Southern accent picked up speed. "Oh dear gawd Mycole, we gots to get you to the hahspitall."

At the bottom of the stairs lay the flattened, furry Frisbee, now looking even larger than I'd remembered. Moe saw it too. "Dear lawd, is that what stung you? You'd better bring it with you, in case the doctor needs to see what kind of bee it is."

Wincing, I held the flattened fur ball in one hand and my crotch in the other, while Moe did his best imitation of an ambulance driver. In a busy emergency room, the two of us filled out forms, and during the extended wait for the doctor, I received no anesthetics or solace. Ten minutes later, a little nun with perfect skin and wire-rimmed glasses came by, asking, "And what brings you into the emergency room today?"

Frazzled, my filter was gone. I held out my hand and said, "See this bee, well it flew up my pants and stung me in the balls."

Two young EMTs leaning up against a nearby wall simultaneously laughed while cringing with sympathy pain, but the diminutive nun just blinked and calmly said, "I see, I'll get you a little cup for it?"

Well I thought, at least someone has some empathy. She soon reappeared with one of those clear plastic urine specimen containers, and Moe and the EMTs were no longer able to hold anything back.

Ten long minutes later, we were called into the examining room by a nurse, who looked like she was way too old to still be a nurse. Handing me a folded paper gown, I told her I'd rather just pull down my pants when the doctor arrived. As stern as she was old, she insisted on the gown, stating definitively, "Oh no you won't. You put this on now…You mustn't expose yourself to me."

I retorted, "Well you don't even have to be in here when the doctor examines me."

"That's not how it works," she said, then once again insisted, "now put this on."

She left the room, and Moe continued his sustained chortle while I got undressed. It took another quarter of an hour before the doctor appeared with my very own Nurse Ratched trailing behind.

Reading the admit form, he snorted a laugh, saying, "Huh, looks like you got a little tangled up with a bee…that must've hurt."

"Yeah it did, and it still does," I said. "It evidently hit the side mirror of my car and popped in…then crawled up my pant leg." Attempting to sound scientific, I told him, "I know it stung me at least three times. Once in my calf, thigh and left testicle."

"Ouch. Well, lay back, and let me have a look."

Once I was horizontal, he took the bottom of the paper gown and threw it back over my head. There I was, stark naked except for my face, which was now covered by the gown. Fuming and humiliated, all I could visualize was that nurse saying how I wasn't supposed to expose myself to her—*yeah, right.* Meanwhile, I could hear Moe doing his worst to stifle a Southern snicker.

A moment later, the doc chuckled, "Hah! Yes, I can see right where it got you. Good thing you're not allergic, otherwise you'd be blown up as big as a basketball…you shouldn't have any problem with this…go home and put some ice on your stings and you'll be good to go."

By the time we checked out of the ER, most of my discomfort was gone and I told Moe to drive me directly out to practice. Walking back onto the field, a miffed staff and full corps stared us down, and the bright sunshine now seemed to be mocking me.

Moe never stopped a practice, but today he did, asking everyone to "gather 'round and take a seat." Staff and members at first seemed puzzled, then visibly worried and murmurs rippled through the ranks.

Once everyone was quietly seated, Moe began, "This mawning I was in my office working, when suddenly, I heard this whoopin' and hollerin'. I walk out of my office and what do I see, but our drum major dancin' around like John Travolta in Saturday Night Disco Fever…"

Telling the story like only he could, with the deceased bumble as the antagonist, and me as its pain riddled protagonist, he left nothing out; coloring it in completely with brilliantly fashioned exaggerations of swelling, swearing, nurses, and nuns.

His epic tale never seemed to end, providing a nonstop laugh fest. Our Southern belle guard members blushed, and drummers traded their sticks for fists, pounding the ground and begging him to stop for fear of wetting themselves. My Emerald Knight buddies looked at me with laughing but sympathetic eyes, as if to say, "Did that really happen?" With my acute pain and embarrassment now distanced by time, even I had to admit, Moe's clever embellishments were pretty damn funny, and I think the only person who wasn't laughing was the hornless Ronbo.

Moe eventually concluded with, "...and that, mah friends, is the true story of Mikey and the Bee."

Thunderous applause filled the little stadium, and my rank instantly rose to that of a true Blue Star. Go figure—baptism by a bumblebee. I know it sounds weird, but with Moe's comedic storytelling, I'd become a worthy character in Blue Stars' folklore. Interestingly, it came with acceptance, and even a modicum of respect from the vets, simply from my ability to take a joke...albeit, a painful one.

A week later we'd settled into our all day practice pattern. With no competitions and little change in weather, the long July days flowed into one another and the only real variations came in the form of our program design and the addition of several new members.

As difficult as the first tour had been, it was harder on some than others. One stoner French horn player cried uncle, and two guard members were taken out, one from mono and another by an appendicitis attack shortly upon return. Management and members networked to find worthy replacements, and driving from one practice site to another, I gave a ride to Dawn Christianson. Attractive, she had short light brown hair, and striking, sparkly blue eyes that were paired with the serious look of a seasoned, no-nonsense veteran.

My instincts were proven right when she told me her story. Joining the Blue Stars' cadet corps as a ten-year-old in '68, she'd gone on to march both as a flag and rifle through '75. A steady boyfriend distracted her for several years, but upon learning we were in a tight spot, she took leave from work, cashed in some savings bonds, and decided to give it one last spin. A drum corps dynamo, she'd learned the drill and most of the guard work in only three days. With our ages and extensive drum corps experience as a common denominator, we became instant friends.

That was one thing about the top competing corps: come August, you almost never saw a hole in the drill. So extensive were the networks of alumni, they could usually find someone, or at least someone who knew of someone that was capable enough to fill the spot. So like last year, barring any more illnesses or mishaps, we'd have a full corps come second tour.

Given our penchant for partying, the challenge would be the "barring" part. Tuesday's special at the Rustic Inn, one of the corps' favorite watering holes, had "four for a buck night." The little green bottles were seven-ounce hand grenades of Blatz Light Cream Ale that went down really easy after a hot day of practice, and while beer wasn't exactly my flavor, I didn't find it too much of a burden to toss back a few, but the evening's planned agenda turned out to be completely different from the usual cool-down.

This being Wisconsin, a UWL guys' dorm had made the Rustic's promotion a worthy drinking challenge, and their record stood at a daunting one thousand and twelve bottles. When practice ended, Schultzie, having previously ensured there'd be a plethora of cold ones waiting, stood in the center of our end of practice huddle, boldly proclaiming, "Tonight the record will fall!"

There were just a couple of hurdles standing in our way: one, it was already 9:30, and two, we could only muster up fifty-six guys and gals to take on the task. The good news was that if everyone pulled hard on their fair share, it'd come out to about eighteen bottles apiece, which was only four dollars and fifty cents' worth? *Heck, anybody could consume four dollars and fifty cents' worth of beer, right?*

Even carrying my mom's Milwaukee-bred genetics, I was still a novice beer drinker. While my first few dollars' worth went down smoothly, the third dollars' worth—uh, not so much, and by the time I was looking at my thirteenth bottle, I decided that the remaining thousand would be up to the other fifty-five Blue Stars. So in bloated awe, I furtively nursed my last one, as I watched my Wisconsin brethren guzzle ale, after ale, after...ale. Some were so certifiably committed, they'd stagger into the alley, purge themselves, and come back for more. It was a glorious demonstration of immoderation fueled by single-minded focus. Brute sized garbage cans had been strategically placed around the bar in preparation for the evening's dare, and they gradually filled to the sound of breaking bottles and jukebox rock.

Nearing two a.m., everyone's favorite Southern Bastard, French horn player Jody, stood wavering on a chair. Holding up the record-breaking beer like it was the Olympic Torch, he was assisted by Roxy the bartender. As they shared the task of snuffing it out, the place went up for grabs.

All choices have their consequences, and the problem with a two a.m. last call is a nine a.m. first call for brass sectionals the following day. Amazingly, everyone arrived promptly, but the morning sun at Riverside Park appeared to be shining a little too brightly on some rather green record setters, and Wolfie, knowing full well of our escapades, quipped, "How 'bout a lap around the park to cleanse the spirit?"

Cleanse the spirit, or cleanse the spirits, I wondered? Off we went, and as impressed as I was by the record-setting evening, it was nowhere nearly as impressive as that half mile jog around the park. There's no denying the diaphragm muscles on DCI caliber brass players, and for the first time in my life, I lay witness to a profusion of arching streams of projectile vomit.

Fortunately, thirteen bottles was apparently my lucky number. I hadn't heaved since I was eleven, and I was grateful that my streak remained intact.

Ten years prior, on an icy winter Saturday after YMCA swim practice, I'd made the mistake of staying for lunch. The Y's youth leader was promoting an All-You-Can-Eat Bean Feed, where for just fifty cents, my teammates and I could indulge in multiple paper plates full of sloppy beans and weenies that we greedily mopped up with Wonder Bread butter sandwiches and washed down with gallons of lip-staining red Kool-Aid. Hungry from the workout, I ate way too much, way too fast, and later that day, I'd returned each little bean and tube steak back into the kitchen sink, regretfully learning that you don't buy all-you-can-eat beans and weenies, you only rent them.

Having been out of barfing practice for quite some time, I was blown away by the experienced resiliency of our vets. Taking a mouth cleansing rinse from the park's water fountain, they staunchly returned to their place in line just as if it were part of their normal morning routine. Damn, ain't drum corps grand!

The following day's *La Crosse Tribune* had a small notice in the personals section from the proprietor of the Rustic Inn. It simply stated: *Congratulations Blue Stars, on your Rustic Inn record setting 1013 Blatz Light Cream Ales.* FCO indeed!

When all else fails, fire the guard instructor, buy some bulk reams of tinsel, and break out the umbrellas.

A lot had happened in the two weeks before DeKalb's DCM Championships— it had to. The tight competition meant if things didn't change we'd be sitting out the evening's finals in Birmingham. So chase after it we did. The guard bid a tearful goodbye to their caption head as a new pair of guard instructors were flown in from New York. They were of Winter Guard International fame: Brady Rouse was best known for his smart choreography, and his assistant, Bruce McCready, was a cleaning machine. Together, the "Killer Bs" had turned a New York high school color guard into one of the premiere competitive winter guards in the country and Dr. K was hoping they'd work their magic on us.

Along with filling the gaps in choreography and cleaning the old work, newly sewn silks were adorned with silver tinsel streamers on both ends of the telescoping flag poles. The tinsel was also thickly layered on a hand-sized wire ring that was designed to be a sparkling sash for the brass players. Tucked into their cummerbunds, the ring was easily removed to add flashing hand accents at the conclusion of "Birdland."

Additional visuals to the drum solo also eliminated the program's only rifle work, as the rewrite had guard members reprising the use of our large blue and red-paneled umbrellas. It marked the fourth straight year we'd used the props and while not as impressive as the rifle toss, it was a trademark effect that was easier to execute.

The classic white bucks were also discarded. Historically they'd highlighted our outstanding marching technique, but now were sadly exposing too many of our rookies' errors, and it was mandated that the brass and percussion would purchase black shoes. To that end, the corps continued to break down every facet of the drill, with Old Man Frank's method of precisely-practiced repetition. Now it was my turn to enjoy watching Jordan, Nelson, Lyman, and Frank feel the jabs of his wry rants.

JULY 28TH ~ DEKALB, ILLINOIS

Standing next to Tippett warming up our brass arc before DCM prelims, our recent endeavors were noticeable in a steadily improving brass sound and our overall appearance, and it wasn't just from the shoes and tinsel sashes. Prior to the first tour, some of the horn players followed Schultzie's lead by getting a basic-training haircut. With the summer's heat turned up both on and off the field, more brass and percussion players had joined in. Noticing some of my hair was already starting to abandon ship, I declined their offer to shave off what was left, but the two dozen members who did called themselves buzz heads, and dressed in uniform, they had a fairly intimidating presence. A few variations on a theme had even appeared, with one lead sop shaving all but a five-point star on the crown of his head, and our big bass drummer complemented his steely-eyed appearance with a truly frightening, Travis Bickle *"You talkin' to me?"* mohawk.

Additionally, six euphoniums had been purchased and were now dispersed throughout the bari section. These were twenty-two pound, two-valve, conical beasts that made baritones look more like sopranos. Adding another layer of depth to our sound, they required vast amounts of air to play and plenty of strength to hold them up. Luckily, we had the players to make it happen, and Schultzie, with his shaved head, biker mustache, and monstrous new horn, looked like he could single-handedly take down the walls of Jericho.

My DeKalb prelim performance was a vastly different experience from last year's embarrassing debut. The show was tight, and from the podium I thought the new stuff came off pretty well. Enjoying my post-performance adrenaline rush, my hypervigilance caught sight of an older man in a fedora who surprisingly looked a lot like my Uncle Joe, and as sightlines expanded, I suddenly recognized my pear-shaped Aunty Em. Then, holy crap, here comes my mom, dad, brother, and sister-in-law pushing a stroller with my new little nephew. Unbelievable. In my mind, they'd been thousands of miles away and suddenly here they were, all smiles and hugs.

My brother had taken a leave from his post in Germany, flying back to the states to show off his new son to the in-laws, and Dad took some vacation as well. I'd resigned myself to the fact that my parents and brother were never going to see me perform, and their surprise had me swelling with gushy family pride. Introducing them to Moe, he asked how long they were around and told them if they came to the Horicon show, I could join them for the two days off we had before leaving on tour. Once again, I'd miss Puker, but what the hell, I hadn't seen my brother in two years and my parents since last winter break.

The unexpected Piskel family reunion at
DCM championships in DeKalb

DCM's prelims had us in fourth place out of the twenty-one competing corps. Scoring a 79.35 validated the three weeks' worth of work we'd crammed into ten days, but everyone else had also improved, and we lagged behind the G-men by over two points. Cavies were almost two points behind us, and the hapless Kilties could only muster a 68.4. Phantom won prelims with an 85.3 and Madison had now closed the gap to less than a point.

In uniform waiting to board the buses for the night show, I saw a disturbing cluster of small black flies circling overhead. I shooed them away but moments later they'd reassembled, and I felt conspicuous, taking note that no one else seemed to be suffering from the same plague. Arriving at the stadium, it was only a matter of minutes before they seemingly had caught back up with me. While not as prophetic as a murder of crows, the whole thing was unsettling, and I couldn't figure out if they were attracted to the white uniform or were trying to tell me something. Thankfully, entering the lights of the field they suddenly evaporated—maybe it'd all been in my mind.

A strangely subdued stadium full of fans sat on their hands during our prosaic performance. It cost us, as the energetic Cavaliers, spurred on no doubt by the partial crowd, edged us out of fourth place by three tenths of a point. *Argh!* I couldn't help but compare our show with theirs, and I simply refused to believe they were better than us, yet tonight's recaps showed that other than marching execution, we fell to them in every caption. *Could that have been what the little black bugs had been trying to tell me?*

Our quest for eighty points would again have to wait, at least until tomorrow. The one positive from the evening was that progress was definitely happening and we were closing the gap on the Guardsmen. Whitewater had them a full six and half points above us, but tonight it was down to less than two. With more potential to explore, our season wasn't close to over.

Phantom was the only corps whose score improved from the afternoon, increasing their spread over Madison by more than three points, and while I was sure home field advantage didn't hurt, they were definitely on a mission of redemption. Their stark white helmets and military appearance aligned with their classically inspired show that was big, loud, angry, and no doubt conceived when they were still very pissed off about last year's second place. All three phases of the corps were incredibly strong, and even the subtle moments of their performance came at the audience in waves of intensity.

Their guard work was just that—work. And what arduous work it was, just watching them tired me out. Having destroyed all comers during their championship winter guard season, they continued to hang on to that same aggressive ferocity. They didn't bother with choreography, unless you count stiff legged goose steps, kicks, and rigid bows as dance moves. Rifles and flags were cleanly spun with baton-like speed and their collective, near perfect execution, was bolstered by sheer Amazonian strength. Their unique style had them finishing many of the moves with definitive snaps that could decapitate any distracted judge.

Phantom's horn line was filled with double tonguing sopranos, ripping French horns, all supported by a robust lower brass section, while their spotless and demanding percussion arrangements kept pace with the rest of the corps. If anyone was going to challenge the California corps in Birmingham, it would once again be Phantom, and watching them perform, I wasn't so sure I'd want to be a judge that put them in second.

~ ∾ ~

This year's version of Horicon's Marsh Days had us in a lineup with six other corps, but Phantom was the only other DCI member. Like last year, Hill loosened the reins on the brass line, and armed with euphoniums and two months of Chop Suey, we lobbed heavy artillery into the jam-packed little stadium. The intimacy of the venue sandwiched my podium between our huge sound and the enthusiastic crowd. It was an amazing place to be for a drum corps show, and I reveled in it.

My now-familiar and disconcerting little cluster of preshow flies had somehow accompanied me to Horicon, but unlike last year, finale wasn't quite the same buggy blitzkrieg on the field. Maybe being downwind from our brass line, we'd blown all the little mother-suckers back to the swamp. Also unlike last year, we didn't break eighty points. Managing just a 78.65, we placed second, and Phantom took home the "Mosquito Bowl Trophy" by almost six points.

After the show, I gathered my gear from the gym and joined my parents for the short ride back to my aunt and uncle's house in Brookfield. After a little catching up, I began to realize my time with them might not be all family fun, as mom went straight into Anita mode.

"Mike, I was cleaning up the house—" *Of course she was.* "— and I found a pan with grape seeds, stems, and ashes in it under the sofa. Do you know what that is?"

Shit! Had I really left that there? I wasn't expecting my parents to come back home before I did, but it was really stupid to leave out the tray I used to clean some buds and roll a joint. I guess I wasn't immune from the same short term memory loss that had infected Ronbo.

Too exhausted to provide any brilliant excuse, I came clean. "Mom, they aren't grape seeds, they're from some pot a friend and I had before leaving for La Crosse. Sorry...it's no big deal."

"What? I don't understand...you smoke that stuff? You know how bad that is for you? We didn't raise you to be like that...Dad and I don't do that. What possesses you to do that?"

In retrospect, I probably should have gone with the grape seeds. I wasn't quite sure which of her questions to address first, so downplaying it as best as I could, I replied, "Mom, it's not like I do it a lot, and it isn't exactly like you think. I'm sorry for disappointing you."

My sullen dad interjected, "Remember what I told you, if I ever caught you doing drugs?"

"Yeah, I know," I sighed, "you'd kill me." Not wanting to engage in any close quarters combat, I left it hanging there.

Mom then instantly switched gears, caustically saying, "Well, when I was cleaning up your little mess, I couldn't find the Electrolux. I'd like to know where you put my vacuum? You didn't take it up to La Crosse…did you?"

Classic Anita. Here I was being shamed about my marijuana use, and next thing I know, I'm being cross-examined about household appliances. Of course I'd taken it, I'd adopted my mom's domestic routines ever since she showed my little four-year-old self how to properly make the bed and clean a room. Nowhere to run, I felt like I was in an episode of the *Twilight Zone*: "Imagine if you will, a young man trapped in the back seat of a car, desperately trying to explain his blatant stupidity…."

Mindful of her tone, I replied, "Yeah, I have it. I didn't think it'd matter with you being gone, but the upright is still there."

"I don't care about the upright, I want *that* vacuum cleaner. You had no right to take that with you. Let one of your friends bring one. That Electrolux is expensive. It could get broken…when we drop you off, I'm taking it back."

Huh? No wonder I constantly struggled with any attempt at being cool. I assumed her frustration was covering up her disappointment over the realization that her son was a dope-smoking fiend. Who knows? Again, I didn't push it—you don't always get to pick your moments, but you do get the choice on how you react to them. An apprentice magician in the making, I did my best to redirect their focus, pointedly asking about Yugoslavia and sharing my summer marching experiences. Thankfully, for the time being, it worked.

As much as I wanted to be with them, our spontaneous family reunion was poorly timed, and I was feeling like a guy who'd spent all day preparing his favorite meal, and after finally sitting down to enjoy it, was interrupted by a sudden knock at the door. From the dark back seat of the car, I realized what I really wanted was to be asleep on a bus that was silently humming its way back to the world's largest six-pack.

The two days off were the slowest part of the summer, and despite the rest and reconnection with family, I wasn't able to shed my drum corps skin. Here I was, having my first grilled steak of the summer, and all I could think about was that I needed to be back in La Crosse. It was like having one of those drawn-out frustrating dreams—the kind where you realize you were signed up for a class that you hadn't been attending all semester, and right then, I would've gladly traded the juicy rib-eye for a beer and a brat.

The following day's three hour car ride back to La Crosse was a different kind of hell, and now I was thinking, *Maybe that's what the little black specters of doom had been trying to tell me?* Wedged between my parents in the front seat, I sat silently as Mom continued to rail against the evils of the devil's lettuce, while my brother played his part perfectly, boxing my ears from the back seat, and laughingly saying, "Yeah dipshit, what were you thinking?

With my parents, brother's family, and the Electrolux all safely on their way to Iowa, I was relieved to learn that Monday's Puker had been deemed a great success, and that no one had been incarcerated or hospitalized. Judging from the sordid stories Jordan and Nelson shared, maybe it was a good thing I'd spent time doing penance in my parent's car. We'd be leaving for Minneapolis at eight a.m. tomorrow, and despite my roommates' morning hangovers, we had a lot to do in preparation for the tour.

Sans vacuum, Jordan, Nelson, Lyman and I were spending the afternoon packing up and cleaning. We had to be completely out of the apartment before we left on tour, and as we were finishing up the phone rang.

Photo courtesy of Tammy Muck

Schultzie and Dr. K share an Old Style moment at the 1979 Blue Stars Puker.

Answering, I heard Frank's mom. "Hello Mike, is Frank there? I need to speak with him."

"Oh hey Mrs. Gorman, Frank's not here. He's out getting lunch with a friend."

She icily responded, "Oh he is, is he? Well, just have him call me as soon as he gets back."

"Sure, no problem," I replied, "but you don't sound very happy...is everything okay?"

"No Mike, it's not," she said. "Evidently, Frank went to Perkins, and then took off, without paying the bill?"

I was completely befuddled. "Hunh...Mrs. Gorman, can I ask how you would know that Frank didn't pay for his lunch, when you're in Cedar Rapids?"

Sounding even more irritated, she explained, "Well, I got a call from the manager of the restaurant. It seems that when Frank was there, he left his dental appointment card out on the table, and after he left without paying, the manager called our dentist and got my number. He said he was going to call the police if Frank didn't show up to pay the check."

Pure Frank. I tried to stifle a laugh. "Hah...Mrs. Gorman, I'll take care of it. If there's a problem, I'll call you back."

"Thanks, but you tell that fool I still want talk to him before he leaves on tour. I'm so mad, he needs to hear it from me."

Chalk up yet another victim to short-term memory loss stupidity. This was going to be too much fun. Frank's faux pas provided the perfect vehicle to pull me from the despair of my parent's car ride and send me straight back into a summer of drum corps craziness. Along with the rest of the Iowa House, I couldn't wait for his return.

Only moments later, Frank sauntered in. Looking totally at ease, he joked, "Hey what's going on guys...you got the apartment ready for my inspection?"

Barely into the apartment, I grabbed him by his T-shirt and pinned him against the wall. Getting right up in his face, I yelled, "Frank you idiot, why didn't you pay your bill at Perkins?"

Small eyes instantly grew to fill in the large frames of his smudged glasses. "How'd...how'd you know I didn't pay my bill?" he stammered.

The other members of the Iowa House cracked up, and holding him there, I continued, "Because, you're so fucking stupid, you left your dental card on the table before you decided to dine and dash. You have no idea how pissed your mom is right now."

Frank bawled, "I must've left it there when I cleaned out my wallet, but Rock didn't pay for his bill either. I only did it to have some money left for tour. If I go back, I'll be almost broke...our bill's about thirteen bucks."

"More like twenty, with the tip you're going to leave. You'd better get going...and don't forget to beg for forgiveness on your pagan soul."

A forlorn Frank rechecked his wallet, shook his head, and sulked out of the apartment.

FRIDAY, AUGUST 10TH ~ BAYONNE, NEW JERSEY

"All things excellent are as difficult as they are rare."

~Baruch Spinoza

THAT'S WHAT IT SAID ON page one of the itinerary that Moe had passed out before leaving on our second tour. Now, inching our way through afternoon traffic to the Bridgemen's show, we were already at the tour's halfway mark. In less than a week we'd be lining up for prelims at Legion Field in Birmingham, and I was hoping we'd finally found some of that rare and difficult excellence.

~ ≈ ~

"National Tour," that's what Moe had dubbed it, but most of us just called it second tour, and while the majority of the time was spent heading east and then south, the first day had us going in the opposite direction for a show in Stillwater, a suburb of Minneapolis.

It seemed our show was going in the opposite direction as well. Maybe it was three days off, or perhaps there was still some hangover from the Puker. Whichever, the evening's performance was as rusty as our buses, and having finally met up with the Blue Devils and Santa Clara, we sobered to the reality that our 76.05 was eleven points back from the world's best. As for me, my reality included the return of my little black aerial escorts.

The next morning, we awoke to a delightful surprise. Moe and Doc had somehow procured enough cash to replace two of our buses with cool, quiet, smooth new rides. Sadly, the mixed nuts would still have to tolerate their roached coach. Regaining our easterly bearings, we left for Michigan City, Indiana, for a show that would live in Blue Star infamy.

Stately Ames Field was a cool little brick stadium near the shore of Lake Michigan, and the following evening it was packed with nearly four thousand fans watching Santa Clara edge out Spirit by a half a point. Once again, during pre-show warm-ups I watched as the cloud of flies circle above me like biplanes in a dogfight, and I wondered if I'd be cursed with their presence for the rest of the tour.

Despite our best brass performance to date, we finished a disheartening fifth out of the eight competing corps, suffering the dual frustration of not breaking eighty, and once again being routed by the Guardsmen. The result sent Hill into attack mode for the post-show critique, where he confronted his old Des Plaines Vanguard mentor, brass judge, Jim Unrath.

In question were the points awarded for musical analysis, and Unrath would have none of it, telling Hill it was a good score. Hill agreed but wouldn't back down. It wasn't the score he was disappointed with—rather, the spread between corps, and he made his case for reconsideration at future performances. Then things got grisly. Strong personalities verbally duked it out, and Wolfie never waned. Rearticulating multiple salient arguments in undeniably astute Don Hill fashion only raised Unrath's ire.

How dare this long-haired upstart mentee challenge him? Coming completely unglued, he tore the score from the bottom of the judges sheet, licked it, and stuck it on Hill's forehead, telling him, "You got the score…now you can wear it!"

Nostrils flaring, a seething Hill returned to the parking lot as we were packing up. Word spread, and brass and percussion assumed parade formation. With Terr-Terr and his scary-ass mohawk banging out a bass drum cadence, we marched back into the stadium, and in surprising solidarity, the members of Santa Clara's horn line joined us.

With most of the field lights off, long thin shadows were cast as we followed the dark cinder track to the critique staged in the end zone. Royer himself walked alongside us, spouting supportive statements regarding how sometimes young people need to show older people how to behave with dignity and class. Upon our reentry, the critique abruptly disbanded.

From there it was a late night run to Marion, Ohio for the U.S. Open. Losing an hour, we arrived at our housing with only time for a little more shut eye before the morning's prelims. It didn't matter. The now-aptly named

"Michigan City Incident" had lit a fire in all of us, and before heading onto the field, we gathered around a fully ticked-off Dr. Kampschroer. It was a short but motivating tirade, telling us how it was "time to stop pussyfooting around and break eighty."

Inspired, we obliged.

Prelims had us in fifth place out of the sixteen competing corps, and our 80.70 was only one point down from the Guardsmen. Getting ready for the show that evening, things were definitely looking up, and in doing so, I was relieved to see that my little escorts had finally gone AWOL.

In front of an enthusiastic full house, the evening's fun performance kept us in fifth place. While across the board scores had dropped, we continued to narrow the gap with the Guardsmen. With plenty more space and time for improvement, we were starting to have fun again, and with momentum on our side, I felt we could catch them by Birmingham.

The Blue Devils edged the Phantom Regiment by two tenths of a point to claim the massive wooden trophy topped with a cast metal screaming eagle. Realizing we'd no chance at a World Championship, I still hoped a Midwest corps could take the crown and wondered if Phantom had enough gas left to catch the Devils.

Two days later, I awoke to light streaking into a gym full of sleeping bodies. Laying there in my sleeping bag on the hardwood floor, I felt like I was playing strip poker with time and running out of clothes. Telling myself it didn't matter—*Just stay rooted in these last few days of summer and enjoy the game, you've worked too hard and sacrificed too much, not to get the most from it.*

There's nothing like the middle of a second tour to gain some perspective on how far we'd come. While the daily grind of my responsibilities was draining, I had to admit, some of it was getting easier. I was free from the curse of second guesses associated with self-doubt. Deb, JB, and I were now a fluid team, and with their support, tension from the vets had vanished. I'd fully assimilated into my role of Blue Stars drum major, and it seemed like everyone had finally found their place too. It had taken us most of the summer to bridge the performance gaps created from a weak offseason, but at long last, having achieved that cherished sense of family, we were finding our groove with our show and more importantly, with each other.

Checking my watch, I realized it was past time for Moe's morning wake-up call. I tiptoed my way through a maze of unconscious bodies to where he was sacked out, and lightly shook him. Startled, he jerked awake and asked me what the problem was. Together we quickly woke up the corps and headed off to Fort Washington, Pennsylvania.

With several shows in the area, we had the luxury of making the junior high school in Fort Washington our home base for the next four days, and at Thursday's show in West Chester, we thankfully put the seventies astern. Popping another eighty plus points, we were a close third to the Crossmen's 81 and the Bridgemen's 81.85.

That night I had the chance to observe the Bridgemen from the backfield stands, wondering why they'd dropped a notch from '78. The music selections for the first half of their show were a redux from their prior two seasons. Opener was '77's rendition from *Pagliacci*, with their drum major dressed as the sad clown, unabashedly conducting the conclusion while facing the audience. They followed that with last year's eerie "Spanish Dreams" and it was noticeably missing Diamond Jim's talent. Using last season's percussion feature, the brass and guard recapped their Bridgemen shuffle. While the crowd still dug it, I felt it lacked the creative spontaneity from the prior years.

The second half of their show was entirely new and initially somewhat perplexing. During their concert of "Boogie Woogie Bugle Boy," they embellished it with three hyperactive and patriotic Andrews Sisters, gyrating old school to loosely executed brass features. From there it just got desperate, as their freewheeling DM yelled, "One more time!" and the corps broke out into a kitschy version of Basie's "Jumpin' at the Woodside," a la *The Gong Show*. Plastering over poor intonation and musicianship with sheer volume, they distracted fans with some bizarre theatrics, including a fake female judge being manhandled by their own exaggerated version of Gene Gene the Dancin' Machine.

The last three minutes of their show was a Civil War Medley, and the guard switched out their rainbow silks for obvious interpretations of union and confederate flags. Staged around competing side one and two brass lines, the guard broke into battle front and center, where two sword wielding and badly-bearded gray and blue clad generals charged each other from opposite sides of the field.

Like a lobbed softball, it didn't take long to hit on Hoffman's genius, and I was positive that once they'd made Birmingham, they'd be rewriting American history. Pure pandering. I wasn't sure what to think but based on my '75 "Dixie" experience in Shreveport, I figured they'd bring down the house.

Riding our wave of increasing momentum, we were tireless and focused. It was what we do, and Hill and Tippett's combined efforts had the brass section finally catching up to the performance level of the percussion section. Miraculously, even "Strike Up the Band" was starting to resonate positively with our audiences, but a lot of our overall progress could be attributed directly to the guard. Having filled in the earlier gaps in choreography, now extensive cleaning by our new East Coast instructional team had raised our overall visual GE scores. Settling in nicely, there was only one last bit of guard work to rewrite, which Brady said would be "the piece de résistance."

All the rage, Zengali's 27th Lancers had introduced double flags to fill the field with pinwheels of color. It was a dramatic effect, and the Killer Bs thought an arc of thirty-six guard members surrounding our ensemble with pulsating spins for the last minute of our show would provide the perfect visual accompaniment. So throughout the first week of tour, Deb and a handful of guard members spent their limited free time cutting and sewing new green and orange silks with blue center panels. Now finished, they'd be unveiled in Bayonne.

Surprisingly, the Bridgemen's home show was a rather casual neighborhood affair at a local high school, and the raucous Friday night crowd that filled the stadium appeared to be well lubricated. Despite the small venue, there was nothing intimate about the evening and we did our best to satisfy the "higher, faster, louder," needs of the crowd, backed by the dramatic effect of our new guard work, but the real histrionics came during the finale.

Front and center, I was flanked on either side by Deb and JB, where we joined the 27th Lancers, Cavies, Scouts, and Crossmen drum majors. Killing time for show officials to crunch the last few scores, the announcer introduced the Bridgemen's drum major. Armed with a baritone, he attempted the National Anthem and the crowd reflexively rose to their feet. Only six identifiable, but poorly executed, notes into the first phrase, he embarrassingly stopped. Then audaciously laughing, he blew a few more indiscernible notes and cleared the spit from the horn. I cringed as ripples of sympathetic and/or intoxicated laughter ran through the crowd.

JB looked over at Deb and me saying, "Disgusting…that's the most unpatriotic thing I've ever seen…if he comes up to us, don't shake his hand."

Gritting my teeth, I quietly replied, "Have you looked at this crowd? They'll crucify us!"

No doubt considering her options, Deb remained silent.

Mercifully, his second attempt at the anthem was much better than his first. Cheesing it up, upon completion, he pumped his fist to the ripe, overly appreciative fans. That sealed it for me. There was no way I was pushing those buttons. JB was on his own.

Sure enough, as placements were announced, the cocky dude greeted each drum major with a smile and an outstretched hand. Listening to the scores, I puckered up a bit as the Cavies took last place, followed by the Crossmen, who had shockingly dipped below eighty, and we followed in third with a score of 81.15. *Not too shabby*—too bad I couldn't enjoy it.

After our salute, the Bridgemen's drum major went in for the handshake and JB sternly shook his head no. Turning back to the crowd, he shrugged, and stuck his hand out once more for emphasis. JB stared straight ahead in defiance. That started the scattered boos throughout the crowd—the boos, as in, "Boo, Boo Stawz. Po spahts, po spahts. Boo Stawz ahh po spahts…Boo, Boo Stawz."

Their pimped-out DM gave JB a sarcastic smile before moving over to me, where I quickly took the third-place plaque and reluctantly shook his hand. Deb followed my lead, but with the finger already out of the dike, the crowd would have none of it, and the finger was exactly what we were getting.

When Madison was announced in first place, we couldn't get back to the corps fast enough, and playing ourselves off the field, the crowd continued to hurl their Jersey-tinged verbal assaults, and I was relieved they were the only things thrown our way. A confused Moe met us in the lot and asked me what the hell that was all about.

The morning of the DCI East Regional Championship, we woke to cool temps and cloudy skies. A lengthy and intense practice the day before was spent cleaning the needy parts of our show and we were fired up to see its impact. Allentown would be our last significant competition before heading south, and the lineup included the entire East Coast contingency, along with a handful of other DCI member corps.

You perform like you practice, or so the saying goes, and our hard work was finally starting to pay off. Prelims went better than well, and it reminded me of the initial success the corps had in Allentown last year. There was something about this stadium and its fan base that made drum corps really fun.

Coming off the field, I caught voices from over the sideline fence, requesting an autograph from that amazing Italian drum major and outside the stadium I discovered the amusing comments had come from my dad's sister and her family. As a kid growing up, we seldom traveled out to Pennsylvania, and I was humbled that they'd made the trip down from Hazelton. They followed us back to our housing, where we shared some time and a picnic dinner, while hearing that we'd tied the Crossmen for fifth, earning a season high 83.3. Our score was also good enough to barely beat the Bridgemen for the first time since Midwest Prelims. JB loved it.

Misty rain and Allentown's urban renewal traffic slowed our commute back to the stadium for the evening's finals. The delay left the percussion section with just enough time to off-load equipment and reprise their DCI Midwest duck-waddle dash to the starting line. Maybe that was the secret to a loose relaxed performance, because for those thirteen minutes we were bringing it.

The seventh corps on, we were under the full effect of stadium lights. Wet chrome and tinsel twinkled like Christmas Eve. Other than Deb, JB and me, the corps took the damp field without our plumes, and the shiny helmets looked oddly naked, but tonight they'd keep water off serious faces.

The light rain was no match for us or the enthusiastic East Coast fans. In fact, it might have actually helped, as our final's performance glistened like a jewel cut with precision tools. Spurred on from the energy generated by receptive fans, our bluesy brass inflections during the opener's company front swung unabashedly, snares and tenors nailed "Birdland's" tight syncopation, and "La Fiesta" exploded into something otherworldly when Haynes pulled off a revised version of his solo that boldly climaxed into a raw, ear-piercing dramatic resolution. The fans were going completely bonkers, and it only continued to get better from there. Throughout "Strike Up the Band," perfectly flowing tempo changes formed coherent musical phrases, and during the guard's seated flag exchange they seemed oblivious to the wet field. Despite soaked uniforms and mud splattered legs, their execution was sparkling clean.

With a summer's worth of strength and conditioning, the corps stoked the fire of anticipation for our show's finale with "Children of Sanchez." Now expertly employing Tippett's technique of playing solidly through the phrases, the soprano line powered their way through the ending. Upon conclusion, the roar of the crowd had us realizing the emotional connection we'd been driving for all year. It was great to find "the zone" in the heart of drum corps country.

Me? Well, it was my best show too. Holding nothing back, I was unashamedly tripping on my ego. Immersing myself into each phrase of the music, I became lost in the emotions of our performance and the crowd's reaction, and my only disappointment came from the brevity of the moment.

Maybe it was just a timing thing—do anything repeatedly and you're bound to eventually get it right. After a year's worth of instruction and effort all crammed into three short months we finally did get it right. We were ordinary people, collectively doing extraordinary things, and as the sweat of our performance mingled with the evening's rain, it came together in a perfectly maxed out show. From the podium, it was truly spectacular.

With on and off showers, the finale was limited to just drum majors. In the back stands, small gangs from competing corps hung out in street clothes, segregated only by their corps jackets. As the scores were announced, three East Coast corps simultaneously spewed obscenities as the announcer had us solidly in fourth place. Crazy—we'd actually defeated the Bridgemen, North Star, and Crossmen by over a point, right in their own fucking backyard.

Sure, the Blue Devils had outdistanced the second place Scouts by almost six points, breaching the first ninety of the summer, but tonight, having earned the judges' acknowledgment for the subtle and not so-subtle complexities of our show, we too had reason to celebrate. Returning from the field, I joined other excited Blue Stars mingling in the parking lot; everyone was in a rocking good mood, and after climbing back on the guys' bus, we put its suspension to the test.

FRIDAY, AUGUST 17TH ~ BIRMINGHAM SOUTHERN COLLEGE

"In the works of man as in those of nature,
it is the intention which is chiefly worth studying."

~Johann Wolfgang von Goethe

It was one more of Moe's choice quotes sprinkled through our tour's itinerary sheets. Having now studied the Blue Stars for two seasons, there was absolutely no ambiguity in our intent. Mission-bound for excellence, we continued to grind out lengthy practices in the dripping heat of the South, and we continued to incrementally improve. Our last performance in Tifton, Georgia, we scored another season high of 83.7. Taking second to Madison, the consensus was that we were ready for Birmingham.

Bathed in the wonderful air-conditioned dormitory housing, I recognized several more similarities to last year's World Championship experience. Once again, we proudly boasted the prowess of two more individual events champions, as serious Southern Bastard Jay Pennisson, took the medal in the multi-percussion category, and Tom Nanni expanded his legacy with his number one disciple, cerebral Cliff DeArment, earning the keyboard title.

Exactly like last year, Moe had me rooming with another young third soprano, Sean McKinney. I guessed he must've appreciated the big brother instincts I'd carried over from the Emerald Knights. I did have some empathy for the kid and was proud he'd made it through the season. A young fifteen, Sean tagged along with an experienced brother and sister team who'd marched with the Salinas Silver Sabres. Throughout the season he reminded me of a nervous little squirrel foraging directly under the flight path of migrating raptors, and I was sure the summer had taken a lot out of him—hell, it'd taken it out of me, I'd dropped twenty-five pounds—and considering the kid was underweight when he arrived in La Crosse, I was surprised he hadn't already completely disappeared.

As dog-ass tired as I was, my little roommate had already beaten me to the punch, snoring so loudly, it sounded like someone was dragging furniture across the room. Tired but wired, I couldn't sleep anyway, and I kept ruminating over our eighth place World Championship prelim finish. *Eighth place— eighth place—not fantastic, then again, we were solidly in finals, and hadn't that been our main goal?* What I knew for sure was, it was a hell of a lot better than the Crossmen's results.

Those fickle prelim scores had them in thirteenth place, as in, "The Dreaded Thirteenth Place," where a mere two tenths of a point had sorrowfully put them out of tomorrow's big show. I didn't get it, here was a corps that was beating the Bridgemen, 27th Lancers, Cavies, and us for half the summer, somehow failing to make the night show. *What was it about that corps' annual August melt? Had the Troopers really improved enough to slip in front of them?* If so, it was a miraculous six-point upgrade in just four days. More likely their astonishing jump came from an early prelim slot, combined with their ability to somehow enter that elusive zone.

While we hadn't entered the zone, today's prelim performance was about as good as we could expect. However, focusing on my greater responsibilities, I'd felt none of the energy and excitement of Denver's prelims. In fact, the biggest sensation I had was pure, unrelenting fatigue, and I wasn't alone. We were all feeling it, as last year's heat in Denver was now accompanied with Spanish moss hanging humidity. It made every move feel like we were swimming in sand, and luckily for us, we were strong swimmers.

Going on just after one in the afternoon, we were in the thick of the heat and also the middle of the block of DCI member corps, yet the stands in Legion Field were only about half-full and the fans seemed to have already stagnated in the sticky air and were seemingly stuck in their seats. Getting only modest support, we plowed through the show, manufacturing our own excitement by summoning up the last of our adrenaline reserves. It was good enough for an eighth in percussion, tenth in brass, and tenth in GE, but black shoes, clean marching, and even cleaner guard work made up the difference. Finishing a strong sixth in M&M, helped push us to a season high 84.45.

As dictated by our FCO motto, we'd peaked exactly when and where we needed to, and the more I thought about it, the more it seemed like that was a pretty fair position. We'd become a damn good corps, unfortunately just not a great one. This year's show design was one where its ability to generate orgasmic excitement was slippery at best, and on a heavy, muggy day, in a huge, half-empty stadium, it had been all the more difficult to pull people to their feet.

Used with permission from
Sights & Sounds Inc., Publishers of
Drum Corps World

Resume march!
1979 World Championship
Prelims

The judges had us barely clipping the North Star and while we hadn't seen the Guardsmen since the U.S. Open, we took them by a full point. The Cavies and Troopers filled out the last two finals spots.

For the first time since the advent of DCI, every corps making finals had been there at least one time before, and the top three were a shuffled version from the prior two years. As most pundits predicted, the Blue Devils took prelims with a 91.75, and Phantom, down by a mere tenth of a point, followed closely in their wake. Santa Clara had yet to break ninety, and it'd be a challenge for them to repeat last year's victory. Spirit, 27th, and Madison were too far back to be contenders, so tomorrow's drama would come from the choice between menacing classical music or lush wide-open jazz. Frankly, since we weren't part of the mix, I really didn't care. Tomorrow we'd be performing in front of thirty thousand fans and take part in a live four-hour PBS broadcast with Maynard accepting an invitation to do color commentary, as far as I was concerned that'd be good enough.

Moments before taking the field, I stood behind the guard in the darkened tunnel near the back field entrance. The North Star's show reverberated through the walls, as a solemn Don Hill approached.

"Mike, you did a good job this year...big crowd out there, there'll be a tendency to rush. Don't do anything different from how you've done it all year, and we'll be fine...you doin' okay?"

I assured him that I had it all under control, but the intensity in his voice initiated another release of adrenaline and I welcomed the familiar buzz that thankfully overshadowed the clinging fatigue from my shitty night's sleep. Confident and psyched, I had this. At least, I felt like I did—*I'd been in big shows all season, why should this one be any different?* Moments later, a show official, armed with clipboard and stopwatch, signaled us onto the field.

Moving out of the dark chute and into the bright field lights revealed the concert side of the double decked stadium now completely packed with 32,000 fans—we were rock stars once again. Over a hollow thumping in my chest, I focused on Hill's words and purposefully slowed down our pre-show preparation. Once set in our opening formation, I heard Brandt Crocker's iconic voice, "Drum Major Mike Piskel, is your corps ready?"

Facing a dozen silks with anxious eyes, I gave them a knowing smile before giving the command that sent their flags spinning. Turning on count, and presenting my acknowledging three-part salute, the guard synchronized their move with a fanned-out arc of flags behind me. Framed like a picture, I took it all in until hearing Crocker's response echoing across the field, "Blue Stars, you may enter the field in competition." It was the best part of the evening.

With six blasts from center snare Randy Knox's police whistle, we were off and running, clipping along on the brighter side of our prescribed tempo, but after the company front's swinging ritenuto, the tempo settled in comfortably. From there, the opener was on autopilot. Cutting through the dank air, our brass sound was bright, robust, and tight, with inflections and phrasing that were as good as our finals at DCI East. Upon completion, I would have thought the bluesy tune would have connected more with the Alabama crowd, but evidently St. Louis wasn't quite far enough south, and despite our solid effort, we received only respectable applause.

Drum solo's catchy upbeat brass sextet, featured flag exchange, tinsel accents, umbrellas, and high-paced gunshot finish, sparked our first spirited ovation from the crowd. Settling in, we were gaining comfort with the time, place, and current carrying us along on the white-water rafting trip that was our show. Taking the plunge so many times, we were used to the g-forces associated with the rapids, fast drops and back eddies, but it was a quiet pool where I momentarily lost focus.

With a bank of a dozen large umbrellas spinning behind the percussion section, I retook the podium, and counted off the first four slow beats to "La Fiesta's" introduction. A dark cymbal roll preceded the suspenseful larghetto keyboard feature, during which the brass line began their slow march into concert formation. It was one of several spots in the drill where both sides of the horns were facing away from me, and Deb and JB's peripheral conducting roles were critical in coordinating the exposed pianissimo brass entrance.

Show after show, I'd made eye contact with Deb to bring in the side one horn line, but for reasons unexplained, I glanced once over to JB and then returned my focus to the mallet section. Upon the brass's entrance, I sensed our raft capsize in slow motion, and the wrinkle in time lasted for eight long counts.

Like a poorly-folded envelope, the corners didn't quite match up, initiating a dreadful chain reaction. As brass players came to an unsteady stop, marching intervals were compromised, and a bizarre side-to-side echo challenged a melody that was scored to build mystery and suspense. Standing on the podium gave me all the mystery and suspense I could take, and I felt like a raft guide frantically looking for the bobbing heads of his dump-trucked crew.

Damage done—it required immediate triage. Thankfully, the short phrase ended on a held chord, and preceding its release, I sharply conducted four downbeats of the upcoming tempo in hopes of regaining the necessary timing for the ensuing fortissimo attack.

Hitting the phrase with everything we had provided a wash of relief and returned our composure. I lamented my mistake, but it was behind us now, and as a corps we left it there. With our capsized craft now righted, we headed back down the river. By the end of the piece, Haynes' horn had once again brilliantly cut through the thick air, and hopefully it had blasted away any memory of the tempo tear.

Our extensive time on task paid off, and the rest of the show unfolded as intended. The guard's seated flag exchange and subsequent sit circle were executed perfectly. Combined with the solid ensemble work throughout "Strike Up the Band," we garnered multiple positive crowd responses. Then, being the last of three straight corps to perform "Children of Sanchez," I recognized the restless sounds from impatient fans behind me. Even with its challenging rhythmic intro and sorrowful mellophone solo, the audience's whispers depreciated it to that of a mere transition for the show's powerful Spanish coda.

During the last forty seconds of our performance, with the brass and percussion pushing towards the stands and the guard cranking hard on their double flags, we filled the stadium with a volume commensurate with the impact of a fist to the face. Trying to knock out the remaining frustration of a tough show for a tough crowd, we delivered repeated blows with a punishing wall of sound, and as I pushed the tempo, Deb and JB held on tight to the very end. Horns uniformly snapped down, the audience rose in seemingly requisite appreciation of our effort.

Turning around to salute the anonymous mass of faces, it was done. A good show, too bad not a great one. The journey had ended with some ripping class-four rapids, and unfortunately one unexpected hair-raising class five. Finding myself still in one piece, wasn't I supposed to be saying, "Damn that was fun! Let's do it again?" Yet the only voice I heard was Hill's, reminding me, *"Mike don't do anything different from how you've done it all year."* There'd be no forgetting this one. I was feeling a lot of stuff inside, but most of it was overshadowed by full-servings of relief that it was over and regret that it wasn't our best.

Drum corps is a hard religion. Head up, I followed the corps off the field.

Moe and our staff members quietly joined our circle formation behind the stadium, and because there was a lot of unspoken love in my second family, not one staff member mentioned the phasing. Instead, in Zen-like calm, they did their best to assuage the disappointment of a less than perfect performance. *Maybe it wasn't as bad as I'd imagined.* Evidently Hill and Tippett were actually pretty pleased with the overall brass performance, and Brady told the guard that they had indeed captured the moment with their best execution of the season. Briefed by Moe on the timing for the finale, we were dismissed to the back stands.

Catching the last minutes of the Bridgemen's show, I watched the revised version of history come to life, or should I say, death? The guard's mock battle ended with the Confederate general in attack mode, and the Union general in a fearful posture, after which, only rebel flags remained slightly upright. It took a beat for the crowd to recognize the significance, before losing their collective minds. Although my thoughts were muffled by the thunderous ovation, they clearly told me there was no way we were going to be beating them tonight.

It was hard watching a drum corps show from the back side of a stadium, and even harder to watch that. Sitting there, my mind wandered aimlessly throughout the remaining performances until the Blue Devils took the field. An entire summer of competitions, yet I hadn't seen a single one of their performances.

Setting up on the field, the Devils' mature appearance exuded class and lots of money well spent. The blue color palette ranges far and wide, and the cool blue of their richly-appointed cadet jackets fit somewhere between sapphire and the sea. Their traditional look was highlighted by white-ruffled tuxedo blouses and sparkling silver details. Pearl finish shells on the battery section completed their stunning appearance.

While Phantom came at the crowd with ferocious tenacity, the best description of the Blue Devils' on-field presence was huge, smooth, and laid back. Utilizing double and triple intervals as they spread across the field, they appeared twice the size of everyone else. Accompanying their ensemble was a fluid guard, whose equipment handling appeared to be expertly performed by one and perfectly mirrored by all the others. With gracefully controlled, straightforward guard work, they went about their difficult business with relative ease, and not one dance step.

Even from the back field, the blend of brass and percussion produced a studio-quality sound with impressive balanced dynamics, intonation, and tempo control. The crowd was digging them, and during their well-paced, contrived musical and visual impacts, they blew the house down. As precise as Phantom was, after watching the Devil's performance, I wished them good luck with all of that—they were going to need it.

~ ~ ~

Before heading back on the field, Deb asked if she could join me front and center for the awards ceremony. Confused, I hadn't assumed otherwise, and told her I wouldn't have it any other way. As far as I was concerned there'd be safety in numbers and I wanted all three of us together.

Informing JB of our plans, we killed some time goofing around rehearsing the salute that would acknowledge our score. It was obvious that JB had joined his age-out pals at a pub across the street from the stadium after the performance, and I tried to imagine them bellied up to the bar in their uniforms, downing multiple beers in front of bewildered barflies. Still somewhat compromised, I hoped the sights and sounds of the finale would sober him up for our last on field responsibilities.

With all twelve corps bathed in the bright lights of the stadium, Deb, JB, and I moved front and center to a spot on the end of the growing line of drum majors. Standing before the huge crowd and TV cameras, I felt the symptoms of anxiety creeping over me. With four corps all within a point and a half after prelims I knew the phasing error would come with significant cost, and I hoped we wouldn't be too embarrassed by the results.

After all the blah, blah, blah about what an amazing spectacle we made, and how the kids that make up drum corps are the future leaders of our country, Crocker announced the Troopers in last place with only a 77.9, the Cavies followed with a 78.5. Next, hearing the pause after a score of 83.05 was announced, my gut had the uncomfortable feeling it was going to be us, and sadly, Crocker confirmed it. Behind me, our guard's sit circle unfolded their flags to reveal a raised National Flag while we perfectly executed our salute. Then DCI's executive director, Don Pesceone, came over to shake hands. I was sure my face clearly bore the disappointment of falling two places, and in knowing consolation, he took my hand, and patted it three times as if my mom had just died.

North Star was appropriately announced a quarter of a point above us, and hearing the next score of 84.5, going to Madison, I was suddenly snapped from my self-pity. Only two points better than their score from back in DeKalb, I couldn't believe the placement, and neither could their obviously insulted drum major duo. Stepping out from the line of drum majors to salute the crowd, they held their pose for an obviously uncomfortable length of time.

After their silent protest, Pesceone avoided shaking hands. It was a good move on his part, as Madison's lead DM backed into line, and clearly let loose with the mother of all rhetorical questions, "What kind of fucked-up shit is this?"

Once again, it was crazy times front and center. Definitely the place to be, Deb and I tried not to lose it, while wondering if the comment had been heard on national television. I caught Crocker looking plaintively at his notes, then swallowing hard before he moved on with his announcement of the Guardsmen in seventh, followed by the Bridgemen, and 27th.

A three and a half point jump in scores put Spirit in fourth, followed by Santa Clara, whose fifth bottle dance in eight years couldn't slide them above third.

With the stage set, Crocker expertly conveyed the drama on his microphone, echoing, "In second place...with a score of 92.75..."

In that brief space between score and corps, I whispered over to Deb, "Phantom." Their score would end up being the second highest finals score in DCI history, yet this year it was somehow attached to a heartbreaking second place, now for a third year in a row.

With that, the Blue Devils won their third World Open Class Finals, scoring a record 93.55. As of now, the California corps had accounted for every DCI World Championship but one, and this year, there was little question of their superiority.

Walking backfield to rejoin our corps, it was *The Wide World of Sports* in living color. Right beside each other, the Blue Devils were caught up in the thrill of victory, breaking ranks, hugging, and high-fiving, while Phantom collectively grieved with body shaking sobs and streaming-tears in the agony of their defeat. Meanwhile, Madison fumed, Guardsmen and 27th celebrated, Bridgemen did, well, whatever it was the Bridgemen do, and the whole time Santa Clara remained unflinchingly classy.

For such a festive event, it sure seemed like there were a lot of miserable people on the field. Strangely, I found this atmosphere of despair oddly comforting but what I really wanted was to get off the field. As much as I loved drum corps, I suddenly felt like a high school senior come May; I was definitely ready to move on.

Passing in review, in the time-honored tradition, most of our age-outs had left their shoes on the field. The last notes of the Blue Stars' season poignantly came from our somber yet hopeful closer, and parading past the remaining nine corps, I watched JB maneuver himself to the end of the brass section. Stripping his gloves from his hands and throwing them to the ground, he faced the stands, raised up both arms, and gave the entire world an emphatic, double barreled, one finger salute.

Ouch! I felt for him. I knew having to fill the position of assistant DM wasn't the way he wanted his marching career to end, and I was positive this evening wasn't even close to how he'd envisioned it. Now with his inhibitions stripped free, I read the abject pain in this public act of frustration, and I hoped no one of consequence saw him.

Showers and bad pizza helped to shake off some of our malaise, but what many of us would have preferred was cold beer—or something much stronger. Unfortunately, there wasn't a drop to be found. Lyman joined the percussion section in taking our placement pretty hard. Banging on locker room walls and cursing up a storm, it was the most emotion I'd seen from him all summer, and I wondered if he'd had a less-than-stellar show, or if he was just lamenting the fact that it marked the season's end.

Lyman finally calmed down after Hill and Tippett gathered the brass line together, proudly telling them how we'd once again captured fifth place in overall brass. Considering where we'd started from and the number of newbies in our soprano line, it was an amazing achievement. Unfortunately, the remaining subcategories found us in ninth in both M&M and percussion, and only tenth in GE.

Hearing the scores reignited my thoughts of the phasing into concert, and I started playing a little "if only" game, before recognizing its futility. There were a lot more poignant aspects of the season to reflect on and commiserating with Dawn and a few other age-outs helped bring about a more tranquil closure to our marching careers.

Eyes stinging, bodies aching, and hearts slightly scarred, we got to the point where none of our conversations were making much sense, and I dragged myself back to the dorm room where even the snores of my little roommate didn't prevent me from diving headfirst into deep sleep.

The bus trip back to La Crosse was the perfect therapy to transition me out of my season-ending funk. Sleep will do that. Blissfully unaware of each passing mile, I took little note of the gradual change in latitude. Waking only briefly for pit stops and meal breaks along the route, I felt like a space traveler put in suspended animation for a lightyear journey, and pulling into the UWl parking lot, I never even felt the bus stop.

Outside, the Monday morning sun and much lighter Midwestern air woke me up, rejuvenating my spirit—I wasn't alone. Contagious upbeat moods beamed from everyone. Much like the farewell scene at a successful family reunion, we unpacked gear, snapped last minute photos, and made solemn vows to return for the Oktoberfest parade. Tippett gave me his patented bear hug before the comforting reminder that we'd soon be reunited back at Iowa, and I thanked Hill and Moe for a hell of a summer. Then seeking out Deb, Dawn, and JB, we said warm goodbyes.

Nelson and Frank shared their plans to spend a last day celebrating in La Crosse before heading back with Jordan and Lyman, and I couldn't wait for the solitude of a private road trip. In three short hours I'd be home, and tomorrow I'd be back in Iowa City with Beth.

No sense dragging it out. I turned the ignition and the stale car took a second to fire up. I was off, hoping that a summer's worth of repairs to the Great River Road had it ready for me and my little yellow Toyota. Windows down, but more mindful of bees, I turned off the car stereo, wanting to absorb the scenery and its accompanying silence and to be able to clearly hear any worthwhile thoughts that might come to mind.

Filtered sunlight danced through the trees, and off to my right, the Mississippi ran a wide, slow, muddy-blue. The winding road followed the river and the thoughts from eight years of drum corps were meandering as well. All suddenly rolled together, I considered their collective impact. Wisely, I let go of the regrets. Instead, realizing that given the chance to do it all over again, there wasn't any doubt I'd take it. While I wasn't exactly sure what my life without marching would bring, I knew exactly what I'd gained from the past eight years.

My days in corps had been the perfect gift, and whether others understood that or not really didn't matter. I'd found a community where I belonged, I'd made what I believed would be a lot of lifetime friends, and hopefully only a few temporary enemies. Drum corps had been a fantastic training ground, providing me with a variety of eye level experiences in preparation for that "real life" that was now staring me straight in my face—I knew I wouldn't flinch.

I had learned a lot about people, especially what it takes to get along and work productively in tight quarters. I'd learned a lot about acceptance, perseverance, forgiveness, and tolerance, and I learned how to deal with all of that and still manage to have a blast, but most importantly, I'd learned a lot about myself and my own human potential. I'd figured out how to breathe—how to be patient. I'd developed a goal-oriented work ethic, I'd mastered self-doubt, and developed some resiliency from the numerous detours and setbacks, realizing that most difficult situations weren't permanent, and usually came with a variety of options that could offer a sense of control and a degree of optimism. I'd also acquired the necessary confidence I needed to move forward—then, ironically, almost as if it'd been scripted, the Celica's engine sputtered and lost power.

The irony continued as I realized I was stranded just north of Prairie du Chien, that pivotal place in my life where I'd made a bold move forward. Coasting over to the shoulder of the road, I sat there for a moment—as good as I was feeling about working with people, was as bad as I felt about working with combustible engines. There was enough gas in the tank and no engine light on. I got out, popped the lid, and did dumb stuff like check the oil. Everything seemed to be in order—as if I knew what the order should be.

Hunh? Maybe the car was trying to tell me something—maybe I should've stayed another day in La Crosse, or maybe I shouldn't be so damn full of myself. Maybe, just maybe, I wasn't ready to give it all up and move on. *Nope, don't go there*—I might be stuck on this road, but I wasn't about to let myself go down that one.

Not quite sure what my next move should be, I got back in the car, tried the ignition, and the car miraculously fired up. Elated, I tentatively pushed the accelerator and it slowly lurched ahead, but only a few miles down the road, it chugged twice and came to another disheartening stop. Again, I briefly waited and again it came back to life.

Slowly driving down the main drag, I scanned both sides of the road for a service station with an actual garage, but no luck. Not wanting to be stranded on the narrow bridge, I held my breath as I crossed the Mississippi over to Iowa. Safely in tiny neighboring McGregor, I saw a small two-pump service station. The attached garage had a car on a lift, and I pulled in.

The lonely, skinny attendant wasn't long out of high school but at least he seemed like he knew cars. With both of us hunched over the engine, I explained its symptoms, and he said it sounded like a fuel filter, but without the part, there wasn't a lot he could do. I figured I'd have to stagger my way back home, until he told me he had an idea. Pulling the filter off the line, he back washed it with gas and hit it with the air hose. With that, the car came back to life. I was ecstatic. I topped off the tank and tipped him my last ten bucks.

I couldn't believe my luck. Then again, I realized I'd been on a lucky streak all my life, so why not run with it? Pulling out of the service station, I reflected on the last quote of Moe's itinerary:

"If well thou hast begun, go on;
it is the end that crowns us, not the fight."

~Robert Herrick

Herrick's words now rang clear, and I knew it was time—time to take the skills I'd gained and go forward, time to make new stuff happen, time to get on with my real life—as I was positive there was a lot of it ahead of me. Besides, now it'd be easy to move forward, just keep following the river downstream. So on I went. Plugging in a jazz mixtape, I cranked it up.

Overlooking the Mississippi from the Iowa side of the river, the unobstructed bright sunshine and the ringing tones of Chick Corea's electric piano filled the car. He was joined by Latin diva Flora Purim, and she beckoned me to follow her to a better place, a place where I would become as light as a feather, a place where I'd be free with music all around. Hearing her siren's voice, I got one of those cold shivers and thought, *Yeah Flora, you can take me there right now.* Instantly, I did feel as light as a feather. I punched the gas pedal. The car agreed, and I headed for home.

Finis Coronat Opus

ACKNOWLEDGMENTS

SINCE MY FIRST ATTEMPT AT blowing air through a bugle, the stories from the people associated with my time in drum corps have rumbled around in my brain, like rocks being polished in a tumbler. Finally I had to do something about all the noise, so I decided to write them down as best as I could. That process has been arduous and frustrating as I am not a writer, but it has also been an exciting, and intriguing exercise in the art of self-reflection, and the best side effects to come from it were the conversations that it generated with family and friends. Their assistance helped to color in the details of events caught between intervals of retrograde amnesia as well as resolving many of the false memories that form when reminiscing about events that took place a half century ago.

Thanks to all of my Emerald Knight friends who shared their time, recollections, photos, and encouragement: Lori Baker, Matt Daugherty, Tom Daugherty, David Dean, Scott Dickinson, Lori Ellickson, Frank Gorman, David and Robin Nelson, Dee Ann Rexroat, and Kim and Pete Wyatt. I am especially indebted to the detailed research gathered by past Emerald Knights, Cindy Hadish, as the writer and editor of the exceptional, *Marking Time, A History of the Drum and Bugle Corps in Cedar Rapids, Iowa,* and Rich Severa, for his phenomenal photographic memory of the Emerald Knights from 1972 through 1977. Tremendous gratitude also goes out to my childhood friend, Roger Dickinson, who loudly pushed me in a direction that would forever change my life.

Helmets off to all the past Blue Stars for their willingness to help me relive our glory days: Brian (Bubbs) Albrecht, Cindy Albrecht, Dawn Christianson, Cliff DeArment, Kevin Donka, Robert Fayard, Rob & Shelly Franzblau, Kevin Hanson, Mike Haynes, Don Hill, Robbie Hochstetler, Brett Johnson, Colin Klos, Larry LaSuer, Moe Latour, Tammy Muck, Sue (Reichardt) Pochop, Penny Reedy, Deb (Peters) Scheckler, Steve Severance, Steve Smith, Steve Steuck, Helen (Dornbusch) Timmreck, and David Tippett.

Many of the details of people and events involved in the evolution of drum corps would not have been possible without the notable information provided by Steve Vickers, editor of *Drum Corps World* and *The History of Drum and Bugle Corps, Volumes 1 And 2,* and posthumous DCI journalist and author,

Michael Boo. Other notable contributors to the historical references in the book include: Ron Allard for his outstanding Diceman Radio podcasts; Jari Villanueva, and Scooter Pirtle, for their extensive research on the evolution of the bugle; Jim Reilly, Pat Forker, George Lavelle and Bert Lync for their detailed history of the Bridgemen; Bob Zinko, a singularly great American Legion Drum Corps Historian; Doug Peck of the Osage Precisionaires; and the World Drum Corps Hall of Fame website.

Thankfully, much of the information regarding drum corps' performances, scores, and show results have been preserved via the internet and were obtained from the following web sites: dcxmuseum.org, fromthepressbox.com, youtube. com, and dci.org.

Throughout the past several years I have relied heavily upon the suggestions from my partner and wife, Beth, daughter Sophie, and brother Tommy. I appreciate their patience and willingness to humor me through many ragged rough draft readings. I also garnered significant encouragement and valuable feedback from my steady and longtime friends, Stewart Cohen, Tim (Dode) Daugherty, Jenny Jordan, Mark Jordan, Charlie Lilly, and Nancy Meyers. Additionally, I would like to express my sincere appreciation and gratitude to Audrey Brock and Dawn McGarrahan Wiebe of Windy City Publishers.

I would especially like to thank my good friend, author, and honorable colleague, Paul Pryma. As principal of the high school where I taught, he inspired a tremendous faculty with his vision, purpose, knowledge, and humility. Upon his retirement, he continued to positively influence my life by enthusiastically encouraging me to write, especially when the writing got tough (which was most of the time). Without his incredible positivity, advice, and support, I would never have completed this journey.

Finally, I would like to posthumously recognize my loving parents, who I know were completely befuddled with their son's infatuation with tooting a horn and waving his arms in front of others tooting theirs. This story would not have happened had they not been initially tolerant, and ultimately supportive, of my passion to take the field in competition.

ABOUT THE AUTHOR

MIKE PISKEL is a retired high school science teacher from Glenbrook North High School where he taught from 1981 until 2018. During his career, Mike was a Glenbrook North Distinguished Teacher, a Golden Apple Teacher of Distinction, and the recipient of The Friends of the Chicago River Educator of the Year.

Mike and his wife, Beth, reside in Northbrook, IL, where he works as an ecologist specializing in native landscaping and restoration ecology. He also continues to support his high school in a variety of capacities. Mike's hobbies include travel, fishing, food rescue, exploring the great outdoors, and taking in concerts and drum corps shows with his family and friends.

Made in the USA
Middletown, DE
18 October 2022

12932915R00176